NEW Opportunities

Education for Life

Upper Intermediate

Language Powerbook

Contents

Michael Harris
David Mower
Anna Sikorzyńska

with Hanna Mrozowska

PEARSON
Longman

1 Identity

Papatybis cmpoŭne mus

1 Vocabulary

1 Personality adjectives
Complete the description with the words in the box.

> cheerful, hard-working, outgoing, reckless, reliable, sensible, sociable, sympathetic

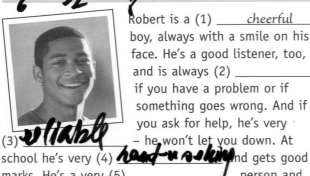

Robert is a (1) _____cheerful_____ boy, always with a smile on his face. He's a good listener, too, and is always (2) _____ if you have a problem or if something goes wrong. And if you ask for help, he's very _____ – he won't let you down. At (3) *reliable* school he's very (4) *hard-working* and gets good marks. He's a very (5) _____ person and would never do anything (6) *reckless* . Robert is a popular student with lots of friends; he's very (7) ___sociable___ and (8) *outgoing* .

2 Personality adjectives
In your notebook, write sentences about a person you know using the cues.

> Eva tends to be a bit careless with her homework.

1 tends to/a bit
2 can be/rather
3 deep down

3 Wordbuilding
Complete the table.

Noun	Verb	Adjective
_____	create	_____
decision	_____	_____
_____	_____	different
_____	help	_____
_____	imagine	_____
thought	_____	_____
_____	tolerate	_____
_____	co-operate	_____

4 Wordbuilding
Complete the sentences with an adjective or noun. The first letter is given.

1 One minute he's cheerful, the next he's miserable. He's a very _____moody_____ person.

2 They are h_elp_____ the economy will recover.

3 Choosing a new car is a difficult d_ecision_ to make.

4 He couldn't see the i_mportance_ of what I said.

5 Her a_im_____ is to travel round the world.

6 She listened to my problem with great s_____ .

7 There's nothing to do. I think I'll die of b_oring_ !

8 Don't do anything silly – use your common s_ense_ .

➡ Lexicon, Students' Book, pages 157–158

5 ᴬ/z Dictionary work
Are the underlined words nouns, adjectives, verbs or adverbs?

1 I could feel the sun on my face and I could touch the leaves of the plants. ___n___

2 She picked me up and held me close. _____

3 In my quiet, dark world I didn't feel sorry for doing it. _____

4 We walked down to the well. ___n___

5 That living word awakened my soul, gave it light. _____

What are the underlined words in these sentences?

6 Turn round and face the wall. ___verb___

7 The train leaves at 8 o'clock. ___noun___

8 The hotel is very close. ___adj___

9 He's afraid of the dark. _____

10 She plays chess well. ___adj___

11 Your bag is very light. _____

Remember

1 ⋆ Modal verbs of prohibition, permission, obligation and exemption

The new coach of a basketball team is talking to the players. Fill the gaps with modal verbs: *must, can, mustn't, needn't*.

If you want to become full-time players in our team …

1 You _must_ be present at all training sessions.

2 You _can_ talk to journalists or give autographs if you don't feel like it.

3 You _mustn't_ drink alcohol.

4 You _can_ go out of town but always let me know well in advance.

5 You _mustn't_ take any forbidden stimulants.

6 You _needn't_ wear the team sweatshirt all the time, if you don't like it.

7 You _can_ put on weight.

8 You _must_ drink only water and fruit juices.

9 You _can_ use the club's sauna and jacuzzi whenever you like.

10 You _must_ do whatever I tell you.

2 ⋆⋆ Modal verbs of speculation

Look at the picture on the right and speculate about the two people in the past and present. Use the modal verbs *must, may, might, could, can't* and the expressions below. Write the sentences in your notebook.

be husband and wife, go to the same school,
fall in love when they were young, have a large family,
be retired, go fishing, be very attractive, be fit,
do some gardening, have grandchildren,
be fashion-conscious, talk about the weather,
work full time, buy some presents for the kids

They must be husband and wife.

3 ⋆⋆ Modal verbs in the past

Complete the text with: *had to, used to, would, should/shouldn't, could/couldn't, was/were able to*. Change the form of the verb in brackets if necessary.

City life, country life

Sam and Frances Bates (1) _used to_ (live) in London. She was a market analyst and he worked as a journalist. They (2) _had to work_ (work) very long hours and (3) _couldn't spend_ (spend) much time with their three children. To relax, they (4) _used to get_ (get) into the car at weekends and spent all the time they (5) _were able to manage_ (manage) in the country. Then one day they decided that they (6) _couldn't go on_ (go on) living like that any more – they (7) _had to_ (change) their lives.

Sam found a cottage in Sussex, which the owner wanted to sell quite cheaply. They (8) _were able to buy_ (buy) it without selling their house in London. But then it turned out that the cottage required massive repairs and they (9) _had to sell_ (sell) their London house because they (10) _couldn't afford_ (afford) to pay for the repairs.

Now Frances grows and sells flowers and Sam writes DIY guides. They sometimes think that they (11) _shouldn't leave_ (leave) London but they never really regret their decision. As Frances says, 'I think we (12) _had to move_ (move) years ago. We wasted so much valuable time.'

2 Grammar

REVISION OF TENSES

1 ⋆ Question tags
<u>Underline</u> the auxiliary verbs in the sentences.
Then add question tags.

1 Laura's been learning Japanese for some time,
   <u>   hasn't she   </u> ?

2 He's out, _____ ? *(handwritten)*

3 You don't usually eat meat, _____ ?

4 Jim can't help you with this, _____ ?

5 The train will certainly be late, _____ ?

6 We're eating out tonight, _____ ?

7 The Johnsons haven't phoned yet, _____ ?

8 Lucy didn't cook it herself, _____ ?

2 ⋆ Time adverbials and tenses
Put these time adverbials in the correct part of the
table. Some of them can go in more than one box.

> at the moment, occasionally, at 9 p.m. last night,
> next Saturday, this year, tomorrow, these days,
> from time to time, in a moment, for ages, soon, always,
> already, since my birthday, just

Present Simple	at the moment
Present Continuous	
Present Perfect	
Present Perfect Continuous	
be going to	
will	
Past Simple	
Past Continuous	
Past Perfect	

3 ⋆⋆ Time adverbials and tenses
Now write eight sentences about your classmates in
your notebook, each time using a different time
adverbial and a correct tense.

> Victor is playing tennis at the moment.

4 ⋆⋆ Tenses
Put these responses in the right places. Use the
information in brackets.

> I do it all the time.   I'll do it.
> I've been doing it for weeks.   I'm doing it.
> I'll have done it by the weekend.   I've done it.
> I was going to do it.

1 A: The sink is full. Can anyone do the washing-up?

   B: Not me again. <u>*I do it all the time.*</u>
   (this is your routine household chore)

2 A: Can we plan the surprise party for Jack's birthday?

   B: Can't you see? <u>*I'm doing it*</u> *(handwritten)*
   (you're involved in the planning right now)

3 A: Who could walk the dog?

   B: <u>*I'll do it*</u> *(handwritten)*
   (you feel like taking some fresh air)

4 A: I'd like you to lay the table for dinner.

   B: <u>*I've done it*</u> *(handwritten)*
   (the table is ready)

5 A: Could you tidy the kitchen? I'm so busy.

   B: <u>*I was going do it*</u> *(handwritten)*
   (this was your intention but you haven't managed to
   do it yet)

6 A: You never clean the bathroom.

   B: What are you talking about?
   <u>*I've been doing it for weeks*</u> *(handwritten)*
   (actually nobody else but you has cleaned the
   bathroom for a month)

7 A: Could you tidy up these documents? We have to
   fill in our tax declaration next week.

   B: OK, <u>*I'll have done it by...*</u> *(handwritten)*
   (you promise to finish doing this before that time)

5 ⋆⋆ Tenses
Continue each statement in a logical way. Use the
cues in the correct tense.

1 You are totally exhausted! <u>*Are you training for*</u>

   <u>*the marathon?*</u>
   (train for the marathon?)

2 I'm the best runner in the school. _____

   _____
   (win every race in the last two years)

3 I'm afraid I didn't see the accident. _____

_____

(read a newspaper/it happen)

4 I can't come tonight. _____

_____

(take part in a school performance)

5 I'm so depressed! _____

_____

(fail my driving test yesterday)

6 I don't usually eat out but now I'm on holiday and

_____

(eat out every night)

7 I can understand why she is furious. _____

_____

(the children paint her car pink)

8 I know everybody in this street. _____

_____

(live here all my life)

9 Get ready! The performance _____

_____

(begin in ten minutes)

6 ★★★ Tenses
Put the verbs in brackets in the correct tenses.

At 6 p.m. yesterday a fire (1) __broke out__ (break out) at 16 Chestnut St., Otley, in an old building which (2) _____ (be abandoned) for years. The neighbours (3) _____ (call) the local fire brigade who said they (4) _____ (come) at once.

The fire engine driver, who (5) _____ (receive) his professional licence only a few days before, (6) _____ (drive) a little too fast and (7) _____ (crash) into a tree. The firemen (8) _____ (call) the headquarters to inform them about what (9) _____ (happen) only to find out that the villagers (10) _____ (manage) to put out the fire on their own.

'We (11) _____ (extinguish) fires in this area for years and nothing like that (12) _____ (happen) before,' says Bill Hogan, the head officer for this area. 'I'm sure the driver (13) _____ (be punished) as the crash (14) _____ (be) clearly his fault.'

Prepositions

After adjectives
Sometimes adjectives and prepositions go together.

Examples:
*I'm not very **good at** judo.*
*I've been very **busy with** my exams.*

1 Write each adjective next to a suitable preposition in the table.

bad, clever, disappointed, disgusted, enthusiastic, impressed, interested, kind, pleased, polite, proud, responsible, rude, shocked, similar, useless

disapointed, with	about
bad	at
	by
upasing	for
interested	in
proud	of
kind	to
im pused	with

➡ **Lexicon, Students' Book, pages 167–169.**

2 Complete the letter with suitable prepositions.

Dear Andrea,

Thanks for your letter. Jenny was delighted (1) __with__ the birthday present you sent her. You've always been very kind (2) __to__ her. As you can imagine, at sixteen she's a typical teenager. She says she gets bored (3) __with__ our company and goes out with her friends at weekends. At home she gets annoyed (4) __with__ little things and she's often rude (5) __to__ her father. Don't get me wrong – we're still very proud (6) __of__ her! I'm sure it's just a passing phase.

I've been busy (7) __with__ our holiday arrangements. We were disappointed (8) _____ the apartment last year in Greece. This year we're renting a farmhouse in France. I was surprised (9) __with__ the price but we're very enthusiastic (10) __about__ it. I've been learning French, but I'm useless (11) __in__ learning languages!

Love,
Margaret

PS: I was very impressed (12) __with__ Sonia's new paintings! Have you seen them yet?

3 Communication

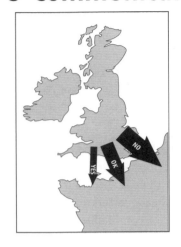

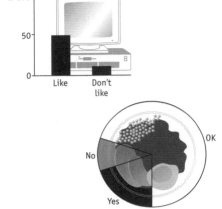

1 Expressing preferences
Look at the diagrams and complete the text with these words.

> would love to, can't stand, don't mind, not keen on, really into, really keen on, wouldn't mind, wouldn't want to

Surprisingly most teenagers are not interested in living abroad. In answer to our question: 'Would you like to live abroad?' only 10 percent say they (1) _would love to_ , 15 percent say they (2) _wouldn'h_ living abroad for a short time, but the majority say they definitely (3) _____ live in another country. More predictably, nearly 50 percent of the 15–18 age group say they are (4) _____ computers; only 10 percent say they are (5) _____ new technology; the others say they don't care! Finally, in answer to the question 'Do you like traditional British meals?' the majority of teenagers say they (6) _____ . Twenty percent are (7) _____ them, but one in ten (8) _____ our traditional Sunday roast dinner!

2 Expressing preferences
Circle the correct verb in each dialogue.

1   A: I *love*/*would love* skiing. We go twice a year.
    B: It looks exciting. I *love*/*would love* to try it one day.

2   A: I *like*/*would like* to go to the USA next year.
    B: Me too. I wouldn't mind *visiting*/*to visit* the Grand Canyon.

3   A: I *love*/*would love* to live abroad when I finish university.
    B: I *don't want*/*wouldn't want* to be away from home for too long.

4   A: He *doesn't enjoy*/*wouldn't* enjoy his French classes.
    B: No, he's not keen on languages. I *love*/*would love* to be able to speak French.

3 Expressing preferences
Write true sentences about yourself for each topic.

Example: *I'm really into music from the sixties. I can't stand jazz.*

music

1   I'm really into _____

    _____

    _____

2   I can't stand _____

    _____

    _____

travel

3   I'd love to _____

    _____

    _____

4   I wouldn't want to _____

    _____

    _____

sport

5   I'm really keen on _____

    _____

    _____

6   I wouldn't mind _____

    _____

    _____

food and drink

7   I'm not keen on _____

    _____

    _____

8   I don't mind _____

    _____

    _____

school subjects

9   I can't stand _____

    _____

    _____

10 I'm really keen on _____

    _____

    _____.

MULTI-PART VERBS

1 Multi-part verbs

Replace the verbs crossed out in the phone conversation with these verbs in the correct form.

> take off, drop (somebody) off, get back, get on with, get to, look forward to, perk up, pick (somebody) up, put up with, take after

Tania: Hi, this is Tania. The plane ~~left~~ (1) ___took off___ a bit early and we ~~arrived at~~ (2) _get to_ the airport about twenty minutes ago.

Olivia: Great! How is Mark?

Tania: Well, we had to ~~tolerate~~ (3) _get on with_ his bad temper on the plane. He said he couldn't wait to ~~return~~ (4) _get back_ home! He ~~behaves like~~ (5) _____ his father when he's travelling, but he ~~is looking more cheerful~~ (6) _____ now.

Olivia: Glad to hear it! I'm sure once he's here he'll ~~have a good relationship with~~ (7) _get on with_ my kids. They are ~~waiting hopefully~~ (8) _looking forward to_ seeing him.

Tania: Great. Anyway, when can you ~~collect us~~ (9) _pick us up_

Olivia: I'll be there in about twenty minutes. I'll ~~leave you~~ (10) _____ at the apartment and we can meet later, OK?

Tania: Sounds great!

2 Verbs with prepositions

Look at the pictures and complete the sentences with these words:

> down, across, ahead, at, over, through, by, into

1 She got ___down___ from her horse.

2 They got _across_ the river.

3 The cat can't get _____ the bird.

4 She got _____ by a few metres.

5 The man was in front and she couldn't get _____ .

6 He got _____ a taxi.

7 He managed to get _____ the wall.

8 The robbers got _____ the wall to the bank.

3 Multi-part verbs with *get*

Now use the same words from Exercise 2 to make multi-part verbs with get in these sentences.

1 He's very ambitious and wants to get _____ .

2 She's quite shy but she gets _____ her ideas very clearly.

3 Don't let all these problems get you _____ .

4 He failed his driving test but soon got _____ the disappointment.

5 We somehow got _____ a conversation about national identity.

6 He's impatient and he's always getting _____ me for being late.

7 She never listens. I can never get _____ to her.

8 We don't have a lot of money but we get _____ .

➡ Lexicon, Students' Book, pages 170–176.

4 Focus on Writing

1 Linking

Complete the sentences with a word from the box.

> but, after, although, anyway, because, before, so, when

We aren't keen on football,

(1) _____but_____ Steve's dad gave us free tickets for the match. (2) _Although_ United lost, they didn't play badly.

(3) _After_ the match, Steve went straight home (4) _because_ his team lost. He gets moody (5) _when_ his team loses. (6) _Anyway_ , it wasn't late (7) _so_ we went for a burger (8) _before_ going home.

2 Linking

Complete the second sentence so it has a similar meaning to the first. Use the cue in brackets.

1 I'll take my mobile phone so I can give you a call.

  I'll use my mobile phone _if I want to_ give you a call. (if)

2 They are very proud; they are law-abiding, too.

  They are very proud _____ _____ law-abiding. (well)

3 Many people are suspicious of despite living in a multicultural society.

  Many people are suspicious of foreigners, _____ in a multicultural society. (although)

4 I've applied for a summer job because I need the money.

  I haven't got much _____ _____ for a summer job. (so)

5 The hours are long, but I'll have to do it.

  _____ , I'll have to do it. (despite)

3 Style

Read this letter of application for a summer job in Britain. What is wrong with it? Cross out the underlined words and replace them with these words and expressions.

> accompany, as requested, children, enclosed, I look forward to hearing from you, referees, thank you, would like, yours faithfully, assisted

Dear Sir / Madam,

(1) [Thanks] ~~Thank you~~ for the brochure. I (2) ~~want~~ [would like] to apply for a job as a monitor in your summer camp and I am writing my application in English (3) ~~because that is what you asked people to do~~ [as requested].

I have some experience with (4) ~~kids~~ [children]. I give tennis classes after school and sometimes I (5) ~~go with~~ [accompany] a class on school trips at weekends. Last year I (6) ~~helped out~~ [assisted] with an action summer holiday and learned how to canoe.

I've (7) ~~put in~~ [enclosed] the names and addresses of two (8) ~~people who can give me a reference~~ [referees].

(9) ~~Write soon~~ [I look forward to hearing from you],

(10) ~~All the best~~,

Carl Strombolsky [Yours faithfully]

4 Editing

Correct these extracts from a formal letter. Mark the mistakes S (spelling), P (punctuation) or G (grammar). There may be more than one type of mistake.

1 Dear Sir / Madame,

  [S] _Dear Sir / Madam,_ _____

2 I am writting to apply for a job at your summer camp.

  [ ] _____

3 I don't have any formal qualifications however I have some experience

  [ ] _____

4 Could you tell me how many students there will be in each group

  [ ] _____

5 I look forward to hear from you.

  [ ] _____

6 Yours sincerelly

  [ ] _____

5 Guided writing: Paragraph plans
Read these sentences from a personal letter and match them to the correct parts of the paragraph plans.

a) *Anyway, I'm writing to ask if you want to come and visit us this summer.*

b) *I saw Karen last week, and she's looking for a new dog.*

c) *Thanks for your letter. It was lovely to hear about your dog.*

d) *Well, I must go now because I've got to do my history project.*

e) *The best time for me is the end of July or beginning of August.*

f) *Don't forget to send me that photo.*

g) *Are you going to keep any of the puppies?*

PARAGRAPH PLANS	
Introductions often ...	
1 refer to a previous letter	c
and/or	
2 ask questions	☐
and/or	
3 include some chat.	☐

Then give your ...	
4 reason for writing	☐
and	
5 details.	☐

Letters often end with ...	
6 an excuse to finish	☐
and/or	
7 a request.	☐

6 Leaving out words
In personal letters we often miss out words. What words are missing from these extracts?

1   Thanks for the present. Very useful in winter!

_____

2   It's my birthday party on Saturday. Can't wait.

_____

3   I met old Mr Williams yesterday. Remember him?

_____

7 Introductions to letters
Write three introductions to personal letters. Include sentences about each of the topics.

> *How are you? The weather here is terrible – it's been raining for weeks. How is the cat? Still in trouble with your neighbours?*

1   the weather/a pet

_____
_____
_____

2   school or university/an old friend

_____
_____
_____

3   a neighbour/a party

_____
_____
_____

4   holiday/swimming

_____
_____
_____

8 Finishing letters
Write three excuses to finish personal letters.

> *Well, I must finish now because someone is at the door.*

1   Well, I must go now because _____

_____

2   Well, _____

_____

3   _____

_____

Word Power

1 Personality adjectives: Opposites
Replace the <u>underlined</u> words in these school reports with negative adjectives in your notebook.

Oscar is quite a <u>mature</u> and <u>sensible</u> student. He is always very <u>patient</u> if he doesn't understand and he is very <u>careful</u> with his written work.

Sonia is a very <u>outgoing</u> girl, and sometimes too <u>chatty</u>! She is <u>reliable</u> and can be quite <u>hard-working</u>.

Characteristics

Match these descriptions of people (a–f) with the quotations (1–6).

a) family-oriented
b) law-abiding
c) competitive
d) reserved
e) conservative
f) tolerant

1 *I think everybody's different and we should respect each other's views.* [f]

2 *I like to play a sport to win – not just for fun!* [ ]

3 *I obey the rules even though I might not agree with them.* [ ]

4 *I think it's important that children spend a lot of time with their parents.* [ ]

5 *I'd rather not comment on that.* [ ]

6 *I don't like too many changes – we should keep our traditions.* [ ]

➡ Lexicon, Students' Book, pages 151 and 159.

3 Collocation with *do*, *have* and *get*
Complete these sentences with *do*, *have* or *get*.

1 Don't worry about the exam. Just __do__ your best.

2 You _____ a real talent for painting.

3 My sister wants to _____ law at university.

4 I usually _____ home from school after six o'clock.

5 Can you _____ me a favour and open the door, please?

6 It's stuffy in here. Let's go outside and _____ some fresh air.

7 She _____ angry when she doesn't understand.

8 They're great friends; they _____ a lot in common.

9 I've been unemployed since I left school; I just can't seem to _____ a job.

10 I'd like to _____ a summer course in England this year.

11 He's OK when you _____ to know him.

12 You usually _____ well in exams.

➡ Lexicon, Students' Book, page 162.

4 The verb *feel*
Replace the words in brackets with words and expressions from the box.

felt, felt homesick, felt sorry for, felt the sun on my face, felt very happy

1 I (was really pleased) _____ when I heard she'd passed the exam.

2 He (regretted) _____ shouting at his son.

3 My grandparents (believed) _____ they were Scottish, not British.

4 When I went away, I (missed home) _____ _____ after the first week.

5 Once I (was in the sunshine) _____ _____ , I began to cheer up.

5 Vague language
Complete the dialogue with these words and expressions.

> fiftyish, about, some kind of, something like, sort of, what's-his-name

Tim: I saw Mr Shipley, our old English teacher, after the match yesterday, at (1) _about_ six o'clock.

Rob: Really? How old is he now?

Tim: Well, he's (2) _____ , I suppose. He was wearing a (3) _____ sports shirt and looked like (4) _____ , that funny weatherman on the BBC.

Rob: Oh yeah? What's he doing now?

Tim: He's working at (5) _____ special school for kids with problems. Sounds interesting.

Rob: Yeah, I thought he might do (6) _____ that one day.

6 Vague language
Write six sentences of your own using the words and expressions from Exercise 5.

> My neighbour looks like what's-his-name, that old American comedian.

1 _____
_____

2 _____
_____

3 _____
_____

4 _____
_____

5 _____
_____

6 _____
_____

7 Confusing words
Complete each sentence with a word from the box.

> alone, angry, kind, lonely, nervous, only, sensible, sensitive, sympathetic, unique

1 Don't shout at her. She's very _____ and will be upset.

2 She's very _____ to animals.

3 She has no friends and is really quite _____ .

4 He was the _____ person I knew at the party.

5 I'm very _____ about tomorrow's exam.

6 He's very _____ and wouldn't do anything silly.

7 She's a _____ artist; there's really nobody else like her.

8 I was very _____ when he broke my favourite glass.

9 He has lived _____ since his wife died.

10 My friends were very _____ when my dog died.

AZ Check your answers in a good dictionary.

8 Extension: Describing people
Complete the definitions with the words in the box.

> bore, layabout, chatterbox, gossip, snob, troublemaker

AZ Use a good dictionary to help you.

1 A _____ is a person who likes talking about other people's business.

2 A _____ is a person who causes difficulties for other people.

3 A _____ is a person who can't stop talking.

4 A _____ is a person who dislikes people of a lower social class.

5 A _____ is a person who talks in an uninteresting way.

6 A _____ is a person who is extremely lazy and never does any work.

Language Awareness

1 ★ *a* and *the*

Match each sentence with the correct response (a or b).

1	I've seen the film.	a	Really? It's the first time for five years.
2	I've seen a film.	b	At last! Did you like it as much as I did?
3	You can book the flight at a British Airways office.	a	Which of them is the nearest?
4	You can book the flight at the British Airways office.	b	I know, but it's so far from my place.
5	Can you give me a hammer?	a	I can't see it anywhere.
6	Can you give me the hammer?	b	The big one or the small one?
7	Jenny's bought a gold watch.	a	You're kidding! She said she didn't like it.
8	Jenny's bought the gold watch.	b	She's trying to impress people with her money.
9	I'm looking for a black dress.	a	I'm afraid we only have black skirts.
10	I'm looking for the black dress.	b	I took it to the cleaners' yesterday.

2 ★★ Determiners

Circle the correct options in the sentences below.

1 We've bought *a/the* new dictionary for Tom but it's not very good – we'll have to look for *the other/the second/another* one.

2 I was asked *a lot of/several/much* questions at the interview. I remember *the other/the second* question because it was *a/the* most difficult one.

3 Could you get me *some/any* water?

4 I like *all/much* fruit and I also eat *a lot of/much/many* vegetables.

5 Let's hurry, we have *some/any/no* time to lose.

6 He doesn't have *any/much/some* furniture in his room – just *some/a* bed and *a/an/another* old desk.

3 ★★★ Determiners

Complete the text with the correct determiners.

After that, Holmes explained (1)_____ clues about (2)_____ hat to Watson. Then Peterson, (3)_____ door attendant, came into (4)_____ room carrying (5)_____ enormous diamond. His wife had found it inside (6)_____ goose. (7)_____ diamond had been stolen from (8)_____ countess at (9)_____ London hotel. Two hotel servants had been involved. One was (10)_____ butler, James Ryder, and (11)_____ was John Horner, a plumber. Horner had been working in (12)_____ countess's room when Ryder noticed that (13)_____ diamond had been stolen. Since then, Horner had been in prison for (14)_____ days.

Sherlock Holmes decided to advertise (15)_____ goose and hat in (16)_____ newspapers. That evening (17)_____ man appeared; it was Baker. Baker did not know about (18)_____ diamond but Holmes and Watson managed to locate (19)_____ butchers who had supplied (20)_____ goose. They went there and saw (21)_____ man asking about (22)_____ goose. Holmes invited (23)_____ man back to his house . It was Ryder, (24)_____ butler from (25)_____ hotel. Holmes mentioned (26)_____ diamond and (27)_____ man nearly fainted and confessed that he had stolen it. After Horner's arrest, Ryder had gone to his sister's house to hide (28)_____ diamond. There had been (29)_____ geese in (30)_____ garden and Ryder had put (31)_____ diamond into the mouth of one of them and then asked for (32)_____ goose for Christmas. Later, he had taken (33)_____ goose away and killed it but there was (34)_____ diamond there! He had chosen (35)_____ wrong goose! Holmes had enough proof to put Ryder into prison, but he decided to let (36)_____ man go. In the end, Horner was released from prison and (37)_____ diamond returned to (38)_____ countess.

slewspy
fad
spike
contnary

Exam Zone

USE OF ENGLISH

TIPS for error correction

1 Read the whole text to get an idea of what it is about.

2 Read it again sentence by sentence to understand the meaning.

3 It may help if you 'say' the words to yourself.

4 Search the text for any unnecessary words and cross them out:

determiners (e.g. *a, the, some, any, this*)

auxiliaries (e.g. *be, do, have*)

prepositions (e.g. *to, from, at*)

pronouns (e.g. *he, something, them*)

relative pronouns (e.g. *who, which, that*)

linking words (e.g. *but, so, however*)

Read the text and look carefully at each line. If a line is correct, put a tick (✓) in the space on the right. If a line has an unnecessary word, write it in the space on the right. (20 marks)

The choices we make as consumers today affect the lifestyles we lead them	0	*them*
tomorrow. As the consumers, we all have a role in influencing the	1	
market, because consumer choice is something what drives the market.	2	
We are all consumers of electricity. We use it in the most of the things	3	
we do, whether it's lighting our homes, listening to music, washing our	4	
clothes, refrigerating our food or running our computers. But there is no	5	
any doubt that electricity is an essential part of our lives.	6	
We must have little choice when it comes to consuming electrical energy.	7	
But we do have had a choice when it comes to purchasing electrical	8	
energy. Since the recent introduction of competition into the energy	9	
market, consumers are able not to choose their electricity supplier.	10	
Traditionally, the electricity has been generated by burning fossil fuels – oil,	11	
gas and coal. Lately, nuclear energy has to become a major source of	12	
electricity. Now, because due to technological advances in the industry,	13	
that choice is being broader. We can also produce electricity from	14	
renewable kind resources.	15	
Renewable energy makes use of the power of wind or water or the sun's	16	
rays. While using these sources of energy does not destroy the world's	17	
resources, or pollute the environment. Renewable energy is the energy of	18	
the future. And you may be too pleased to hear that you can choose to be	19	
supplied with this energy from right now.	20	

20

READING

Multicultural Britain

The following are extracts from a speech given by Robin Cook, the British Foreign Secretary, in April 2001.

(A) Tonight I want to celebrate Britishness. Sadly, it has become fashionable for some to argue that British identity is under siege, (1)_____ . I want to argue that where the pessimists identify a threat, we should instead see developments that will strengthen and renew British identity.

(B) The first element in the debate about the future of Britishness is the changing ethnic composition of the British people. The British are not a race, but a gathering of countless different races and communities. It is not their purity that makes the British unique, but the sheer pluralism of their ancestry.

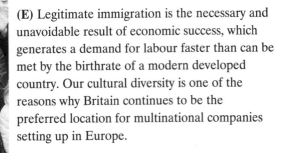

(C) London was first established as the capital of a Celtic Britain by Romans from Italy. They were in turn driven out by Saxons and Angles from Germany. The great cathedrals of this land were built mostly by Norman bishops, (2)_____ . Outside our Parliament, Richard the Lionheart proudly sits astride his steed, a symbol of courage and defiance. Yet he spoke French much of his life, and depended on the Jewish community of England to put up the ransom that freed him from prison.

(D) The idea that Britain was a 'pure' Anglo-Saxon society before the arrival of communities from the Caribbean, Asia and Africa is fantasy. But if this view of British identity is false to our past, it is false to our future too. The global era has produced population movements of a breadth and richness without parallel in history. Today's London is a perfect hub of the globe. It is home to over thirty ethnic communities of at least 10,000 residents each.

In this city tonight, over 300 languages will be spoken by families over their evening meal at home. This pluralism is not a burden we must reluctantly accept. It is an immense asset that contributes to the cultural and economic vitality of our nation.

(E) Legitimate immigration is the necessary and unavoidable result of economic success, which generates a demand for labour faster than can be met by the birthrate of a modern developed country. Our cultural diversity is one of the reasons why Britain continues to be the preferred location for multinational companies setting up in Europe.

(F) (3)_____ . Our lifestyles and cultural horizons have also been broadened in the process. It reaches into every aspect of our national life.

(G) Chicken Tikka Massala is now a true British national dish, not only because it is the most popular, (4)_____ . Chicken Tikka is an Indian dish. The Massala sauce was added to satisfy the desire of British people to have their meat served in gravy.

(H) The modern notion of national identity cannot be based on race and ethnicity, (5)_____ . Some of the most successful countries in the modern world, such as the United States and Canada, are immigrant societies. Their experience shows how cultural diversity, allied to a shared concept of equal citizenship, can be a source of enormous strength. We should draw inspiration from that experience.

1 Read the text carefully. Match the sentences (a–f) with the gaps in the text (1–5). There is one extra sentence that you do not need. (2 marks each)

a   And it isn't just our economy that has been enriched by the arrival of new communities

b   perhaps even in a state of terminal decline

c   because of the linguistic variety of the population

d   but because it is a perfect illustration of the way Britain absorbs and adapts external influences

e   but the religion in them was secured by the succession of a Dutch prince

f   but must be based on shared ideals and aspirations

| 10 |

2 Choose the best answer according to the text – a, b, c or d. (1 mark each)

1 What, according to the speaker, makes British people unique?
 a their racial purity
 b their recent history
 c their mixture of races
 d their fashion

2 In paragraph C, why does the speaker talk about British history?
 a To show how the English language developed.
 b To show that the British are not a pure race.
 c To show Britain has a parliament.
 d To show important changes of governments.

3 What should the British attitude to immigration be?
 a It is inevitable and so should be accepted.
 b It improves cultural and economic life.
 c It leads to a population increase.
 d It is changing pure Anglo-Saxon society.

4 Immigration is necessary for Britain because
 a multinational companies want to do business in Europe.
 b it leads to a successful economy.
 c it had an empire in Asia and Africa.
 d there aren't enough people to do the work.

5 The speaker uses the United States and Canada as examples of successful countries because
 a immigrants have contributed to their development.
 b they have a similar national identity.
 c modern societies must have a mixture of races.
 d they share the same ideals and aspirations.

[5]

3 Find words in the text which have a similar meaning. Paragraph references are given in brackets. (0.5 mark each)

1 attack (A) _____
2 argument (B) _____
3 horse (C) _____
4 money (C) _____
5 centre (D) _____
6 something heavy (D) _____
7 very large (D) _____
8 legal (E) _____
9 part (F) _____
10 idea (H) _____

[5]

WRITING

Below is an extract from a letter you have received from a friend in Britain. Write a reply, telling your friend about your plans for his visit. Write about 150 words. (20 marks)

I'd love to come and stay with you. It will have to be in August because, as you know, our summer holidays are not as long as yours. Tell me when the best dates for you are. What will the weather be like? Should I bring any special clothes? What sort of present would your parents like? Would you like me to bring you anything special? Write back soon and give me all the details. I can't wait!

See you soon!

Tony

[20]

2 Laughter

5 Vocabulary

1 Laughter: Expressions
What are people doing in the following sentences? Choose the phrases to match the sentences.

> telling a joke, being sarcastic, pulling someone's leg, describing something ironic

1 I'm sorry, but I've broken your new expensive vase. I'm sure I can fix it. (*pause*) Only kidding! _____

2 Oh, fantastic. The way he missed that goal was absolutely brilliant. You have to be really clever to miss such an easy goal.
_____

3 What's the longest word in the English language? 'Smiles' – because there's a mile between the first and last letter!
_____

4 He knows nothing about football, but amazingly he predicted the results of all the matches last weekend! _____

▷ Lexicon, Students' Book, pages 151–152.

2 Collocation
Complete the sentences with the words from the box.

> pale, breath, cold, concern, control, land, opinion, order, practice, rain, sense of humour, sleep

1 When he heard the bad news he *turned* ___pale___ and nearly fainted.
2 I haven't been sailing for years. I'm a bit *out of* _____ and I'll be glad to get back on *dry* _____ .
3 He always *expresses* his _____ clearly in meetings.
4 I was completely *out of* _____ after running for the bus.
5 According to the weather forecast it's going to _____ *heavily* throughout the night.
6 I'm afraid our phone is *out of* _____ . You'll have to use your mobile phone.
7 You _____ so *heavily* that it's always difficult to wake you.
8 Jim has got a very *dry* _____ . He can be quite witty.
9 The parents *expressed* their _____ about the amount of traffic near the school.
10 I'm taking a sweater in case it *turns* _____ .
11 The lorry went *out of* _____ and crashed into a shop.

▷ Lexicon, Students' Book, pages 160 and 165–6.

3 AZ Dictionary work
Look at these words. Which is a noun and which is a verb? Mark them N or V.

breath ☐   breathe ☐

Match the expressions (1–6) with the definitions (a–f).

1 breathe a sigh of relief ☐ c
2 breathe new life into something ☐
3 don't breathe a word of ☐
4 get your breath back ☐
5 speak under your breath ☐
6 take someone's breath away ☐

a don't mention
b talk in a low voice or whisper
c feel calm again after being nervous
d to surprise or shock someone
e make something more interesting or exciting
f be able to breathe easily again

Remember

1 ★★ Past Simple and Past Continuous
Use the cues and *when* or *while* to write sentences.
Use the Past Simple and Past Continuous.

1 I write an essay/computer crashed

   I was writing an essay when my computer crashed.

2 I drive from London to Cambridge/car wheel fall off

   _____

3 Jane read a fashion magazine/Peter watch a
   basketball match on TV _____

   _____

4 I break tooth/eat muesli for breakfast _____

   _____

5 we finish lunch/I make tea _____

   _____

6 my dad sleep in front of the TV/Michael Owen score
   a goal _____

   _____

2 ★★ Past Simple, Past Continuous and Past Perfect
Put the verbs in brackets in the correct tense: Past
Simple, Past Continuous or Past Perfect.

The President (1) _went_ (go) through a painful
experience yesterday. While he (2) _____ (go)
to the parliament to deliver a speech about the National
Health Plan, he (3) _____ (realise) that the text of
his speech (4) _____ (be left) in his office.
It was too late to go back and he (5) _____
(be force) to improvise the speech. While he
(6) _____ (talk), he (7) _____ (forget) the name
of the Minister of Health, who (8) _____ _____
(be appointed) only a few days earlier, and
(9) _____ (call) her the wrong name. The MPs
(10) _____ (boo). At that moment the President's
secretary, who (11) _____ (go) back to the
office to get the speech, (12) _____ (want) to hand
it over to him. As he (13) _____ (approach) the
President, he (14) _____ (trip) over a wire and
(15) _____ (break) his arm. The session
(16) _____ (have) to be interrupted so that the
poor man could be taken to hospital. The President
(17) _____ (apologise) to the Minister of Health and
(18) _____ (finish) his speech.

3 ★★★ Past Simple, Past Continuous and Past Perfect
Match sentences 1–3 with the timelines a–c, then
draw your own timelines for sentences 4–6.
The symbols are:

> → – timeline
> x – a single event
> ⏜ – a prolonged activity
> ↶ – returning to an earlier event

1 When John came home, he watched the news. ☐
2 When John came home, his wife was watching the
   news. ☐
3 When John came to work, he told us that he had
   watched the six o'clock news. ☐

a) ⏜ ———— x ————→
b) ———— x ———— x ——→
c) ———— x ———— x ———— x ——→

4 When I was stopped by the police, I suddenly
   realised that I had left my driving licence at home.
5 While Joanna was preparing dinner, he laid the
   table, lit the candles and poured the wine.
6 All evening Peter was reading his old letters, then
   the next day he threw them away and said that he
   had broken up with his girlfriend.

4 ★★ *would* and *used to*
Complete these sentences about Eddie Murphy.
Decide where you can use both *would* and *used to*, or
only used to.

1 *He used to* _____ be very amusing as a child.
2 _____ imitate people's voices.
3 _____ live in Brooklyn.
4 _____ write and perform his own
   acts.
5 _____ dress very elegantly when
   he was at school.
6 _____ study at Nassau Community
   College in New York.
7 _____ take part in comedy
   contests.
8 _____ believe that he would
   succeed.

6 Grammar

PAST TENSES

1 ★★ Past Simple, Past Continuous and Past Perfect
Put the verbs in brackets in the Past Simple, Past Continuous or Past Perfect.

1 While a man ___was washing___ (wash) his hair, he _____ (notice) that it _____ (fall) out in handfuls. It _____ (turn out) that he _____ (take) a bottle of bleach instead of shampoo.

2 A prison warden _____ (sit) in his watchtower when suddenly he _____ (see) a beautiful girl at the gate. What he _____ (not know) was that some prisoners _____ (plan) an escape for that night and they _____ (hire) the girl to help them. He _____ (go) up to her and when they _____ (talk) about her car, which she claimed _____ (break) down, 32 prisoners _____ (climb) over the prison wall and _____ (escape).

3 A comedian _____ (prepare) for his act when he _____ (realise) that he _____ (leave) his most important prop – a white pigeon – at home. He _____ (replace) it with a cat, which _____ (run) away in the middle of the act because it _____ (see) a mouse backstage.

4 A Formula 1 driver _____ (drive) off at high speed and _____ (not notice) that his repair team _____ (wave) at him frantically. It was only after one of the wheels _____ (fall) off that he _____ (find out) that they _____ (not manage) to tighten the screws properly.

2 ★ Past Perfect Continuous
Write answers to these questions by putting the expression in the Past Perfect Continuous.

1 Why was Hugh out of breath when we met him? (jog)
   He had been jogging.

2 Why did Emma cry so much when the cake fell on the floor? (decorate it all morning) _____

3 Why didn't you have any dinner last night? (feel sick all day)
   _____

4 Why did no one laugh when Nick told a joke? (listen to his jokes all evening) _____

5 Why didn't Lucy want to drive to the theatre? (drive all day)
   _____

6 Why was the doctor so exhausted? (operate for nine hours)
   _____

7 Why did the teacher arrive late? (talk to the head teacher)
   _____

8 Why was Jane cross with Steve? (gossip about her with his mates)
   _____

3 ★★ Past Perfect and Past Perfect Continuous
Use the cues and ask questions in the Past Perfect or Past Perfect Continuous to find out why Mike crashed his car.

1 drive too fast
   Had he been driving too fast?

2 drink
   _____
   _____

3 fall asleep
   _____
   _____

4 the brakes fail _____
   _____
   _____

5 listen to the radio
   _____
   _____

6 see something unusual
   _____
   _____

7 talk on his mobile
   _____
   _____

8 think about Louise
   _____
   _____

9 look at the stars
   _____
   _____

4 ★★★ Past Simple, Past Perfect and Past Perfect Continuous

Write sentences using the pictures and the verbs.
Use the Past Simple, the Past Perfect or the Past Perfect
Continuous. Link the sentences with *after* or *because*.

1 buy/save

They bought a car after they had saved their money.

2 imprison/rob _____

_____

3 move out/live _____

_____

4 get married/meet _____

_____

5 fail/go out _____

_____

6 retire/work _____

_____

Prepositions

In fixed expressions

Many prepositions occur in fixed phrases and expressions.

Example:

At that very moment, a face, head and shoulders emerged from beneath the water.

Complete the text with these prepositions. Some of them are used more than once.

on, at, by, in, under

➡ Lexicon, Students' Book, pages 165–166

EXAM CHAOS

Angry students have written to the Minister of Education after they were told to go to the wrong place for an exam.

'It's just (1) *not __on__ ,' said one student, Colin Bolton. 'We all turned up (2) _____ *good time* for the exam, but ten minutes before it was due to start they told us we had to go to another place! My mother was (3) _____ *home*, so she came and picked me up in the car.'

Taxis, cars and a mini-bus had to rush the students to the place where the exam was taking place.

'(4) _____ *the time* we arrived, the exam was already (5) _____ *way*,' said another student, Lynn Sharples. 'They gave us some extra time (6) _____ *the end*, but I couldn't concentrate.'

A spokesperson for the council said: 'The local Education Office has been (7) _____ *a mess* since the government introduced all these new exams. I understand there were some problems this morning, but (8) _____ *the end* they were sorted out. *From now* (9) _____ , we'll contact the students personally if there's a change of exam venue.'

'(10) _____ *a way*, it was quite funny,' said Stephen Smithson after the exam. 'There was a nursery school next to the exam centre and the kids were really noisy. You have to laugh, really!'

7 Communication

1 Language used for jokes
Complete the dialogue with words from the box.

> have you heard the one about, and then, anyway, eventually, go on, guess what, just can't, luckily, or something like that, right, so, well

A: (1) _Have you heard the one about_ the diver?

B: No, (2) _____ .

A: (3) _____ , one day, a diver goes down ten metres underwater, (4) _____ . (5) _____ he notices a man down there, but with no diving equipment. (6) _____ , the diver goes down another five metres, but a minute later the man joins him. Then he goes down five more metres, and (7) _____ ?

B: He sees the man again?

A: (8) _____ . The same man joins him. (9) _____ , they go all the way to the bottom. The diver is very confused. (10) _____ , he has a waterproof board and pen, (11) _____ he takes them out and writes: 'I (12) _____ believe it. How can you stay underwater all this time without equipment?' And the man takes the board and pen and writes, 'I'm drowning, you idiot!'

2 Telling a joke
Put the sentences in the correct order to tell a joke.

a   Eventually, he found a dog that could actually walk on water to retrieve a duck! He was sure none of his friends would ever believe him. ☐

b   The pessimist watched, but didn't say a word. ☐

c   He decided to tell a friend of his, a pessimist who refused to be impressed with anything. His new dog, surely, would impress him. ☐

d   One day a hunter needed a dog to retrieve ducks when he shot them. ☐

e   On the way home, the hunter asked, 'Did you notice anything unusual about my dog?' ☐

f   He invited his friend to hunt with him and his new dog. Every time they fired and a duck fell, the dog ran across the water to retrieve the bird, never getting more than his paws wet. This continued all day. ☐

g   'Yes, I did,' replied the pessimist. 'He can't swim.' ☐

3 Tenses in jokes
Complete the joke below with the verbs in the correct tense – Present Simple or Present Continuous.

A man (1) _is staying_ (stay) in a hotel. One evening he (2) _____ (go) down to the hotel bar for a drink before dinner. He (3) _____ (order) an orange juice and decides to stand at the bar. While he (4) _____ (drink) his juice he (5) _____ (hear) a voice say: 'That's a nice tie.'

The man looks around, but nobody is near him. Then he hears the voice again: 'Nice shirt, too.'

The man (6) _____ (think) maybe the barman (7) _____ (talk) to him, but the barman (8) _____ (clean) glasses at the other end of the bar. Suddenly the man (9) _____ (hear) the voice again: 'Your jacket is really smart.'

The man can't understand where the voice (10) _____ (come) from, so he (11) _____ (ask) the barman about it. 'Excuse me, (12) _____ (you talk) to me?'

'No, sir,' says the barman. 'That'll be the complimentary peanuts.'

> **complimentary** *adj* **1** given free to someone: *We got two complimentary tickets for the game.* **2** Saying that you like something and think it is good: *He wasn't very complimentary about the food.*

MULTI-PART VERBS

1 Multi-part verbs
Complete the film review with the verbs in the correct form.

get on, crack up, dress up, get into, get out of, go in for, make out, make up, put on, turn off

TOOTSIE

Dustin Hoffman plays an out-of-work actor named Michael Dorsey who just can't (1) _____ in the acting world.

   In desperation, he (2) _____ as a woman named Dorothy Michaels in order to get a part in a TV soap opera. He has to (3) _____ a different voice and (4) _____ that Dorothy is an older woman. At the job interview he (5) _____ a story about his acting career and gets the job!

   Everything goes well until Dorothy becomes a national sensation. Then things go from bad to worse. Michael falls in love with Julie Nichols (Jessica Lange), one of the soap's leading women, but can't (6) _____ a love affair because she thinks he is a woman. The scene that really (7) _____ me _____ is when Julie's father makes Dorothy a proposal of marriage and Dorothy has to say no to

(8) _____ it. Julie's father is so disappointed!

   Another amusing sub-plot is the relationship between Dorothy and one of the leading actors. He thinks he is attractive to women, but really he (9) _____ them _____ , and Dorothy uses every opportunity to make him look foolish. Eventually, Michael reveals his true identity on a 'live' edition of the show.

   If you (10) _____ wacky comedies, then *Tootsie* is a film for you.

2 Verbs with and without an object
Look at the multi-part verbs in these sentences. If the verb has an object, <u>underline</u> the object.

- Some (transitive) verbs take an object:
  *He took off **his jacket**.*
- Some (intransitive) verbs do not take an object:
  What time did you get back?

1 You need more exercise. You should *take up* swimming.
2 They *turned up* late.
3 Have you *set up* the equipment?
4 *Turn down* the TV, please.
5 We don't have much money but we *get by*.
6 He *made up* an excuse for being late.
7 They *get on* well.
8 She *put on* her new boots.
9 He *takes after* his father.
10 A bomb *went off* in the main square.

3 Verbs with and without an object
Add an object to these sentences if necessary.

1 They went away _____
2 I can't put up with _____
3 Why don't you put on _____
4 Come on, hurry up _____
5 He doesn't get on with _____
6 The train pulled out _____
7 I asked my teacher to go over _____
8 She tried out _____
9 The plane finally took off _____
10 I don't go in for _____

⇨ Lexicon, Students' Book, pages 170–176.

8 Focus on Writing

1 Linking
Complete the text with words from the box.

eventually, unfortunately, during, in the end, especially, although, one day, despite, all in all, after that, such as, in addition, or, apart from

Seventeen by Booth Tarkington is one of the funniest novels I've ever read. (1) _____ it was first published in 1918, it still remains a classic comic novel. It is set in the American Middle West (2) _____ one hot summer and tells the story of a young man in love.

Willie Baxter, (3) _____ William Sylvanus Baxter as he calls himself, is the main character of the book. He has just turned seventeen and, in his own words, he is not at all interested in girls. But (4) _____ , a beautiful stranger comes to Willie's town, and Willie falls head over heels in love with her. (5) _____ , Willie follows his beloved Miss Pratt everywhere and worships her with all his heart. (6) _____ , he is not alone as many other boys are also in love with Miss Pratt. (7) _____ , members of Willie's family, (8) _____ old Genesis and his dog Clematis, constantly get in his way and ruin his chances of

making a good impression on Miss Pratt. (9) _____ , she leaves the town and life returns to normal.

The book's greatest strength is its timeless humour. (10) _____ being written so long ago, *Seventeen* describes what it's really like to be a teenager. The love-stricken Willie Baxter is a wonderful comic character, (11) _____ when he steals his father's evening dress to impress Miss Pratt. But (12) _____ making us laugh at Willie's misfortunes, the book also laughs at human nature. (13) _____ , Willie doesn't marry the adorable Miss Pratt but his next door neighbour who seemed so irritating at first.

(14) _____ I definitely recommend *Seventeen*. It will make you laugh and help you understand adolescence.

2 Sentence building
Use the following simple sentences and the words in brackets to make longer, complex sentences.

1 Rob is depressed and has nothing to do on Sunday. He decides to visit his parents. He misses home. (as, because) *As Rob is depressed and has nothing to do on Sunday, he decides to visit his parents because he misses home.*

2 He travels all the way to their home. He finds they're not in. (after) _____

_____

3 He starts to walk away. His mother calls him from the house on the other side of the road. (when)

_____

_____

4 Everyone at the party is having a great time. Rob realises his parents' life has changed. Rob finds it confusing and unhelpful. (while, which) _____

_____

_____

5 Rob goes to a movie with his parents and their friends. Rob doesn't feel any better in the cinema. The people he is with make him feel even worse. (although, where) _____

_____

_____

3 Editing

**Read the text. If there is a word missing, indicate where it goes (/\ )
and write the word on the right. If a line is correct, put a tick (✔).**

Laughter therapy		
There is increasing evidence /\ laughter is good for people with cancer	1	_that_
and it could help prevent other diseases as well. Studies from the USA	2	✔
have shown that laughter increases body's natural immunity. While you	3	_____
laughing, levels of important components of the immune system go up;	4	_____
the amounts white blood cells and natural painkillers in your blood rise	5	_____
considerably. Laughter is also good exercise. It increases heart rate,	6	_____
improving the flow of air to lungs. Some hospitals in Canada now use a	7	_____
'laugh mobile'. Patients select items from trolley containing humorous	8	_____
books and videos. The Canadians also point that patients with smiles on	9	_____
their faces are easier for the nurses to deal with. However, one	10	_____
laughter therapist says that is important to watch out for patients who	11	_____
don't join in. Although most people are suitable for laughter therapy,	12	_____
those have recently had an operation should avoid laughing too much	13	_____
at first. The initial increase in blood pressure might be enough to	14	_____
cause heart attack. But at least you'd die laughing!	15	_____

4 Style

**Read the texts below and decide whether they are
from:**

a   a book review in a popular newspaper.
b   an essay about a book in an English language exam.
c   an essay by a student of English literature.
d   a book review in a quality newspaper.

1 ☐
Fernand Braudel's three-volume history of the Mediterranean must remain one of the classics of twentieth-century history, with its breathtaking scope, fascinating observations

2 ☐
Cathy Conrad's latest novel has just hit the bookshops but it is already a runaway bestseller. Don't miss another adventure with her super-cool detective Guy Gurney sorting out all the crooks of LA. Go out and get your copy now!

3 ☐
The use of irony and humour in Graham Greene's dialogues is illustrated clearly in *The Quiet American*, a novel in which the themes of colonialism and culture shock are dealt with masterfully.

4 ☐
All things considered, in my opinion, it is one of the best detective novels I have ever read. If you enjoy crime stories, I would really recommend you read it.

5 Guided writing

**Write a short book review in your notebook based on
the information below. Or follow the plan to write a
review of a book you have read recently.**

Paragraph 1 Introduction
Title: *The Snow Queen*
Author: Rose Cartwright
Category: historical novel

Paragraph 2 A summary of the plot
young queen goes from Denmark to Ruritania –
adventures on the way – problems in Ruritania –
escapes from castle – saves prince from execution –
happy marriage with prince

Paragraph 3 Good and bad points
plot exciting at start/confusing at end/not historically accurate
style complex + repetitive/good use of dialogue
characters/heroine interesting/others not believable/especially the king

Paragraph 4 Conclusion
fun to read/interesting theme/not a great book/poor research

Word Power

1 Confusing words

Circle the correct word.

1 He got up in a bad *humour/ mood* this morning; he was very miserable.

2 The meal was delicious; it was a very *enjoyable/funny* evening.

3 If you are *dissatisfied/ unsatisfied* with the service, complain to the manager.

4 She *dressed/wore* a lovely red blouse for the party.

5 Hurry up, or we'll *lose/miss* the bus!

6 I *passed/spent* a lovely weekend at my aunt's house.

In your notebook, write sentences using the other words.

2 Word families

Complete the diagrams with the words in the box.

chat, cling to, glance, clutch, glimpse, grasp, handle, hug, mention, mutter, observe, shout, spot, whisper, witness

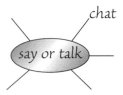

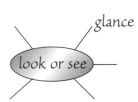

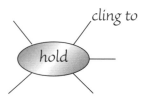

3 Word families

Replace the words in brackets with a more suitable verb from Exercise 2 in the correct form.

1 He ____glanced____ (look quickly) at his watch and left the room.

2 'I feel sick,' she said, and _____ (hold tightly) her stomach.

3 You must _____ (hold) it very carefully; it's fragile.

4 He slipped and had to _____ (hold desperately onto) the window ledge until help arrived.

5 'Help! Help!' he _____ (say very loudly).

6 Nobody _____ (see) the accident.

7 I only _____ (see for a very short time) him; I couldn't possibly describe him.

8 She _____ (say) something to herself under her breath.

9 'Can you keep a secret?' she _____ (say very quietly).

10 My baby sister _____ (hold) her teddy bear tightly when she goes to bed.

11 They didn't _____ (say anything about) the results.

12 Suddenly I _____ (see) my friend in the crowd.

⇨ Lexicon, Students' Book, page 163.

4 Reactions

Write reactions to these statements to show what is indicated in brackets.

1 A: My dog died yesterday. (*sympathy*) _____

   B: _____

2 A: My dad passed his driving test. (*surprise*)

   B: _____

3 A: It's too long, don't you think? (*agreement*)

   B: _____

5 Pronunciation: Word stress

Put these words into the correct group according to the stress pattern.

ambitious, amusing, considerate, conventional, enjoyable, entertaining, humorous, impatient, likeable, popular, reliable, romantic, sensible, sensitive, sociable, sympathetic

1 oOo	2 oOoo	3 ooOo	4 Ooo
ambitious			

6 Extension: British and American English

Replace the American English words in italics with the British English words from the box.

> autumn, biscuits, crisps, film, flat, ground floor, lift, motorway, petrol, shop, sweets, to

1 I rented a new *apartment* _____ in the *fall* _____ . There's no *elevator* _____, but fortunately it's on the *first floor* _____.

2 We ran out of *gas* _____ on the *freeway* _____.

3 If you're hungry, help yourself to some *candy*, *potato chips* _____ or *cookies* _____ .

4 There's a good *movie* _____ on TV tonight.

5 The *store* _____ is open Monday *through* _____ Saturday.

7 Extension: Expressions

Complete the dictionary definitions with the colloquial expressions from the box.

> Jekyll and Hyde, piece of cake, red carpet, red tape, white elephant

1 Something can be described as a _____ if it is very easy to do.

2 A person can be described as a _____ character if he or she has big changes of mood or personality.

3 _____ treatment means very special treatment.

4 A _____ is something that is useless, unwanted and usually expensive.

5 _____ means rules that delay action.

A→Z Use a good dictionary.

8 Extension: Newspaper stories

Read the headlines (1–5) and match them with the extracts (a–e).

1 REX GETS RED CARPET TREATMENT ☐

2 'TOP STAR WAS JEKYLL AND HYDE' CLAIMS BOSS ☐

3 DOME WAS WHITE ELEPHANT, SAYS POLL ☐

4 IT WAS 'A PIECE OF CAKE', SAYS WINNING CHEF ☐

5 POLITICIAN ATTACKS RED TAPE ☐

a) A local survey shows that people in the North believe it was a waste of money. Not many made the trip down to London to visit it, and most thought the money could have been better spent.

b) The dog was given a medal at a special ceremony near the house where the rescue took place. He had his photo taken with the mayor – and then was served his favourite food in a silver bowl.

c) Local MP Jack Mann said it was difficult to get anything done because work was constantly passed from one government department to another.

d) Manager Metcalfe defended his decision to transfer Shannon. 'He was so unpredictable. One week he'd train hard and play well, the next he'd miss training or make no effort in the match. We need consistent players at this club.'

e) The winning entry needed over 2,000 eggs and 500 bags of flour. Mick Taylor, who baked it in a specially designed oven, said: 'It took longer to prepare, but apart from that it was just like baking a normal-size cake.'

9 Extension: Onomatopoeia

A word is onomatopoeic if it sounds like the action it is describing. Below, the word splashing resembles the sound of water:

*After a lot of **splashing** and struggling, Mr Pickwick was finally rescued.*

Complete the sentences with these onomatopoeic verbs in the correct form.

> chuckle, crack, drip, howl, mutter, patter, tick

1 The ice _____ and he fell in the water.

2 I couldn't sleep because the clock was _____ loudly.

3 The rain was _____ on the roof, the wind was _____ and water was _____ from the ceiling.

4 He _____ something about coming back tomorrow.

5 She was reading a book, _____ happily to herself.

Language Awareness

1 ★ Tenses
Match each sentence with the correct response, a or b.

1	I've washed the car.	a	Don't tell me you haven't finished!
2	I've been washing the car.	b	Great! I won't feel embarrassed when I park it in town.
3	We had lunch when John arrived.	a	So he won't be hungry now.
4	We were having lunch when John arrived.	b	I hope you invited him to join you.
5	Why was she so cold?	a	She had been swimming in the sea.
6	Why was she so proud?	b	She had swum five kilometres.
7	Why are you writing in pencil?	a	I'm allergic to ink.
8	Why do you write in pencil?	b	I've left all my pens at home.
9	She's on a diet for a month.	a	So she probably isn't eating sweets.
10	She has diabetes.	b	So she probably doesn't eat sweets.
11	What time do you go home?	a	I don't know yet. I may have to stay late.
12	What time are you going home?	b	Usually at five o'clock.

2 ★★ State or activity verbs?
Put the verbs in brackets into the correct tense, using either the simple or the continuous form. Paraphrase the verbs and say if they are state (S) or activity (A) verbs.

1 I _have been thinking (= using my mind = A)_ about what you said and I _think (= have an opinion = S)_ buying a mountain bike is a very good idea.

2 Come on, I _____ (not look) at your boyfriend, I _____ (look) at his tie. It _____ (look) horrible.

3 You know Sarah _____ (see) Gary! I _____ (see) them yesterday holding hands in the park.

4 We _____ (have) dinner at a restaurant when a waiter, who _____ (have) a tray of drinks in his hands, tripped and fell to the floor.

5 Look, Peter _____ (taste) this Australian wine. He'll tell us how it _____ (taste).

6 Suzi isn't here. She _____ (go out) with Carl. They _____ (go out) for quite a long time.

3 ★★ Simple or Continuous?
(Circle) the correct form of the verb.

Mike: What (1) *have you done/have you been doing* recently? I (2) *haven't seen/haven't been seeing* you around for years.

Chris: Well, I (3) *have worked/'ve been working* abroad for a while. I'm in London for a holiday.

Mike: Where (4) *do you stay/are you staying* in London?

Chris: At my brother's. He (5) *lives/is living* in our parents' old house in Wimbledon.

4 ★★★ Simple or Continuous?
Tick (✔) the correct sentences and rewrite the others correctly in your notebook.

1 He wasn't understanding why we had left earlier.

2 Do you try to unlock that box? Forget it. Nobody has managed it for years.

3 I haven't been cooking anything so there's nothing to eat.

4 I'm not sure if they're knowing about your party.

5 They showed this film for a month last summer.

6 He had been training really hard before he won the championship.

7 They are resembling their father quite a lot.

8 I wasn't asleep at 2.30: I had a cup of tea and read the paper.

Check Your Grammar

1 Past tenses, *would* and *used to*

Put the verbs in brackets in the correct tenses: Past Simple, Past Continuous, Past Perfect or Past Perfect Continuous. Use used to or would in front of the verb where possible.

Charles Spencer Chaplin was born in 1889 in London. He (1) __had__ (have) a very difficult childhood. As a boy, Charlie (2) _____ (work) to earn his living, and before he was fifteen, he (3) _____ (see) his mother being put into an asylum. Charlie (4) _____ (watch) his mother from backstage while she (5) _____ (perform) and it was then that he first (6) _____ (think) about taking up such a career for himself.

When Chaplin (7) _____ (tour) the US twice with the famous Fred Karno group, he was head-hunted by the American Keystone film company. He (8) _____ (work) for them for three years before he discovered he could direct for himself.

Along with Douglas Fairbanks and Mary Pickford, Chaplin (9) _____ (form) United Artists in 1919, with whom he (10) _____ (make) most of his classic films. He (11) _____ (appear) in his first talking film, *The Great Dictator*, in 1940.

In 1952, after McCarthy's Commission (12) _____ (accuse) him of communist sympathies he (13) _____ (emigrate) to Switzerland, where he (14) _____ (live) with his family until his death in 1977.

3 Determiners

Circle the correct determiner.

Save the Children

As you read this, there are 20 million children who have been torn from (1) *the/their/these* homes by armed conflict and violence – that's more than (2) *some/all/every* the children in the UK.

Of these, 7 million escape to (3) *another/other/the other* country as refugees. (4) *So/All of/ Such* children can remain uprooted for six years or more. (5) *More/Much/Many* never return home.

Save the Children is working with displaced children in over 13 countries. It's our goal to create (6) *the/a/the* second world where (7) *other/many/all* children are safe, healthy, educated and happy.

It's two years now since Ginda's father was murdered and the surviving members of (8) *the/this/a* family fled to a shanty town. It's not (9) *the/an/any* ideal place to grow up, but now, thanks to Save the Children, Ginda is back at school. For her, school is a safe place, where she is able to share her experiences with (10) *other/another/all* displaced children. In this supportive environment Ginda is gradually putting the traumas of her past behind her.

This is just (11) *some/an/no* example of the way Save the Children is working to protect child refugees. By placing an order from this catalogue, you can help thousands of (12) *many/other/all* children like Ginda.

2 Simple or Continuous?

Match each sentence with the correct response, a or b.

1	Why do you think Paul won first prize?	a	He had written the best poem.
		b	He had been writing the best poem.
2	Are you ready to go?	a	Yes, I've been packing everything.
		b	Yes, I've packed everything.
3	Are you on holiday here?	a	Yes, and I'm doing babysitting occasionally.
		b	Yes, and I do babysitting occasionally.
4	I can speak Japanese.	a	How long have you learned?
		b	How long have you been learning?
5	Were you at home when there was a power cut?	a	Yes, I typed an essay on my computer.
		b	Yes, I was typing an essay on my computer.
6	He's never had a car.	a	Does he walk to work?
		b	Is he walking to work?

3 Style

9 Vocabulary

1 Opinion adjectives
Answer the questionnaire with your opinions. Use the words in the box.

> attractive, chic, classy, cool, dated, elegant, smart, stylish, tacky, trendy, ugly

Style questionnaire
1 What do *you* think of these fashions for men?
   a) very short hair ....
   b) big earrings ....
   c) white nylon shirts ....
2 What do *you* think of these fashions for women?
   a) bright red leather skirts ....
   b) long skirts and dresses ....
   c) long hair ....
3 How fashionable are these things at the moment?
   a) mobile phones ....
   b) tattoos ....
   c) fur coats ....
4 What things are really cool at the moment?
   ....

2 Opinion adjectives
Complete the text using the cues in brackets.

The Domino Club is a good place to go to as it's very (1) _fashionable_ (fashion) and it's got good, (2) _____ (date) music. A lot of (3) _____ (style) people go there – the staff are very friendly and (4) _____ (work). The decoration is quite (5) _____ (class) but there is a big statue at the entrance which is a bit (6) _____ (taste), in my opinion anyway. The only disadvantage is that the club is in a (7) _____ (run) area of the city. Some of the people around there look a bit (8) _____ (menace) and (9) _____ (aggression), especially when you come out of the club at three in the morning!

3 Common verbs with different meanings
Complete the text with the correct form of the verbs *make*, *have* and *get*.

The government have just (1) _made_ the decision to legalise busking on the London Underground. Musicians who want to busk will (2) _____ the chance to take a test to prove their musical talent. If they pass, they will (3) _____ licences to play at different underground stations around the capital. We asked some passengers who were (4) _____ the Tube to work this morning what they thought. Some (5) _____ negative feelings towards buskers.

'They (6) _____ a mess and some buskers (7) _____ a terrible noise too, don't they?' said one man. 'Personally, I (8) _____ fed up with them begging for money.'

One elderly woman thought that buskers were lazy. 'They (9) _____ money by doing nothing, don't they?' she said. 'Why don't they go out and (10) _____ proper jobs?'

However, others thought that 'official' buskers would (11) _____ a good effect on the Underground. 'They perk you up and (12) _____ you feel better,' replied a student. One woman thought buskers would (13) _____ a positive influence on tourism. 'Last year, when I was in the Paris Metro there were some great musicians,' she commented. 'I (14) _____ a great time listening to a group of African drummers. I now (15) _____ a CD they (16) _____ and I listen to it all the time!' In fact, many famous musicians have (17) _____ a living from busking, before (18) _____ to the top.

⇨ Lexicon, Students' Book, page 163.

Remember

1 ★ more/less than, as ... as
Compare the pairs of objects in the pictures using the adjectives provided.

1 spacious, classy, beautiful, modern

   The black car is more spacious than the white one.

   _____

2 fast, dangerous, friendly, nervous

   _____

   _____

3 traditional, trendy, simple, expensive

   _____

   _____

2 ★ Comparatives and superlatives
Put the adjectives in brackets into the comparative or superlative form. Use *the* in front of the adjective if necessary.

1 Dolphins are among *the most intelligent* (intelligent) mammals in the world.

2 Mars and Venus seem _____ (likely) to have life than Earth.

3 The results of experiments with an AIDS treatment are _____ (bad) than expected.

4 This wonderful sun-powered engine is _____ (promising) of all that have been designed so far.

5 Peter is _____ (bright) of the two brothers.

6 Emotional intelligence is probably _____ (trendy) term in modern psychology.

3 ★★★ Comparatives and superlatives
Complete the book review with adjectives from the box. Use comparatives or superlatives.

> beautiful, dark, influential, witty, good, expected, good-looking, interesting, lively

Love is Blind by Mary Watson
On arrival at a quiet guesthouse situated in (1) __the most beautiful__ mountainous setting you can imagine, Eileen meets Colin, who introduces himself as a doctor and is (2) _____ than a film star. Within days Eileen falls in love, unaware of Colin's (3) _____ side. Then one night she accidentally hears him talking on the phone to one of the country's (4) _____ people and realises Colin is blackmailing the man.

From now on the love story changes into a thriller and becomes much (5) _____ . The dialogue gets (6) _____ and the characters (7) _____ . We read on until we get to the (8) _____ , yet convincing ending. (9) _____ holiday read available!

4 ★★ much, more and less
Put *much*, *more* or *less* in the gaps.

1 Tonight's performance is __much__ more interesting than yesterday's.

2 Models have a _____ rigorous diet than other people.

3 _____ expensive clothes are not always better quality.

4 VCRs are normally _____ expensive than DVD players.

5 The cost of living in Europe is _____ higher than in Africa.

6 Driving is _____ difficult to learn than riding a bike.

7 We're looking for a _____ older person for this job.

8 In the past people were _____ _____ interested in protecting the environment.

10 Grammar

PARTICIPLE AND RELATIVE CLAUSES

1 ★ *-ing* and *-ed* participles
Circle the correct participle.

1 The police are examining the evidence *collecting*/*collected* during the investigation.
2 Some kids discovered the stolen money *hiding/hidden* in a garden shed.
3 The police on this motorway are very busy *fining/fined* people for speeding.
4 I've often met people *collecting/collected* shells on the beach.
5 The escaped prisoner *hiding/hidden* in a forest near Nottingham was seen yesterday in a village shop.
6 Drivers *fining/fined* for speeding risk losing their licences.

2 ★ Types of relative clauses
Underline the relative clauses and circle the words they refer to.

1 The winner who has been unanimously selected by the judges, is Marion Wong.
2 We need to see a film that will cheer you up a bit.
3 This completely unknown Van Gogh painting which has been hidden in an attic for years will be auctioned in London next week.
4 This is the man whose books have been so popular recently.
5 We had lunch at The Three Bells where they serve traditional English food.
6 The eggs we had for breakfast weren't very fresh.

3 ★★ Relative pronouns
Add relative pronouns and commas where necessary.

1 Heathrow, *which* is one of the biggest airports in the world, handles hundreds of flights every day.
2 Some people would do anything _____ could increase their promotion prospects.
3 The Prime Minister _____ has just arrived will make a speech tonight.
4 The show was put on by four young designers _____ have won major prizes this year, and _____ work has become very fashionable.
5 The style _____ fashion designers are trying to promote this year can only appeal to very young people.
6 Jack Nicholson _____ talent is versatile and unanimously appreciated has received three Oscars so far.
7 The lecture was called off five minutes before it was due to start _____ annoyed the audience enormously.
8 We landed in San Diego _____ the plane was supposed to refuel.

4 ★★ Relative clauses
Rewrite the sentences changing the information in brackets into relative clauses. Add commas where necessary.

1 My oldest brother is a paediatrician. (He has four children of his own.)

    My oldest brother, who has four children of his own, is a paediatrician.

    _____

2 The TV breaks down all the time. (This makes us listen to the radio more.)

    _____
    _____
    _____

3 The fire brigade haven't managed to put out the fire. (It broke out at 5 a.m.)

    _____
    _____
    _____

4 The report describes human rights violations in Asia. (Amnesty International published it this month.)

    _____
    _____
    _____

5 Charles Perry will host a chat show on TV5. (His lifestyle is constantly being discussed in the popular press.)

    _____
    _____
    _____

6 Some African animal species have to be helped by international organisations. (They are threatened with extinction.)

    _____
    _____
    _____

5 ★★★ Relative clauses

In your notebook, add comments to these facts. Use *which*.

> Mobile telephones emit radiation, which might be dangerous.

1 It's difficult to find a job if you don't have basic computer skills, ___

2 English has practically become the world's international language, ___

3 Some countries refuse to sign a ban on producing chemical weapons, ___

4 The 2008 Olympics will be held in China, ___

6 ★★★ Relative clauses

In your notebook, write statements to which you could add these comments.

> My painting won first prize, which was quite unexpected.

1 ___ , which made me mad.

2 ___ , which I really appreciated.

3 ___ , which changed my plans for the future.

4 ___ , which scared me to death.

7 ★★★ Relative clauses

Read the story and complete it with suitable relative clauses. Add commas where necessary.

Peter was getting a little worried about his friend Sam (1), *who was looking really depressed* . He was living alone in a big house (2) _____ _____ . Sam's parents (3) _____ _____ had died and his girlfriend Sara was studying in the States.

One day Peter (4) _____ found Sam with a letter. He saw an American stamp on the envelope (5) _____ .

'Sara wants me to join her in California,' Sam said. 'I think I'll go, although I hate flying (6) _____ _____ .'

Two weeks later Peter took Sam to the airport (7) _____ .

The next evening Peter (8) _____ _____ got a phone call. Sam's plane (9) _____ _____ had been forced to make an emergency landing in Manchester (10) _____ _____ . Sam had been offered another flight, but he had decided to come home to wait for Sara.

Prepositions

In informal sentences

Look at these examples.

Ordinary speech (written and spoken)
*He's the man she's been going out **with**.*
*She found the earring she had been looking **for**.*

Very formal
*He is the man **with whom** she has been going out.*
*She found the earring **for which** she had been looking.*

Complete the less formal relative clauses for each sentence.

1 Tahiti is the place
  a from which the word 'tattoo' comes.
  b which *the word tattoo comes from*

2 This is the eyebrow
  a through which they pushed the needle.
  b which _____

3 He is the man
  a with whom we had our interviews.
  b who _____

4 It's her left arm
  a on which she's got a tattoo.
  b which _____

5 Mick is the specialist
  a by whom I had my tongue pierced.
  b who _____

6 Body piercing is something
  a about which people are often nervous.
  b which _____

7 Look at my necklace
  a for which I only paid £10.
  b which _____

8 He is a person
  a of whom I am very fond.
  b who _____

⇨ Lexicon, Students' Book, pages 166–169.

11 Communication

1 Describing people (1–6)
Match the sentences and replies (a–f).

1 Tell us about this girl you're going out with! ☐

2 Why do you like her? Is she good-looking? ☐

3 What does she look like? ☐

4 So she looks like Jennifer Lopez? ☐

5 And what's she like then? ☐

6 And what sort of things does she like? ☐

a I think so.

b Well, she's very nice.

c She's quiet but she's got a good sense of humour.

d She's really into music.

e Not really. She's better-looking!

f She's tall and slim with dark hair.

2 Modifiers
Circle the best modifier in the description.

My friend Esther is (1) *very/absolutely/much* friendly. She is (2) *really/much/quite* taller than me and she has got (3) *absolutely/totally/very* long blonde hair. She knows how to dress (4) *slightly/totally/pretty* well. She loves parties and is (5) *a bit/totally/fairly* brilliant at dancing – she can dance (6) *a lot/really/ quite* better than me! The only problem with Esther is that she tends to be (7) *absolutely/a bit/a lot* lazy. She (8) *quite/pretty/really* loves lying in bed in the mornings and talking to people on her mobile phone. She also (9) *quite/absolutely/a bit* hates doing any kind of physical exercise. She takes the bus to school even though it's (10) *an extremely/a much/a totally* short walk of about five minutes!

4 Describing people
Choose a friend. Complete the description about him or her. Use the cues or other modifiers and adjectives.

1 *He/She* is *very/not very – tall/short*

   He is not very tall. _____

2 *He/She* is _____ than me.
   much/a bit – taller/shorter

3 *He/She* is _____ good-looking.
   extremely/quite/not very

4 *He/She* has got _____ eyes.
   quite/really – big/small

5 *He/She* looks a bit like _____
   e.g. *Julia Roberts/George Clooney*

6 At first, *he/she* comes across as _____
   a *bit/quite/very/extremely – shy/outgoing*

7 *He/She* tends to be _____
   rather/very – scatty/shy/impatient/lazy

8 *He/She* is a bit on the _____
   side. *serious/nervous/untidy*

9 What I like best about *him/her* is that

   _____

5 Describing people
Look at the photo of Penelope Cruz. Write sentences about her in your notebook. Use modifiers.

She is extremely good-looking!

3 Modifiers
Look at the table. Cross out the modifiers which *cannot* go with the adjectives.

1	~~very~~/really/pretty/absolutely/~~much~~	**strong opinion adjectives:** e.g. fantastic/amazing/terrible/awful
2	a bit/quite/much/a lot/very/slightly	**comparative adjectives:** e.g. better/smaller/more intelligent
3	extremely/very/a bit/totally/absolutely/ rather/slightly/fairly/really/pretty	**descriptive adjectives:** e.g. dark/tall/short/thin
4	very/a bit/quite/really/pretty/totally	**positive opinion adjectives:** e.g. nice/witty/good/friendly
5	much/slightly/very/a bit/a lot/really/ extremely	**negative adjectives:** e.g. scatty/boring/lazy/aggressive

MULTI-PART VERBS

1 Two-word verbs

Complete the description with the correct form of the verbs in the box.

> take out, fall for, take after, keep on, get on (x2),
> put on, come across, show off, point out, go off, get to

This guy has been (1) _taking_ my sister _out_ for four or five weeks. At first we (2) _____ quite well because he (3) _____ as a really friendly, outgoing person. Unfortunately, I've (4) _____ him since then. He thinks he is funny and (5) _____ telling really bad jokes. The problem is that he always starts howling with laughter before he (6) _____ the end. He also (7) _____ in front of everybody and tries to (8) _____ accents, imitating famous people. I've (9) _____ this _____ to my sister but she thinks he's really funny. She says he (10) _____ his dad, who's an actor. His dad's (11) _____ now but apparently he used to be on TV when he was much younger. All I can say is I don't think much of my sister's taste. She always (12) _____ the wrong sort of man!

2 Three-word verbs

Complete the verbs with the prepositions in the box.

> to (x3), of, for, with (x4)

1 I am *looking forward* _____ going on holiday.
2 I *get on* _____ my sister really well.
3 I don't like it but I have to *put up* _____ it.
4 I finally *got round* _____ tidying my room. It was a real mess.
5 I *go in* _____ collecting mugs from all the different places I go to.
6 He's very clever and he always knows how to *get out* _____ trouble.
7 I was nervous about doing the bungee jump but in the end I *went through* _____ it.
8 I really should *get down* _____ doing some work but I just don't feel like it.
9 Why don't you start walking? I'll *catch up* _____ you in five minutes.

⇨ Lexicon, Students' Book, pages 170–176.

3 Three-word verbs

Use the verbs from Exercise 2 to write sentences about the pictures.

1 _____
_____

2 _____
_____

3 _____
_____

4 _____
_____

5 _____

6 _____
_____

12 Focus on Writing

1 Describing places
Look at the pictures and complete the sentences. Use these words:

> not as … as, nearly as … as, much/ a bit/a
> lot/less/more … than,
> …er than

The cottage …

… and the mansion.

1 (cost) The cottage *is much less expensive than the mansion.*

2 (cost) The mansion _____

3 (age) The cottage _____

4 (age) The mansion _____

5 (size) The cottage _____

6 (size) The mansion _____

7 (distance) The cottage is _____

8 (distance) The mansion is _____

2 Descriptions with *too* and *enough*
These two people are looking for a new house. What would they say about the houses in Exercise 1? Complete the statements using *too* and *enough*.

Alexandra: *a rich businesswoman with a big family.*

1 The cottage is much ___*too small for my family*___ (size/family)

2 It hasn't got _____ (rooms/children)

3 It isn't _____ (distance/London)

4 The mansion has got _____ (garage space/cars)

Sam: *a single retired man with £80,000 savings who wants to live in the country.*

5 The mansion is _____ (high cost)

6 It's _____ (distance/London)

7 The cottage is _____ (size)

8 The cottage has got _____ (rooms)

3 Linking
Use the cues to write sentences with *so … that* and *such … that*.

1 (Sue/lazy/get up) *Sue's so lazy that she doesn't get up before lunch!*

2 (he/loud voice/not need a microphone) _____
_____

3 (car/expensive/afford) _____
_____

4 (big garden/get lost) _____
_____

5 (a lot of pollution/not breathe) _____

6 (Paul/scatty/forget) _____

7 (house/old/fall down) _____
_____

4 Giving examples
Complete the sentences using these linking words.

> such as, like, particularly, for example

1 I read newspapers *such as 'The Times' and 'The Guardian'.*

2 I am not very good at some subjects _____

3 I love going to films, _____

4 Some brands of clothes are expensive, _____

5 I'd love to meet a film star _____

5 Editing

Read the text carefully. When a line has an extra word, circle the word and write it on the right. When a line is correct, put a tick (✔) on the right.

People often wonder how to make their home more cosy, or that is warmer and	1 ____*or*____
more comfortable. One idea is a fireplace. Fire has always being been	2 _____
associated with warmth and positive feelings. If you can't have a real one, try	3 _____
putting in a good gas or electric fire. It is also important to have had a mantelpiece on	4 _____
which you can put your family or our friends' photos, souvenirs from trips abroad and	5 _____
interesting postcards. Something else that gives the effect of a real	6 _____
home is appropriate furniture. Armchairs and sofas with plenty of cushions so as	7 _____
well as wooden bookshelves create a feeling of	8 _____
comfort and relaxation. As for the floor, it is good to have natural wooden planks	9 _____
but a good carpet with a few matching the rugs will make it even more	10 _____
inviting. The next point worth careful and planning is how to light your home.	11 _____
As a general rule, you should avoid one central source of light, for example the one	12 _____
in the middle of the ceiling. Instead, choose of a couple of side lamps and put	13 _____
them on the coffee table or on the floor next up to the most comfortable armchair.	14 _____
Finally, think of some personal things. Favourite your paintings and posters on	15 _____
the walls, flowers on the window-sill, and other than details such as an old family	16 _____
clock or mirror, will work like miracles to change your place into a cosy home.	17 _____

6 Style

Read the two texts below. Which is a formal description of a house by an estate agent ☐ and which is a colloquial description? ☐

A

My uncle Keith's house is really cool 'cos it's right on the beach. It's great 'cos you can hear the waves at night when you're crashed out in bed. I guess his joint's a bit like Uncle Keith himself, very laid-back and relaxed. He's forty-something and used to play in a rock band, so you can work out what sort of guy he is. The coolest place in the house is the verandah. You can just lie back in the hammock, listening to Keith's jazz records and gazing out to sea. Ah, one more thing. It's got a great little pool you can cool down in when it gets hot. Not something that happens too often down in Cornwall!

B

This is an impressive detached house located next to a beautiful Cornish beach. It is set in a large garden and has superb sea and rural views. The property has a spacious living room with French windows leading out to a verandah. The kitchen is well-equipped and there is a large entrance hall. Upstairs there are three bedrooms, one of which has an en-suite bathroom. It also has a heated outdoor swimming pool and a double garage.

7 Guided writing: Completing notes

Read the texts in Exercise 6 again. Make notes on these topics in your notebook.

- **Uncle Keith's house**
  location _____
  good things about the house _____
  best place in the house _____
- **Uncle Keith**
  character _____
  past life _____
  interests _____

8 Guided writing: Descriptions

Use your notes from Exercise 7 to write a description of the house and its owner (maximum 100 words). Write in a neutral style.

⇨ Lexicon, Students' Book, page 152.

Word Power

1 Connotation
Read the sentences below. Decide how the <u>underlined</u> words are used *in the context*: with a *positive* meaning, with a *neutral* meaning or with a *negative* meaning.

1 She's so <u>trendy</u> (*negative*) she's always changing her look. One moment she's wearing <u>chic</u> (*positive*) dresses and the next she's got jeans on.

2 I really love <u>old-fashioned</u> (_____) cinemas. They've got such a <u>romantic</u> (_____) atmosphere, haven't they?

3 Can't you stop getting at me? I've had enough of your <u>funny</u> (_____) remarks about my <u>new</u> (_____) hairstyle.

4 She's such a <u>competitive</u> (_____) tennis player that she never ever gives up. But she's too <u>individualistic</u> (_____) to be a good doubles player.

5 I suppose it's quite an <u>original</u> (_____) sculpture, if you like that sort of thing. But personally, I'm not very keen on <u>contemporary</u> (_____) art.

6 He's very <u>slim</u> (_____) but he's got a <u>fair-sized</u> (_____) nose, hasn't he? And it's <u>pierced</u>, (_____) which doesn't help much, does it?

2 Compound adjectives
Match the two parts of the adjectives.

11	absent-	a	air
12	laid-	b	fashioned
13	old-	c	to-date
14	fair-	d	down
15	anti-	e	minded
16	African-	f	social
17	short-	g	back
18	run-	h	sized
19	up-	i	American
10	open-	j	lived

2 Compound adjectives
Match five of the adjectives from Exercise 2 with these pictures.

1 _____

2 _____

3 _____

4 _____

5 _____

Think of five people or places you know that could be described by the adjectives under the pictures.

_____

_____

4 Confusing words
Read the text and (circle) the correct words.

My cousin Jade is now a (1) *respected/respectable* fashion designer who works for most of the year in Milan. In fact she has just set up her own company and it is already making (2) *profits/benefits*. Jade has always been rather unconventional as far as clothes go. When she was at university, where she did a (3) *career/course* in design, she never used to (4) *dress/wear* in the (5) *last/latest* styles. She would always make her own (6) *clothes/dresses*, even her own jeans and shirts. Jade loves bright colours (7) *alike/like* reds, yellows and greens and when she was younger her clothes often used to scandalise her (8) *fathers/parents*. Sometimes, she gives me (9) *advice/council* about what to wear, but I am afraid I never listen to her. I am much too conventional and I (10) *prefer/rather* wearing dark suits and ties.

5 🔤 Words with more than one meaning

Look at the underlined words and try to guess their meanings from the context. Write your answers in your notebook and check them in a dictionary.

1 What kind of gear should I wear for the party?
2 She is a good driver and changes gear when she comes to corners.
3 He is very smart and is always well-dressed.
4 It is a smart phone and has a mini-computer which you can programme.
5 The temperature has just gone up 10 degrees in a day. The climate's going mad!
6 She did two degrees, one in economics and the other in law.
7 Yesterday, I bought myself a brand new car.
8 It is the most expensive brand on the market.
9 I don't like wearing bright colours.
10 She's extremely bright and has just got 'A's in her exams.

6 Colloquial expressions

What can you guess about the person from the luggage in the picture below? Complete the dialogue with words from the box.

> professional tennis player, reader, sports, tennis, books, sandals, sports journalist, messy, tennis balls, teddy bear

A: Well, the person obviously likes (1) _____ such as football.
B: You can say that again. The person must be dead keen on (2) _____ , I mean look at the racket. And there are loads of (3) _____ , aren't there?
A: Must be a big (4) _____ too! There are (5) _____ all over the place.

B: Mmm, that's true. And I think the person must be really (6) _____ . I mean everything's chaotic, isn't it?
A: Right. And look at that great big (7) _____ . It's a bit over the top, isn't it?
B: That's true. And those (8) _____ are a bit tacky in my opinion – they can't be very comfy.
A: I think the person must be a (9) _____ _____ , someone like that.
B: Maybe, or the person could be a (10) _____ _____ , covering football and tennis.

7 Extension: People's appearance

Put the labels in the right places.

> scar, lines, wrinkles, freckles, Adam's apple, receding hair, sideburns, double chin, rosy cheeks

Exam Zone

USE OF ENGLISH

**1 Read the text and think of the word that best fits each gap.
Use only one word in each gap. (25 marks)**

If you want to keep the traffic moving, ban buses (and bicycles)

By Minette Marrin

The Mayor of London, in announcing his grand new traffic congestion scheme, claims that he (0) *has* finished his long consultation with Londoners. Not so. No one has consulted me, (1) _____ the fact that I have been driving around London and using public transport almost all my adult life, and could (2) _____ said to know something about it.

So, I offer the Mayor the benefit of my experience of London traffic. It is not (3) _____ late, even though he has already issued his ambitious plan, because it is almost entirely unworkable, and he will (4) _____ to change it.

(5) _____ far the major cause of congestion, pollution and road rage on the streets of London is not the cars, as he (6) _____ to think, but the buses. Belching out diesel, buses stand still for unaccountably long periods, (7) _____ up the traffic.

Buses are quite useless to anyone who is obliged to (8) _____ to a timetable. Two weeks ago at Russell Square, I found three parked together, at the same stop with the (9) _____ number, any of which could have taken me close to my destination. (10) _____ three were quite unmanned.

These useless buses (11) _____ obstructing a large square footage of public highway. Perhaps it is a sophisticated form of covert traffic calming, (12) _____ the mysterious roadworks everywhere, which are quite clearly unnecessary.

It is not, (13) _____ , simply that buses are inexcusably unreliable and obstructive. They also seem to be faster and (14) _____ dangerous. I don't know how bus drivers are trained or recruited (15) _____ days, but to see them jump in and out of the bus lane without (16) _____ signalling, or speed round narrow intersections of ancient (17) _____ , swinging up onto pavements (18) _____ they go, is to despair and to hold your children close. Buses are too big for these streets, and these drivers, and these days.

And what is the Mayor's solution (19) _____ all this? Not to keep out the real culprits, but to exclude the cars. And without a remotely usable public transport (20) _____ in place instead. It is mad. Cars are not the problem; dependence on cars is a symptom of the problem.

Here is my suggestion. We should dump the red buses and use the (21)

_____ smaller, privately run, Hong Kong-style people-carriers (22) _____ . We must pour billions into the Underground. Until then, the Mayor must (23) _____ force yet more people on to public transport; if he does, (24) _____ will be riots and deaths from overcrowding,

overheating and public panic.

(25) _____ , all buses and large coaches, all outsize lorries and vans should be excluded from London: small vehicles only. Oh, and no cyclists; they are the most irresponsible, lawless and dangerous of the lot.

`25`

2 Read the text and choose the answer (a, b, c or d) which best fits each gap. (15 marks)

Let elephant live, say victim's family

by Richard Duce

The parents (0) _b_ Darren Cockrill, the zookeeper crushed (1) _____ by an elephant at the Kent animal park (2) _____ by the millionaire John Aspinall, asked yesterday (3) _____ the creature to be (4) _____ .

'Elephants were Darren's life. We (5) _____ want anything to happen to La Petite,' Barry and Patricia Cockrill told Port Lympne Animal Park. Mr and Mrs Cockrill

yesterday (6) _____ a trip from their home in Canvey Island, Essex, to the 270 acre zoo (7) _____ Hythe for a meeting with Jane Osborne, its (8) _____ , to discuss Monday's tragedy.

La Petite, (9) _____ is 14 years old and was thought to be placid, (10) _____ now been isolated from all (11) _____ Indian elephants at the animal park and in future will be treated as a bull, (12) _____

means she will have minimal contact with people.

Mr Cockrill was last seen (13) _____ at 11.30 a.m. on Monday when he went to tend La Petite. Half an hour later he was found dead by Steve Seath, (14) _____ head elephant keeper. Five elephants appeared to be (15) _____ guard over Mr Cockrill's body when he was discovered.

0	a for	b of	c by	d with
1	a to die	b to dead	c to dying	d to death
2	a belonged	b owned	c had	d seized
3	a that	b about	c for	d if
4	a spared	b killed	c punished	d saved
5	a can't	b don't	c do	d not
6	a got	b had	c did	d made
7	a by	b to	c near	d from
8	a director	b headmistress	c conductor	d boss
9	a she	b that	c what	d who
10	a is	b was	c will	d has
11	a other	b rest	c the other	d others
12	a which	b what	c that	d and
13	a alive	b living	c awake	d asleep
14	a a	b the	c that	d one
15	a holding	b doing	c standing	d taking

`15`

READING

**1 Choose the most suitable heading (a–g) for each paragraph (1–6) of the article.
There is one extra heading. (10 marks)**

a The teenage market ☐   e New generation technology ☐

b Mobile mania ☐   f Lower bills ☐

c Latest figures ☐   g TV by phone ☐

d Rising numbers ☐

☐ 10

MOBILE MANIA SPREADS as PHONES BECOME the MUST-HAVE GADGET

By Robert Uhlig, technology correspondent

1 More than 24 million Britons now own a mobile phone, according to statistics released yesterday. The growth is expected to accelerate in the next few years as the mobile phone overtakes the personal computer as the most used method of accessing the Internet. No longer a tool only of well-heeled travelling executives and plumbers, the mobile phone is now as likely to be found in school satchels and shopping bags as in briefcases.

2 According to Vodafone, the market leader, of the 24 million cellphones in use, 11.9 million are prepaid, many of which are now used by teenagers. Schools have even taken to banning the use of mobile phones in classrooms and playgrounds.

3 The pre-pay services, using phone cards, have proved the most popular with phone users keen to keep their bills under control. The advent of 'pay-as-you-go' schemes has brought the mobile phone to millions who could not previously afford one or failed the necessary credit ratings. The average pre-pay customer spends £198 a year whereas the typical business customer receives a bill of £556 a year.

4 Around 40 percent of Britons now have a mobile, but by the end of next year, analysts expect the figure to increase by at least half. Even then, we will lag behind Finland, where 71 percent of people own a cellphone.

5 Already, analysts are predicting that within a few years more people will actually watch the six o'clock news or *Match of the Day* on their mobile phone than on television. The phone networks say more people are already using their mobiles at six o'clock each evening than the BBC claims are watching its evening news bulletin.

6 At the end of last year, a new technology called WAP, which enables the Internet to be viewed on a cellphone screen, was introduced. By the end of the year, almost all mobiles will be WAP-phones. Mike Caldwell, of Vodafone, said: 'The average person will not realise it is the Internet that is coming to them on their mobile phone. They'll just use it to watch what they think is television.'

2 Read the article again. Circle the best answer, (a, b, c or d), according to the text. (10 marks)

1 Why is the number of users of mobile phones expected to go up so much?
   a They are going to become cheaper.
   b They will be more popular amongst teenagers.
   c Phones will be used to connect with the Internet.
   d They are so convenient.

2 Who used to be main users of mobile phones?
   a Internet users.
   b Self-employed and business people.
   c People with very big incomes.
   d People who travelled a lot.

3 Why have pre-pay phone cards increased the number of users?
   a The phone calls are cheaper.
   b They are more convenient.
   c Bills tend to be lower.
   d Users have to pay before making calls.

4 What link is there between mobile phones and television?
   a People often use their phones during the six o'clock news.
   b Third generation mobiles will show live TV programmes from the Internet.
   c The new generation of phones will be much smaller than earlier ones.
   d Mobiles are good for watching the news and sports programmes.

5 *Well-heeled* in line 6 means
   a technologically competent.
   b fashionable.
   c tired of travel.
   d quite wealthy.

| 10 |

WRITING

Look at the photo. In your notebook, write a description of the man. Start by writing notes about the things below. Make up information where necessary.

1 Introduction – who he is and how you met him
2 A description of his physical appearance – use the photo
3 A description of his interests and personality
4 Conclusion – why you like/dislike him

Use your notes to write the description in your notebook. Be careful to use a neutral style: not too formal or too colloquial. (20 marks)

| 20 |

4 Beauty

13 Vocabulary

1 Opinion adjectives
Circle the correct adjective in the sentences.

1 That building is not what I would call a thing of *large/great* beauty.

2 The countryside around the cottage is really quite *scenic/glamorous*.

3 I think it is a *magnificent/good-looking* bridge.

4 Personally, I think George Clooney is extremely *handsome/pretty*.

5 She danced so well it seemed almost *striking/effortless*.

6 Westminster Abbey is a really *impressive/scenic* building.

7 She dresses in a very *sophisticated/brilliant* way and a lot of people think she is an extremely *glamorous/picturesque* woman.

8 That painting is a *powerful/real* masterpiece and has a *graceful/powerful* mixture of colours.

9 The views from the top of the tower are really quite *good-looking/stunning*.

10 That old car is much more *graceful/powerful* than all these new ones.

2 Idiomatic language
Complete the definitions of the idioms below with words from the box.

a secret, observe, out of place, obsessed, be physically sick, fierce competition, reads a lot, unsatisfactory

1 to have a bee in your bonnet
to be _____ about something

2 black sheep (of the family)
someone regarded as _____ by the rest of the family

3 a bookworm
someone who _____

4 to feel like a fish out of water
to feel _____

5 to be a fly on the wall
to be able to _____ a situation

6 to let the cat out of the bag
to give away _____

7 the rat race
the _____ of modern life

8 to be as sick as a dog
to _____

⇨ Lexicon, Students' Book, page 164.

3 A-Z Dictionary work
Read the sentences and try to work out the meanings of the idioms in italics in your notebook. Then use a good dictionary to check your answers. Look up the underlined words.

1 I was going to do a parachute jump but at the last moment I *got cold feet* and didn't do it.

2 She's a really irritating person. She's a real *pain in the neck*.

3 I am afraid the whole subject is *out of our hands*. There's nothing we can do about it.

4 I really *put my foot in it* when I told that joke at the party. Nobody thought it was funny.

5 I can never agree with him and we don't get on very well. We just don't *see eye to eye*.

6 I'm very busy. I'm just *up to my eyes* in work.

Remember

1 ★ Passive
Change the sentences into the passive. Use the beginnings provided.

1 A pianist first performed this piece in 1842. *This piece was first performed in 1842.*

2 They are going to sell Jimi Hendrix's guitar for $200,000 next week.

 Jimi Hendrix's guitar _____

 _____

3 They've offered him a job as a sound engineer at MGM.

 He _____

 _____

4 Someone must have told Gina about her promotion. *Gina* _____

 _____

5 Look! They are refurbishing this department store. *This department store* _____

 _____

6 People used to speak French on this island.

 French _____

 _____

7 The police should prosecute illegal parking more severely.

 Illegal parking _____

 _____

8 We had informed him about the accident before he arrived. *He* _____

 _____

9 They are changing the local park into an open-air cinema.

 The local park _____

 _____

10 The company may have dismissed Tom because of his political sympathies.

 Tom _____

 _____

2 ★★ Passive
Put the verbs in brackets into the passive in an appropriate tense.

1 Jeremy ____ *was invited* ____ (invite) to the conference ages ago.

2 The fault in the editing program _____ just _____ (discover).

3 He complained because he _____ (treat) badly by an immigration officer.

4 If nothing unusual happens, this film _____ (award) a few Oscars this year.

5 Roast lamb _____ usually _____ (serve) with mint sauce.

6 Our film _____ still _____ (develop) when we went to collect it.

7 Jack _____ never _____ (tell) that he _____ (adopt).

3 ★★★ Passive and active
Put the verbs in brackets into the passive or active in an appropriate tense.

Frank Martin's new film (1) .... (not recommend) for viewers under eighteen as it (2) .... (include) a lot of violent scenes. Martin, who (3) .... (nominate) for Academy Awards several times, this time (4) .... (choose) to entertain the public with a gloomy psychological thriller. His regular viewers (5) .... (surprise) to see Marilyn O'Neill this time as a bloodthirsty LA mafia boss. Interestingly, although she (6) .... (ask) on numerous occasions to comment on the film, she (7) .... always .... (refuse) to say a word.

4 ★ have/get something done
Rewrite the sentences using *have* (something done) or *get* (something done).

1 We must hire someone to repair the fridge.

 We must have the fridge repaired.

2 The hairdresser is going to dye Susan's hair blonde.

 _____

3 We've made a locksmith replace all the locks in our front door.

 _____

4 A professional gardener designed Lady Agatha's garden.

 _____

5 A man is changing the wallpaper in their living room.

 _____

6 Technicians will install a new computer in the manager's office.

 _____

14 Grammar

THE PASSIVE

1 ★ From active to passive
Change each sentence into the passive by making the underlined phrase the subject of the sentence. Sometimes two possible subjects are suggested. Use *by ...* only if necessary.

1 The government is going to propose a <u>new educational bill</u> next week.
   A new educational bill is going to be proposed by the government next week.

2 Sweden offered <u>John Ngomo</u>, a Kenyan champion runner, <u>their citizenship</u>.
   _____

3 The Prince of Wales has announced <u>a plan to reduce the living costs of the Royal Family</u>.
   _____

4 A computer will calculate <u>the risk of building a nuclear power plant near New York</u>.
   _____

5 An unknown contestant from Jamaica broke <u>the world high jump record</u> yesterday.
   _____

6 The world expects <u>China</u> to change its internal policy.
   _____

7 Someone must keep <u>the business world</u> more aware of social issues.
   _____

8 A famous rock musician is composing <u>a new song</u> to commemorate <u>the anniversary of Princess Diana's death</u>.
   _____

2 ★★ Passive tenses
Change the verbs in brackets into the passive using appropriate tenses.

Ten children in hospital after bus crash

Ten children are in hospital after their school bus crashed into a van in Bristol this afternoon. Both the van and the bus (1) _____were_____ badly _____ (damage).

A spokeswoman for the local Ambulance Trust says ten children (2) _____ (take) to hospital. Most of them (3) _____ (treat) for minor injuries. It is believed that the bus driver, who (4) _____ also _____ (detain) in hospital after the accident, hadn't seen the van come out of a side road.

The bus, which (5) _____ (register) with a small local company, was taking the children for their regular swimming lesson. A spokesman for Bristol City Council, which awarded the contract to the company, says a full investigation (6) _____ (carry out). Police said the road (7) _____ (close) for several hours until the bus (8) _____ (remove).

3 ★ Passive infinitives
Change the verbs in brackets into the passive infinitive (ordinary or perfect) or gerund.

1 I wouldn't like <u>to be disqualified</u> (disqualify) just before the end of the race.

2 _____ (rob) is always a traumatic experience.

3 Dorothy must _____ (give) a tranquilliser. She's so quiet.

4 There's nothing exciting in _____ (fear) by your students.

5 I want _____ (listen) to properly.

6 I think he has _____ _____ (push) if he is to succeed.

7 I've never enjoyed _____ _____ (address) as 'Professor Hill'.

8 The exhibition may _____ _____ (visit) by over half a million people last month.

9 I refuse _____ (speak) to like that. It's rude.

10 He shouldn't _____ (expel) from the university when they found him cheating, and he could _____ (give) another chance.

11 Dogs aren't offended by _____ (tell) what to do.

12 The painting is likely _____ (sell) for more than $200,000.

4 ★★★ Passive or active?
Put the verbs in brackets into the passive or active in an appropriate tense.

Last night an American tourist (1) _____was found_____ (find) unconscious in front of Westminster Abbey. He (2) _____ (take) to hospital but the doctors (3) _____ (be) unable so far to detect the cause of his condition. Apparently, he (4) _____ (not attack) or (5) _____ (mug). He (6) _____ (not drink) either. He (7) _____ (regain) consciousness this morning and (8) _____ (question) now about the incident. His condition (9) _____ (describe) as good and he (10) _____ (not suffer) from any pain or discomfort. He (11) _____ (visit) by the American Consul later today, who wants to know whether he (12) _____ (treat) properly.

5 ★★★ Passive and active
Rewrite the text in your notebook using the passive when it is more suitable.

Someone found an ancient statue in a barn in Devon yesterday. Thieves had probably put it there after they had stolen it from a local collector of antiquities. The police are now investigating similar thefts that people have reported in the last twenty years. It is possible, though, that someone stole the statue much earlier, even before the Second World War. The police are going to call in experts from the British Museum to examine the statue and determine how long it had been in the barn.

An ancient statue was found …

Prepositions

With passive forms

1 Look at these examples:

*The building was totally covered **with** plastic **by** Christo. His projects are paid **for** completely **by** the sale of his own drawings.*

Complete the sentences with these prepositions.

> about, by (x5), in, on (x2), with

1 The patient was operated _____ a famous surgeon from New York.
2 His attention was focussed _____ the smallest painting in the room.
3 This will be dealt _____ immediately _____ our complaints department.
4 Christo's work has been talked _____ a lot and criticised _____ some people.
5 The money will be invested _____ a new museum.
6 The violin solo, composed _____ Tchaikovsky, was played _____ real feeling _____ the Portuguese violinist.

➡ Lexicon, Students' Book, pages 167 and 169.

2 Use the cues to write passive sentences in the past.

1 the museum/build/glass and metal/a young architect
The museum was built of glass and metal by a young architect.
2 the statue/make/wood/a young sculptor from London _____
3 the dish/invent/a French chef/and make/six different kinds of fruit _____
4 the roof/repair/new tiles/a local builder _____
5 the journey/make/three-metre boat/two students from Canada _____
6 the star/discover/a new radio telescope/a French astronomer _____
7 the plants/spray/a pesticide/the gardener _____
8 the Taj Mahal/built/marble/a Mogul emperor _____

15 Communication

1 Opinion adjectives
Complete the adjectives in the text. The first and last letters are given.

The music from the film *Captain Corelli's Mandolin* is really (1) <u>d e l i g h t f u l</u> . The main theme, Pelagia's song, is (2) h_ _ _ _ ing and sad. Some of the music is quite (3) r_ _ _ _ tic but it is not at all (4) so _ _ y or (5) s _ _ _ _ _ _ _ _ al. One of the best pieces is the (6) b _ _ _ _ _ _ t mandolin solo played by Corelli when Pelagia realises that she is falling in love with him. The tragic parts of the story are also reflected in the music with drums played in a (7) s _ _ _ y and (8) si _ _ _ _ er tone. Finally, there are lighter moments, especially the operatic singing of the Italian soldiers which is (9) li _ _ _ y and quite (10) ca _ _ _ y.

2 Agreeing and disagreeing
Agree and disagree with the opinions.

1 I'm not that keen on techno music.
   I am!/Neither am I.
   _____

2 Don't you think Elton John's the best singer around?
   _____

3 Jazz is much better than rock music, isn't it?
   _____

4 I think classical music is great, don't you?
   _____

5 Wouldn't you agree that the best music was from the 1960s?
   _____

6 Personally, I'm not that keen on folk music.
   _____

3 Giving opinions
Complete the dialogue with the words in the box.

> too, admit that, don't you think, I do, isn't it, I wouldn't, that's fair, not really, point, don't you, be honest, that keen, do I, if you ask, meant to be

Todd: Hey, have you heard the latest album by Destiny's Child? I think it's really great, (1) _____ ?

Andy: Personally, I'm not (2) _____ on that sort of music. You know, it's (3) _____ my thing. (4) _____ it's a bit superficial?

Todd: No, I don't think (5) _____ ! Just because you like all that heavy metal.

Andy: Yes, (6) _____ .

Todd: Well, (7) _____ me, heavy metal's horrible. To (8) _____ , the music's just loud and monotonous. It's nearly always the same too, (9) _____ ?

Andy: That's not the (10) _____ . It's (11) _____ loud. What about reggae? I like that a lot, (12) _____ – especially those old Bob Marley songs.

Todd: So (13) _____ , I have to (14) _____ some of them are great. But wouldn't you agree that the best singer in the world is Dido?

Andy: No, (15) _____ !

4 Asking for opinions
Choose the correct sentence (a or b) to follow each question.

1 Don't you like going to the cinema?	a	I thought you loved it.
2 Do you like going to the cinema?	b	We could go together next week.
3 Do you really like that book?	a	I thought it was great.
4 Don't you really like that book?	b	I thought it was awful.
5 Wouldn't you like to watch that film?	a	I've heard it's brilliant.
6 Would you like to watch that film?	b	It sounds awful.
7 Don't you think she's a good actress?	a	I think she's fantastic.
8 Do you think she's a good actress?	b	I don't think she's very good.
9 Did you enjoy the film?	a	I didn't think it was very good.
10 Didn't you enjoy the film?	b	You were laughing a lot.

MULTI-PART VERBS

1 Verbs you can guess the meaning of from their different parts
Look at the verbs in sentences (1–12) and match them with definitions (a–l).
Look at the two parts of the verbs.

1	I couldn't hear the music, so I *turned up* the volume.	a	a increase
2	My trousers were too long so I had them *turned up* five centimetres.		b make someone return in the same direction
3	They asked me to *turn down* the volume because they were studying.		c reduce in length
4	I didn't like the programme so I *turned off* the television.		d reduce
5	We *turned off* the main road when we got to the town.		e leave
6	I *turned out* the lights and went to sleep.		f move head and body towards somebody
7	She *turned to* me and smiled happily.		
8	I *turned on* the radio as soon as I got back home.		g return in the same direction
9	When I asked her about it she *turned away* and looked out of the window.		h not allow someone to enter
10	There were so many people at the concert that they had to *turn away* a lot of them.		i cause something to start working
11	We walked as far as the river and then *turned back* and came home along the road.		j move head and body away from somebody
12	The police *turned back* all the cars because there had been an accident and the motorway was completely blocked.		k cause something to stop working
			l switch off (lights)

2 Verbs you cannot guess the meaning of from their different parts
Circle the correct verb to replace the underlined multi-part verb.

1 She <u>turned up</u> late at the concert and missed the first part. *arrived/came/went*

2 I couldn't find my keys anywhere but they eventually <u>turned up</u> under my chair. *arrived/ appeared/found*

3 I decided to <u>turn down</u> the job because the pay wasn't good enough. *cancel/deny/reject*

4 That comedian <u>turns me off</u>. I don't think he's at all funny. *likes me/leaves me cold/interests me*

5 I thought I had failed the exam. But it <u>turned out</u> that I had done quite well. *appeared to be/ seemed to be/proved to be*

6 He doesn't work very hard but he <u>turns out</u> some good work occasionally. *produces/makes/creates*

7 I have a real problem and just don't know who to <u>turn to</u> for help. *ask/telephone/request*

8 The man suddenly <u>turned on</u> me and started hitting me with his umbrella. *moved/attacked/ shouted at*

3 *up* or *down*?
Read the text and circle the correct word.

'On the day of the exam, I woke (1) *up*/*down* early. I got (2) *up*/*down* and went (3) *up*/*down* to a café on the seafront for breakfast. I sat (4) *up*/*down* at my favourite table in the corner and got (5) *up*/*down* to some revising. Suddenly my mobile rang, I picked it (6) *up*/*down* – it was a friend of mine. There were only ten minutes to go before the exam! She had rung me (7) *up*/*down* to find out where I was. I put (8) *up*/*down* the phone and immediately stood (9) *up*/*down* and rushed out of the café. Luckily, I was running (10) *up*/*down* the hill when a friend stopped and picked me (11) *up*/*down* and took me all the way to the top. I got to the examination hall one minute before nine o'clock, just as everybody was sitting (12) *up*/*down*. In the end, I did quite well in the exam. In future, I'm going to give (13) *up*/*down* revising at the last moment and take (14) *up*/*down* the habit of turning (15) *up*/*down* early for exams!

⇨ Lexicon, Students' Book, pages 165–169.

16 Focus on Writing

1 Linking
Look at the linking words in the sentences. Which of them:

a lists the last of a series of events?

b refers to a part of a film?

c points out that something has happened after a long time?

d sums up what happens in a story?

1 He got on the plane, took control of it and *finally* flew it back home. ⟦a⟧

2 *Eventually*, the heroine saves the world. ☐

3 *In the end*, both the hero and heroine escape and live happily ever after. ☐

4 *Finally*, they fall in love and get married. ☐

5 *At the end* of the film, the story gets confusing. ☐

6 *At last,* here is a film about this important issue. ☐

2 Linking
Circle the correct linking words to complete the sentences.

1 *In the end/At last* I've found someone to go to the cinema with me!

2 I waited ages for a bus but *at the end/in the end* I gave up and walked.

3 First, I went to the bank. Then I bought some stamps. *Finally/At last,* I posted the letter.

4 *Eventually/At last*, the knight kills the dragon and saves the princess.

3 Linking
Read the text and complete it with these linking words:

neither, despite, in the end, both, although, all things considered, one day, unfortunately, after, nor, such, especially

The best film that I have seen recently is (1) _neither_ the blockbuster *Gladiator* (2) _____ the war film *Pearl Harbor*, which I did not enjoy. It is *Chocolat*, directed by Lasse Halström. It is set in a small French town in the middle of the 20th century. (3) _____ , a young woman (Juliette Binoche) and her daughter arrive in the town. (4) _____ that, they rent a shop from an old lady (Judi Dench) and sell delicious things made of chocolate. (5) _____ , it is during Lent, a time when people are not meant to enjoy eating things and the mayor of the town (Alfred Molina) starts a campaign against the shop. However, (6) _____ all the difficulties, Juliette Binoche's character survives with the help of the old lady and a travelling Irishman (Johnny Depp). (7) _____ , the shop is successful and even the mayor comes to enjoy its chocolate. (8) _____ it is possibly too 'politically correct', the film successfully deals with the themes of intolerance and prejudice. The acting is excellent, (9) _____ that of Juliette Binoche. (10) _____ Judi Dench and Alfred Molina are also excellent. There are some dramatic moments, (11) _____ as the fire on the Irishman's boat. (12) _____ _____ , I would really recommend you to go and see this film.

4 Paraphrasing
Complete each sentence so that it means the same as the above.

1 The story takes place during the Second World War.
   The story __is set__ in the Second World War.

2 The Italian army has just invaded the Greek island of Cephalonia.
   The Greek island of _____ Italian army.

3 The filmscript was adapted from the book by Louis de Bernières.
   The film is _____ on the book by Louis de Bernières.

4 The film examines the topics of love and war.
   The film _____ with the topics of love and war.

5 Nicolas Cage plays the main role of Captain Corelli.
   Nicolas Cage _____ as Captain Corelli.

6 However, the film is probably less entertaining than the book.
   The film is not _____ the book.

7 The film has a good cast but the acting is rather disappointing.
   Despite _____ , the acting is rather disappointing.

5 Editing
Correct the two spelling mistakes in each of the sentences below.

1 Personally, I think that wra*p*ping up buildings is not very attractive but it can be quite striking and impre*s*sive.

2 My friend shreiked when he received a feirce blow from a piece of wood weighing almost a kilo.

3 The painting has been critisised but I was mesmerised by it and found it quite exsiting. I realised that it was an exercise in the use of light and movement.

4 Rodin's sculpture is both powerfull and beautiful. It shows a man sitting and looking thoughtfull.

5 The queen, in the centre of the painting, looks fatiged but the countryside behind her is quite picturesqe.

6 The photography is very realistic and some of the senes are breathtaking, but the voices are squeaky and the dialoge is boring.

7 The costumes were glamorous, the main actress gorgous and the dancing sensuous but overall the film was monotonous. I've never seen anything so tedeous in my life.

8 The scene after the assasination was silent and so frightening that I could hear the person next to me breath.

9 The new museum was a real feet of engineering. It has won lots of prises for architecture.

10 He's ancient but he has inspired a lot of modern gitarists, especialy those from California.

6 Style
Change these informal personal opinions into paragraphs in a film review. Use the words and expressions in brackets.

1 I'm in kinda two minds about Woody Allen's film *Melinda and Melinda*. Because, you know, here is good old Allen again, with all his humour and intelligence, and that is what has always made him special to me. But still, isn't this good old Allen a bit boring? After all, each of his films is pretty much the same old story told over and over again. (strength, weakness, on the one hand, on the other hand, traditional, trademark, monotonous, repetition)

2 *Alfie* with Jude Law is good fun, really. What I like about it in the first place is that it uses the story of

Don Juan in a brilliant way, and shows it can make sense in our own time, too. Apart from Jude Law, there are some really great actors in this film, like Susan Sarandon. And finally, as a big Mick Jagger fan, I just love the song *Old habits die hard!* (worth recommending, three main reasons, first/second/third, modern adaptation, cast, starring, soundtrack)

3 *Shipping News* with Kevin Spacey and Julianne Moore is one of the best films I've seen. You know, it's sort of a family saga in which everybody will find something they like. There's a bit of fantasy and legend, a bit of local tradition, quite a lot of surprise, and a love story. What else do you need to enjoy a movie? (particularly interesting, suit everybody's taste, using elements of fantasy/legend/ etc, the most important components of a good film)

7 Guided writing: paragraph planning
Put the notes below in appropriate paragraphs. Write a short film review based on this information.

a band of Vikings are called back to their homeland/ interesting historical background/characters rather stereotypical/title: *The Last Warrior*/the Arabian envoy goes back home/exciting theme/category: historical film/there is a monster invading their land/poor story and characterisation/international cast including Norwegian actors/based on good research/they arrive back home and finally manage to overcome the danger/ starring: Antonio Banderas/using old sagas and epics for the story/not a convincing story/they take with them an envoy from an Arabian country/good cinematography

Paragraph 1: Introduction

Paragraph 2: A summary of the plot

Paragraph 3: Good and bad points

Paragraph 4: Conclusion

Word Power

1 Word families
Use the word trees to classify these verbs:

> stride, cling, whisper, giggle, shout, grasp, chuckle, cackle, roll, spin, stroll, strut, clutch, speak, fall

(walk)

1 _stride_ _____ _____

(move)

2 _____ _____ _____

(hold)

3 _____ _____ _____

(laugh)

4 _____ _____ _____

(talk)

5 _____ _____ _____

2 Word families
Use verbs from Exercise 1 to complete the text.

I was (1) __strolling__ down the street the other day feeling at peace with the world, when something very strange happened. I saw a very small man (2) _____ a newspaper in his left hand and (3) _____ very loudly 'Latest news! Hear all about it!' I stopped and he immediately (4) _____ my hand and (5) _____ very softly to me that the world was going to end at lunchtime. He then (6) _____ to my arm very hard so I panicked and tried to escape. There was ice on the pavement and I slipped and landed on my back. Some coins (7) _____ out of my pocket and started to roll down the hill. When I got up, the little man was (8) _____ to himself with amusement. When I started to pick up my money he began (9) _____ uncontrollably and then walked away (10) _____ along with very long steps and (11) _____ with laughter in a horrible way. Later on I (12) _____ to my dad about what had happened and he told me that the man had done the same thing to him!

3 Wordbuilding
Put the words in brackets in the correct form.

They say beauty is only skin deep, but we're (1) _____obssessed_____ (obsess) with it nowadays, and we want to look as (2) _____ (glamour) as possible. As a result, there's a lot of money to be made from beauty (3) _____ (produce). Magazines are full of adverts showing (4) _____ (beauty) people and they (5) _____ (rare) show Mr and Ms Average. For example, in many shops there are few (6) _____ (fashion) clothes available in larger sizes. Women often complain that the nicest, most (7) _____ (interest) and (8) _____ (attract) clothes are usually only made in the smaller sizes. In the real world there are few women with (9) _____ (spectacle) Barbie-doll figures; in fact, no real women look like the (10) _____ (fame) Barbie. If Barbie were life-size, her (11) _____ (measure) would be 97-57-82, and her neck would be twice the (12) _____ (long) of the average woman's neck!

4 Opposites
Match the opposites.

1	open-air	a	tame
2	elegant (clothes)	b	corny
3	monotonous	c	nervous
4	wild (animal)	d	tacky
5	exciting (film)	e	lively
6	witty (joke)	f	unknown
7	laid-back	g	tedious
8	respected (artist)	h	long-lived
9	short-lived	i	indoor
10	indolent	j	hard-working

Write sentences in your notebook using ten of the adjectives above.

5 Idiomatic language
Complete the sentences with idiomatic expressions.

> walk on thin ice, a short fuse,
> let the cat out of the bag,
> head or tail, right up his street

1 He likes living dangerously.

   He sometimes _walks on thin ice_ .

2 She couldn't understand it at all.

   She just couldn't make _____

   _____ of it.

3 It was just what he wanted.

   It was _____ .

4 He gets angry very easily.

   He's on _____ .

5 He gave away the secret.

   He _____ .

6 Phonemic transcriptions
Write out the sentences from the phonemic transcriptions.

1 /aɪ lʌv ðə ˈskʌlptə əv tuː hændz baɪ ˈrɒdɛ/

   I love the sculpture of two hands by Rodin.

2 /ɪt ɪz meɪd əv ˈmɑːbəl ənd juː kən ˈəʊnli siː ðə hændz/

   _____

3 /ðə tuː hændz ɑː ˈtʌtʃɪŋ iːtʃ ʌðə veri sɒftli/

   _____

4 /ðə hændz ʃəʊ greɪt ˈfiːlɪŋ ənd ɪˈməʊʃən/

   _____

5 /jʊ kən siː ðæt ðə tuː ˈpiːpəl ɑː ɪn lʌv/

   _____

7 Word pairs
Look at the expressions in the two sentences below. Do you have fixed expressions in your language using two words linked by _and_, _or_ and _but_?

> • _We are glad to be in our new home, although we've had the usual **ups and downs** with the builders._
> • _I knew that she would ask me that question **sooner or later**._

Complete the expressions in these sentences.

1 I am _sick and_ _____ of hanging around in the morning waiting for the bus.

2 I don't know why you are making such a _song and_ _____ about it. It's not that important is it?

3 I have nearly done my project and just have a few _bits and_ _____ to finish off.

4 I really like watching old _black and_ _____ films from the twenties and thirties.

➡ Lexicon, Students' Book, page 162.

8 Extension: Word pairs
Complete the expressions below with these words.

> about, later, take, ends, choose, quiet, off

1 I've moved most of my possessions to my new flat. I've just got a few _odds and_ _____ to move.

2 He's recovering from his illness well and I've seen him _out and_ _____ a couple of times.

3 I work _on and_ _____ as a journalist but I also work as a researcher.

4 You can _pick and_ _____ when you want to go on your holiday.

5 I like to have _peace and_ _____ when I am revising for an exam.

6 There were about a million people at the festival, _give or_ _____ a few thousand.

7 _Sooner or_ _____ you're going to have to mend that car. It makes a terrible noise.

Language Awareness

1 ★★ Reference

Read the film review. (Circle) the parts of the text that the underlined words refer to and join the two with a line.

Alfred Hitchcock's *Psycho* is the obvious inspiration behind Michael Bartram's new thriller *On the Edge*. Douglas McPherson, a widowed Scottish aristocrat, (1) whose medieval castle has been transformed into a guesthouse, seems perfectly normal in (2) his dealings with rare visitors. However, he spends most of his time in a mysterious tower, (3) where he keeps all his late wife's belongings and tortures (4) himself with memories of (5) her. When the first guest is found dead, (6) it becomes clear that Douglas has something to hide. Then a few more deaths occur, (7) which makes the police certain that (8) their suspicions are well-grounded. (9) They find evidence: a wig, a mask, a make-up kit. All (10) these point to Douglas but gradually we realise that a completely different solution is also possible.

(11) This and other thrillers are currently being shown at The Galaxy as a tribute to Mr Hitchcock, to commemorate the anniversary of (12) his first release.

2 ★ Pronouns

Complete the sentences with appropriate pronouns.

1 The skater performed two triple jumps, _____ made the audience hold their breath.

2 Just look at _____ – your suit is creased and your tie is stained!

3 This summer holiday was hopeless. We didn't go _____ – just stayed at home in the scorching city.

4 _____ is unbelievable that people are so similar to animals in many ways.

5 The Williamsons aren't so rich: the Volvo is _____ , that's true, but the house is rented by Jim's company.

6 Let's call them again later. _____ is answering the phone now.

7 Soap operas are very popular. _____ seems to be watching them.

3 ★★★ Relative clauses

Finish the sentences so that they make sense.

1 My father drives an old car which _____

_____

2 Sara is a very ambitious young woman, which _____

_____

3 Jennifer collects T-shirts which _____

_____

4 I've never been to Paris, which _____

_____

4 ★★ Pronouns and adjectives

Complete the text with the words from the box.

these (x2), which, it (x4), which/that (x3), you, your (x2), yourself, everywhere, nothing, this (x2), something (x2), anything, someone (x2)

An allergy is (1) _____ 's unusual reaction to substances (2) _____ are normally harmless: animals, pollen, nuts, etc. (3) _____ is hard to believe that items as varied as (4) _____ can trigger the same symptoms. All (5) _____ are common allergens (6) _____ cause various allergic reactions in people. (7) _____ can find them (8) _____ : in the air, in food, at home and at work.

If you are not allergic to (9) _____ , you can be surrounded by allergens and (10) _____ will happen. But if you are allergic to a substance, (11) _____ immune system treats it as an invader and produces chemicals (12) _____ cause symptoms such as skin irritations, runny nose or diarrhoea.

Allergies seem to be genetically transferred. (13) _____ means that if one of (14) _____ parents is allergic to (15) _____ , you may be allergic, too.

The best treatment for allergy is prevention, (16) _____ is avoiding contact with allergens. (17) _____ may mean staying indoors when pollen counts are high, avoiding certain foods, having (18) _____ bathe your pet regularly or even giving (19) _____ away.

(20) _____ is important to act quickly when you notice the first symptoms. If you are scratching (21) _____ regularly or have a runny nose without other symptoms of a cold, (22) _____ may mean that you have developed an allergy to (23) _____ .

Check Your Grammar

1 Relative clauses and participles
Read the text below and decide which answer (a–d) fits each space. There may be more than one correct answer.

REVEALED: DARWIN'S GRIEF OVER DEATH OF GIRL DESTROYED HIS FAITH

By Anna Whitney

Charles Darwin, the Victorian scientist (1) .... challenged the religious doctrine of his time and started a debate (2) ...... went on around the world, will this week be revealed as a man (3) ...... by his own grief. Tender notes (4) ...... by the scholar about his eldest daughter, Annie (5) ...... died of tuberculosis at the age of 10, are to be revealed for the first time tomorrow in an exhibition at his former Kent home.

For almost 150 years, the treasured items (6) ...... Annie's life have been stored in her writing box and handed down through the family. But now, the contents will go on public display for the first time at Down House (7) ...... the Darwins lived for forty years.

A lock of brown hair and a note (8) ...... the child's illness and place of burial, were placed inside the box (9) ...... is covered in Morocco leather, alongside envelopes and pens. A page (10) ...... from a notebook displays a map of a churchyard and the words: 'Annie Darwin's grave at Malvern'. After Annie's death Darwin could hardly bear the mention of her name (11) ...... made his wife (12) ...... that she would be forgotten, gather together all the mementos (13) ...... they had in the writing box.

Darwin (14) ...... lived between 1809 and 1882, was portrayed as 'the Devil's Chaplain' for his work. In reality, he was a committed family man. But Annie's death destroyed what had remained of his Christianity.

	a	b	c	d
1	, who	who	that	whose
2	that	which	, which	what
3	who was tortured	torturing	tortured	being tortured
4	written	he wrote	writing	have written
5	who	when	, who	that
6	that documented	documented	documenting	they documented
7	that	, where	, which	, in which
8	which recorded	recording	recorded	being recorded
9	it	, which	which	that
10	have torn	tearing	torn	tear
11	, what	, which	that	and this
12	, who feared	, fearing	, feared	, that feared
13	that	which	what	who
14	who	, who	that	he

2 Passives, relatives and pronouns
Complete the second sentence so that it has a similar meaning to the first sentence, using the word in *italics*. Do not change this word.

1 We will hire an electrician to fix this socket. *have*

We'll _____*have*_____ this socket
___*fixed by an electrician*___

2 Nothing can make her happy. *anything*

There _____
_____ make her happy.

3 All my family snore and I find it most annoying. *which*

All my family snore _____
_____

4 They have asked Simon to come to their wedding. *invited*

Simon _____
_____ to their wedding.

5 I could do any job as long as it has something to do with English. *that*

I could do any job _____
_____ something
to do with English.

6 It is essential to arrest the suspect as soon as possible. *must*

The suspect _____
_____ as soon as possible.

7 People who take regular exercise are usually healthier. *one*

If _____
_____ usually healthier.

8 They are addressing this issue in their next report. *addressed*

This issue _____
_____ in their next report.

5 New Frontiers

17 Vocabulary

1 Science quiz
Match the scientific words with the definitions.

1	antibiotic	a	microscopic organisms that cause disease
2	bacteria	b	the force that attracts objects to the Earth
3	DNA molecule	c	an independent system of stars in space
4	electricity	d	all the genetic information about a human being
5	galaxy	e	a chemical that carries genetic information
6	gene	f	a substance capable of killing bacteria
7	gravity	g	a form of energy (two types – static and current)
8	human genome	h	a unit of heredity

2 Compound words
Complete anecdotes 1–3 with these words.

good-looking, time-consuming, first name, human being, hard-working, New-Zealand-born, absent-minded, ground-breaking

1
The (1) _New-Zealand-born_ scientist, Ernest Rutherford (1871–1937), did
(2) _____ work on the atom.
He had a student who helped him with his
(3) _____ research and who was very
(4) _____ . One evening he asked the student if he worked in the mornings too.
'Yes,' the student replied proudly.
'But when do you think?' asked Rutherford.

⇨ Lexicon, Students' Book, page 159.

3 Az Dictionary work
Read the information below. Then use a good dictionary to work out the meaning of the words in sentences 1–4.

Some dictionaries, e.g. the Longman Active Study Dictionary, have separate entries for compound words. In other dictionaries, compound words are listed under the first word, e.g. *good*.

1 He is a very *good-natured* person but he is a bit of a *good-for-nothing*.
2 My old uncle is *bedridden* and lives in a *bedsit* in the centre of town.
3 I got very *carsick* on the way to the *car boot sale* in a *car park* outside Croydon.
4 She is a *headstrong* person but she has made a lot of *headway* in her dance classes.

Write example sentences with five of the words in your notebook.

2
Paul Erdös, the brilliant Hungarian mathematician (1913–1996), was very
(5) _____ . The only person who he called by his (6) _____ was Tom Trotter, who he called Bill. Once, Erdös met a mathematician and asked him where he was from.
'Vancouver,' the man replied.
'Oh, then you must know my good friend, Elliot Mendelson,' Erdös said.
'I am Elliot Mendelson!' came the reply.

3
Albert Einstein once met Marilyn Monroe.
She suggested they should have a baby together.
They could produce a fantastic
(7) _____ , intelligent like Einstein and (8) _____ like her. Einstein replied, 'I'm afraid, my dear lady, it might be the other way around.'

Remember

1 ★ *will* and *won't*

Complete the sentences with *will* or *won't* and a suitable verb from the box. Use *'ll* (*I'll*, *we'll*) where necessary.

> remember, pass, buy, cook, take, take, answer, mind

1 I'm afraid Peter ___won't remember___ to bring the book. He is so forgetful.

2 Don't get up. I _____ the phone.

3 We can use Chris's dictionary. He _____ _____ us borrowing it.

4 If there isn't any bread, I _____ some on the way home.

5 I _____ anything special but we can have an omelette and a rice salad.

6 Why do you want to leave so early? It _____ you long to get home.

7 If buses have stopped running, we _____ a taxi from the station to the hotel.

8 The test is quite easy. I'm sure you _____ without any problems.

2 ★ ★ *will*, *may* and *be going to*

Complete the predictions with the verbs in brackets and will, may or be going to.

1 The weather in March is very changeable here. It ___may___ even ___snow___ (snow) tomorrow.

2 That skier is going much too fast. He _____ _____ (fall) in a moment.

3 All his books have been bestsellers and this one _____ probably _____ (make) millions of pounds as well.

4 In twenty years' time, Europe _____ (have) one government.

5 I hope that your holiday _____ (be) very nice.

6 Our team have already given away three goals, so they _____ (lose) the game.

7 I think in 2020 most people _____ (have) university degrees.

8 I'm sure Jim _____ (manage) to lose ten pounds in a month if that's what he's decided.

3 ★★ Arrangements or plans?

Look at Anna's diary for next week. Use the diary to complete Anna's part of the conversation with Ben. Use the Present Continuous for her definite arrangements (*), or be going to for her loose plans (?).

Saturday	7 p.m. visit Great-Aunt Julia *
Sunday	morning – Internet café ?
	4 p.m. ♥ David *
Monday	6 p.m. tennis with Tom *
Tuesday	1.15 p.m. dentist *, revise maths ?
Wednesday	7 p.m. ✗ Katie and Helen *
Thursday	6 p.m. swimming *
Friday	3 p.m. look for Tom's birthday present ?

Ben: Are you doing anything on Saturday night?

Anna: Yes, in fact (1) _____ . She's a very sweet person.

Ben: How about lunch on Tuesday then?

Anna: Sorry, I can't. (2) _____ at lunchtime.

Ben: Sunday?

Anna: Well, in the morning (3) _____ _____ . I need to find some statistics for my project, and in the afternoon (4) _____ .

Ben: David? Are you seeing him every day this week?

Anna: No! On Monday night (5) _____ _____ , on Tuesday night (6) _____ for my maths test – that's on Wednesday – and then (7) _____ a meal with Katie and Helen on Wednesday evening. And on Thursday (8) _____ . You can come too, if you like.

Ben: No, thanks, I don't like swimming. What about Friday?

Anna: In the afternoon (9) _____ _____ .

Ben: Perhaps we could do that together.

Anna: Great! Let's meet at Carlo's café at three.

18 Grammar

1 ★ as soon as, until, after, when
Make sentences from the parts of the table.

1	We'll have coffee		your order has arrived.
2	He can't be offered a contract	as soon as	Martin's finished eating.
3	We'll move in	until	we've cleaned it.
4	We won't start playing rugby	after	the flat's been painted.
5	You can go to your room	when	it's stopped raining.
6	We'll let you know		he's completed his research.

2 ★ Future Perfect
Put the verbs in brackets into the Future Perfect.

1 By Christmas they _____will have sold_____ (sell) over five million greetings cards.

2 By this summer the city council _____ (spend) £2 million on redecorating the old town.

3 By 2030 the climate in Europe _____ (become) much warmer.

4 By the end of this decade our town _____ _____ (invest) $1 million in the tourist industry.

5 By the next Olympic Games many records in sport _____ (be) broken.

6 By the time scientists find a cure for AIDS, many thousands of people _____ (die).

3 ★ Future Perfect
John is a promising young scientist. Use the cues and the Future Perfect to predict his achievements in the future.

1 by 2020/publish eleven books
   By 2020 he will have published eleven books.

2 by end of decade/discover a treatment that can cure all kinds of cancer

3 by the time he's thirty-five/become a professor

4 by end career/receive several honorary doctorates from famous universities.

5 by end of next year/finish writing his PhD

6 by 2010/write a book about genetically transmitted diseases.

7 by next summer/be to fifteen conferences

8 by 2015/do a lot of research on cancer

4 ★★ Future Continuous
Complete the sentences with a verb from the box in the Future Continuous.

give, work, write, watch, drive, put up, use

1 I won't be able to answer the phone in the afternoon. I _'ll be giving____ a talk at a conference.

2 Why don't you drop by on Wednesday night? I _____ a tennis match and it will be more fun if somebody joins me.

3 I _____ to town in the afternoon. Would you like me to give you a lift?

4 _____ you _____ your bike this afternoon? Could I borrow it for half an hour?

5 This time on Saturday I _____ my tent by the lake.

6 We shouldn't disturb them tonight. Tricia _____ her article and Nick _____ on his lecture.

5 ★★ Future Continuous or Future Perfect?
These are predictions about the future of a group of classmates in 2020. Complete the sentences with the verbs in brackets in the Future Continuous or the Future Perfect.

1 Megan will __be working__ (work) as a columnist in a fashion magazine.

2 Patrick _____ (write) at least a few popular cookery books.

3 Kylie _____ (take) part in a few expeditions to the Arctic.

4 Jeremy _____ (receive) two Oscars for best special effects in sci-fi films.

5 Peter _____ (write) best-selling horror stories.

6 Andrew _____ (look) after his children at home.

6 ★★★ Future tenses

Complete the dialogue with the verbs in brackets in the correct forms: Future Simple, Future Perfect, Future Continuous, Present Continuous, be going to.

Claire: I haven't had time to go shopping today.

Rob: Don't worry. I (1) _'ll go_ (go) to the supermarket tomorrow morning. I (2) _____ (not go) to work as the office is being repainted.

Claire: Lucky you! What (3) _____ (you do) all day?

Rob: I don't know yet. I (4) _____ probably _____ (work) a bit at home and in the afternoon I (5) _____ (meet) Frank. He phoned me yesterday. We (6) _____ probably _____ (sit) in the pub all evening, as usual.

Claire: (7) _____ (you cook) dinner by the time you leave for the pub? You know, I (8) _____ (be) in the studio all day and I think I (9) _____ (not have) time to eat anything. I (10) _____ (be) very hungry when I come home.

Rob: I'm afraid I (11) _____ (not have) the time to cook a big meal but I (12) _____ _____ (make) you some soup. (13) _____ (you go out) in the evening?

Claire: No. I (14) _____ (have) a bath and read my book in bed. I (15) _____ probably _____ (finish) it by the time you get home!

Prepositions

Time

1 Complete the text with the prepositions *at*, *in* or *on*.

(1) _At_ the age of ten I had a completely different perception of time from now. (2) ___ the holidays, when we didn't go away, the days always seemed so long. When I woke up (3) ___ the middle of the night, time would seem to go really slowly. I remember once, (4) ___ a stormy night (5) ___ the end of summer when I woke up (6) ___ about 3 o'clock in the morning. I couldn't go back to sleep for ages. (7) ___ about half an hour I fell asleep but it felt like hours. Christmas Eve was even worse. I was always excited (8) ___ Christmas and (9) ___ the twenty-fourth December, time froze. (10) ___ mealtimes I would look at the clock again and again and (11) ___ the end of each hour I would cross off the number of hours to go until Christmas Day. (12) ___ the day itself, time would suddenly speed up. Before I knew it, Christmas was over!

⇨ Lexicon, Students' Book, page 165.

2 Circle the correct prepositions in the sentences below.

1 *During*/For the summer holidays I stayed with my aunt *during*/for two weeks.

2 *Since/From* January I have been working a lot, and *since/from* March to June I got up early every day to study *during/for* a couple of hours.

3 I am going to stay *by/until* July. *By/Until* then I should have learnt to windsurf.

4 *During/For* a few minutes *during/for* the film I was really frightened and I didn't feel relaxed *until/by* it had finished.

5 I went skiing for the first time *during/for* the winter. *By/Until* then I had no idea of how difficult it was to ski but *by/until* the end of the holiday I could ski reasonably well.

6 They met *during/for* the holidays and *since/from* then they have been going out. They have been going out *during/for* almost six months now.

7 I overslept and *by/until* the time I got up there was no breakfast so I had to wait *by/until* lunch to have something to eat.

19 Communication

1 Asking questions
Match the questions and statements (1–6) with the answers (a–f).

1 What I don't understand is how nanotechnology works. `e`
2 Could you explain what an android is? ☐
3 I don't really understand what black holes are. ☐
4 So does that mean that we can see black holes? ☐
5 I'm not sure how radioactivity works. ☐
6 Could you explain why the human genome is so important? ☐

a Don't worry! Scientists don't really understand much about them either. They are 'objects' in space which have collapsed so much that no light or any kind of energy can escape from them.

b Well, it involves the emission of particles by the nucleus of an atom. You see, the particles come from special elements, like radium. Is that clear?

c Right. It is a kind of robot which looks like a human being. There are plenty of robots, like those in factories, that don't look like us at all. However, scientists have produced human-looking robots and, of course, science fiction is full of them.

d Well, it contains a code with all the information about our genetic make-up.

e You see, it works just like any other kind of electronic technology. The difference is merely in terms of scale. It works at a microscopic level and because of this it can't use the same materials as conventional technology.

f Yes, but they are extremely difficult to detect. They are usually located near places where there have been explosions of large stars or supernovas.

Which of the explanations above do you find the clearest?

2 Clarifying
Complete the clarifying expressions in the speech with these words and phrases.

> other words, that means, getting at, means, that, mean, trying, clear, another way, which

Today, I am going to talk about 'bluetooth' technology. Bluetooth is a chip developed by the Swedish telecoms company, Ericsson. It was named after a 10th century Danish king with bad teeth! The chip is a radio transmitter, in (1) __other words__ , it is a chip that can send signals to other machines. This means that in the future machines will be able to 'talk' to each other. What (2) _____ is that they will be able to communicate electronically and control one another.

There are many practical applications for the bluetooth. What I am (3) _____ to say is that the new chip will be extremely useful and will greatly influence our lives. For example, we won't need front door keys any more. We will have an opening device that confirms each person's identity. To put it (4) _____ , a chip will recognise your fingerprint before opening the door automatically.

In fact, the bluetooth will bring in the era of the 'intelligent home'. What I'm (5) _____ is that we won't need cables any more and will be able to work all the domestic appliances in our house from one console – (6) _____ is a screen and a keyboard (7) _____ is the size of a laptop computer. It will be located on the fridge and we will be able to use it to program the heating or the washing machine.

The console will also have a permanent Internet connection. That (8) _____ your fridge will be online 24 hours a day. It will be able to order the shopping or write e-mails. Your fridge will be essential, I (9) _____ you won't be able to live without it! When you are away you will be able to control your house through the internet, for example video your favourite programme or cook the dinner. So, to sum up, bluetooth technology will bring about a revolution in our lifestyle. Is that (10) _____ ?

MULTI-PART VERBS

1 Multi-part verbs

Read the text and complete it with the correct form of these multi-part verbs.

> take over, come out, make up for, get on, make out, give away, get through, carry out, do with, make up of

It looks like robots are (1) _taking over_ some very unusual jobs. Recently, the news (2) _____ about a robot sheepdog called Rover. I couldn't (3) _____ it _____ at first, because the robot works with a flock of geese, not sheep. It has been designed by the Robot Sheepdog Project which is being (4) _____ by three postgraduate students in Britain. The study is to (5) _____ both robotics and animal behaviour and has been a great success. The robots can't move as fast as a dog or a person but this is (6) _____ by the fact that they (7) _____ better with animals than people or dogs. Apparently, research has shown that machines are less threatening to animals than people, so these robots can (8) _____ to the geese. Rover is (9) _____ a robot vehicle, a computer and a camera, it can gather a flock of geese together and move them to a particular place. One thing I'm not going to do is (10) _____ this information to my dog. She's a Welsh sheepdog and I don't think she'd be too happy to hear about Rover!

2 Position of the object

Look at the position of the object in the sentences in Groups 1, 2 and 3. Match the groups of verbs with the rules (a–c).

a   You must put the object after all three-word multi-part verbs.
   Group ☐

b   With some two-word verbs, you must put the object after the second part of the verb.
   Group ☐

c   With other two-word verbs, you can put the object after the first or the second word. However, you can never put a pronoun after the second word.
   Group ☐

Group 1:
I put on my coat.
I put my coat on.
I put it on.
~~I put on it.~~

Group 2:
I get on with Susan.
I get on with her.
~~I get Susan on with.~~
~~I get her on with.~~

Group 3:
I came across my glasses.
I came across them.
~~I came them across.~~

3 Position of object pronouns

Rewrite the sentences below using pronouns.

1 He gave away the secret.
   He gave <u>it</u> away.

2 She is going out with Joe.
   She is going out with <u>him</u>.

3 I would like to try on those clothes. _____
   _____

4 We picked up Anne at five o'clock.
   _____
   _____

5 I am looking forward to the concert. _____
   _____

6 I have gone off carrots. _____
   _____

7 She wrapped up the parcel.
   _____
   _____

8 I finally caught up with Bill.
   _____
   _____

9 She turned on the television.
   _____
   _____

10 I can't put up with that noise.
   _____

11 She made up that excuse.
   _____

12 I finally got back my CDs.
   _____

13 Eventually, we got to the lake.
   _____
   _____

14 I can't work out that equation.
   _____
   _____

➱ Lexicon, Students' Book, pages 170–176.

20 Focus on Writing

1 Linking
Complete the text with these words.

> in order, so as not to, for, in case, so that, a result,
> so as to, caused by, because (x2), due, order that

The Apollo 13 mission was launched in April 1970 (1) ___*in order*___ to continue the manned exploration of the moon. It had nearly reached the moon when the crew heard a loud explosion. An oxygen tank had exploded (2) _____ to the failure of a thermostat, as (3) _____ of this another oxygen tank also failed.

The crew were 200,000 miles from Earth in a spaceship which (4) _____ of the explosion had lost most of its power!

The crew moved to another part of the spaceship and used the booster engines in (5) _____ they might set themselves on course for Earth. The journey back was terrible. There were a lot of problems (6) _____ the lack of power. The crew members drank one fifth of their normal water intake (7) _____ use up valuable water. They had to move air filters to a different part of the ship (8) _____ avoid a build-up of carbon dioxide. When they approached Earth, they got rid of the damaged part of the ship (9) _____ it exploded on entry.

When the crew finally landed, they were greeted as heroes (10) _____ they had shown great courage. The disaster helped NASA to develop procedures (11) _____ rescuing space crews and double-checking spaceships (12) _____ similar accidents would not happen again.

2 Punctuation
Look at these examples of punctuation.

- **Listing in formal writing**
  There are many reasons for this: the increase in cost; the fall in demand; the need for developing new methods of production.

- **Combining two closely related sentences in formal writing**
  The government have already made plans for changing the system; the plans have been developed by experts from three British universities.

- **Giving an explanation in formal writing**
  The new computer is much more powerful: it has two million megabytes.

- **Expressing an afterthought in more informal writing**
  That's probably a good idea – I've never thought of it before.

- **Used like a colon – : or a semi-colon – ; in informal writing**
  I'll be a bit late – I've got a dentist appointment.

Now punctuate these sentences.

1 Give me a ring on my mobile when you get there I'll probably be out.

2 Don't forget a kilo of those tasty apples and a couple of cans of drink.

3 You are advised to bring the following things your passport or identity card two or three good pens a watch so that you can time yourself in the exam.

4 There was an explosion on board the spaceship one of the oxygen tanks had exploded.

5 She arrived late that's typical of her, isn't it?

6 Robots are very useful in some manufacturing processes they are particularly good for the manufacture of dangerous products.

3 Style

Choose words and phrases from the brackets to replace the underlined expressions and make the descriptions (1–4) more vivid, precise and interesting.

1 Yesterday I went to the Polish premiere of a new film by Roman Polański. It was a <u>very interesting</u> event. It started with an <u>interesting</u> presentation by the film production manager who gave a lot of <u>interesting</u> details about their work on the film. One of the most interesting moments of the event was an interview with Roman Polański. (most exciting, really informative, truly fascinating, surprising, incredible, unique, exceptional)

2 My best friend's wedding took place last Saturday. The weather was <u>good</u>. The atmosphere was <u>special</u>. We told <u>funny</u> stories about our school days. Then, the bride appeared in a <u>nice</u> dress. The band played a <u>popular song</u> and we all headed for the church. (electric, sunny, exceptionally warm for the season, gorgeous, designer, silly, amusing, *Love Me Do* by the Beatles)

3 I live in a new district where there are not many shops. Yesterday, we <u>had</u> the opening of the first bookshop in our area. It was one of the most important events I have ever <u>been to</u>. The place was <u>full of</u> objects associated with different kinds of books, such as the hood from Little Red Riding Hood. The organisation was <u>very good</u> and we all had a great time. (celebrated, attended, experienced, excellent, extremely efficient, crowded with)

4 The match yesterday was really <u>great</u>. David Beckham was in <u>incredibly good</u> form and other team members played <u>really well</u>. England scored two <u>great</u> goals before half-time. The rest of the match was <u>not as fantastic as</u> the first half, but all in all, the players <u>did a good job</u>. (brilliant, excellent, good football, top, fantastically, less eventful than, less exciting than, skilfully, gave us our money's worth, proved their superb skills, skilful)

4 Guided writing

Write a description of an event in your notebook. Use the information below.

Paragraph 1: Introduction to the event
a fashion show/where?/new spring collection/young designers
Paragraph 2: A summary of the event
lots of VIPs and photographers/crowded/(not) enough places to sit/a long wait for the show to start/ lighting effects/ models elegantly moving on the catwalk/a reception of tea and sandwiches at the end
Paragraph 3: Focus on one aspect of the event
lighting effects/flashing colours/moments of total darkness/glowing lights on the floor/splendid show/ often difficult to see any details
Paragraph 4: Final comment on the event
fascinating to see young designers' ideas/opportunities to meet VIPs/poor organisation/ controversial lighting effects/ generally interesting but could be better

Word Power

1 Confusing words
Circle the correct words to complete the text.

Scientists are (1) carrying out/ making research into using spiders' cobwebs to (2) do/ produce extremely thin wire. The (3) research/investigation is being (4) conducted/carried by two (5) investigators/researchers from Germany. Michael Stuke and Markus Koch have developed a (6) process/form for reducing spiders' silk to about one twentieth of its normal diameter and then covering it with metal. It is hoped that this new wire will be (7) effective/affective in the growing (8) camp/field of micro-electronics. Stuke and Koch have collected (9) evidence/data on the properties of spider silk. Their (10) work/works has found (11) proof/evidence that the silk of the black widow spider would be the (12) ideal/suitable material for the new 'nanowires'. It seems even the deadly black widow can serve the cause of scientific progress!

2 Oral linkers
Put these sentences from a talk about jazz in the correct order.

a   Well, first I'd like to look at the instruments used in jazz. All sorts of instruments are used, especially the trumpet, saxophone and piano. Jazz violin and guitar are also used. ☐

b   To sum up, jazz is an extremely varied type of music and it has evolved during the 100 years or so of its history. ☐

c   That's all. Thank you. ☐

d   Other interesting sorts of jazz have developed in the last thirty years. Some groups like Weather Report have been playing 'jazz-rock', while other musicians have expanded the boundaries of jazz to produce 'free form jazz'. ☐

e   Right, today I'm going to talk about jazz, one of the most interesting types of modern music. ☐ f

f   So, having looked at its history, what is the future of jazz? It is difficult to tell but it is certain that it will continue to evolve. ☐

g   Of course, these instruments were not all used from the beginning. So where did jazz come from? It started out in New Orleans and spread in the 1920s to other US cities. ☐

h   The 1930s were the era of 'swing' and the large dance bands. Then musicians like Dizzy Gillespie developed 'bop' using smaller bands. In the 50s 'cool jazz' introduced a more relaxed approach with musicians such as Miles Davies and Stan Getz. ☐

3 Wordbuilding
Complete the text with the correct form of the words in brackets.

My aunt is a (1) ___scientist___ (science) and she works in a research institute near London. She is a (2) _____ (biology) and she is researching the effect of machines on animals. She recently made the (3) _____ (discover) that the sound of machines is of less (4) _____ (important) than we might think. She has produced (5) _____ (computer) models of animal behaviour, in particular that of cows. The (6) _____ (inspire) for my aunt's work was her (7) _____ (child) on my grandparents' farm. She disliked household pets like dogs but loved farm animals. My aunt is –(8) _____ (extreme) good with animals and immediately starts up a (9) _____ (relation) with them.

   She has a very nice (10) _____ (person) and I've always got on well with her. She is quiet and modest but is a very (11) _____ (determine) person. She is very 'green' and worries about the future of (12) _____ (human) and other species on the planet. She is my favourite aunt because, in my (13) _____ (judge), she really cares about both people and animals.

4 Fixed phrases

Complete the phrases below from Modules 1 to 5.

1 I'm afraid it's not really *my* thing – I don't like jazz.
2 She came up to me and *guess* ________ ? She kissed me!
3 *Have you* ________ *the* ________ *about* the computer and the spider?
4 I think it's a bit *over the* ________ , myself.
5 *If you* ________ *me*, I think it's really tacky.
6 I'm *sick and* ________ of waiting around for him to arrive.
7 That book's really interesting. I think it'd be *right up your* ________ .
8 She's ________ *keen on* football – she's obsessed with it.
9 He's a nice guy but he's a bit *on the slow* ________ isn't he?
10 ________ *I don't understand is* how the computer controls the other machines.
11 It's very volatile – *in* ________ *words*, it changes all the time.
12 *To be* ________ , I don't really like it very much.
13 *I'm really* ________ diving. I think it's great!
14 I felt ________ *of* relaxed – you know what I mean?
15 I *met* ________ the other day in the street. Chris Carrington – that's his name.
16 *He comes* ________ as a bit reserved at first. But when you get to know him he's really nice.
17 ________ *you can see*, it's not a great day to go swimming.

5 Abbreviations

A lot of abbreviations are used in English, both British and American. Match the initials with the words they stand for.

EU, <u>NASA</u>, GP, MP, <u>NATO</u>, PM, <u>AIDS</u>, BBC, UK, FBI, PC (x 3), IT

a prime minister (Br) ☐
b auto-immune deficiency syndrome ☐
c information technology ☐
d north atlantic treaty organisation ☐
e european union ☐
f british broadcasting corporation ☐
g police constable (Br) ☐
) personal computer ☐
i politically correct ☐
j north american space agency ☐
k member of parliament (Br) ☐
l united kingdom ☐
m federal bureau of investigation (Am) ☐
n general practitioner (doctor – Br) ☐

Pronunciation

The <u>underlined</u> abbreviations are pronounced as one word.
Example: /næsæ/

In the other abbreviations each letter is said:
Example: BBC – Bee Bee Cee

Practise saying the abbreviations above.

6 Abbreviations

Match each abbreviation with its meaning.

1	etc.	a	please note (Latin *nota bene*)
2	i.e.	b	as soon as possible (informal)
3	RSVP	c	care of (sending a letter to somebody at another person's address)
4	e.g.	d	please turn over (a page in a letter)
5	asap	e	postcript (extra message at the end of a letter)
6	PS	f	and so on (Latin *et cetera*)
7	c/o	g	please reply to this invitation (French *répondez s'il vous plait*)
8	NB	h	that is to say (Latin *id est*)
9	PTO	i	for example (Latin *exempli gratia*)

⇨ Lexicon, Students' Book, (inside back cover).

Exam Zone

USE OF ENGLISH

TIPS for word formation

1 Decide what part of speech should fill the gap – noun, verb, adverb, etc.
2 Think of the suffixes used to form particular parts of speech:
   • nouns e.g. *-ment, -tion, -ness*;
   • adjectives *-ful, -less, -ous*;
   • adverbs *-ly*;
   • verbs *-ise, -ify, -en*.
3 Decide if the word should have a positive or negative meaning: negative words use prefixes
   such as *un-, dis-, in-* or *il-*.
4 Be prepared to accept the fact that sometimes word formation rules don't work and you just have
   to know the word required in the gap.

1 Use the word in brackets after each sentence to form a word that fits the gap. (20 marks)

1 Three people have been questioned in connection with the _____ of a four-year-old girl in Brighton. *(appear)*

2 She uses an _____ amount of make-up, which doesn't make her look more beautiful anyway. *(believe)*

3 _____ is a very serious social problem, which can only be solved by a long term government policy. *(home)*

4 She dresses in a very _____ way: mini skirts, low necks and high heels. *(provoke)*

5 Reddening and a rash is an _____ symptom of skin allergy. *(mistake)*

6 The present government treats ecological issues quite _____ from the previous one. *(differ)*

7 The management's _____ has led to a significant increase in the number of accidents on this building site. *(care)*

8 He was sentenced to five years' _____ for tax evasion and accepting bribes. *(prison)*

9 Mrs Roberts's experience and _____ are generally acknowledged. *(wise)*

10 A lot of crimes occur in the _____ zone, from which soldiers withdrew long ago. *(military)*

11 His speaking skills improved _____ after he had spent two months in Britain. *(consider)*

12 Remember that this information is strictly _____ – no one is supposed to learn about it. *(confide)*

13 I'm afraid nausea and dizziness are _____ side effects of this medical treatment. *(avoid)*

14 Mike's _____ to co-operate with the police was interpreted as admission of guilt. *(refuse)*

15 The students never know what their maths teacher will do and it's this _____ that makes their maths lessons exciting. *(certain)*

16 They brought towels and soap quite _____ – the hotel provided them. *(necessary)*

17 Students often demonstrate a lot of _____ , especially in making up practical jokes. *(invent)*

18 If you want to work here you have to _____ yourself with some most important office software. *(familiar)*

19 It's so easy to hurt Miriam, her extreme _____ has been a problem since she was a child. *(sense)*

20 The _____ of this gadget is highly questionable. I don't think anyone will ever need it. *(use)*

20

2 Read the text and complete the gaps with words formed from the words in brackets. (20 marks)

THE SILVER LAKE HOTEL

The Silver Lake Hotel is (0) __situated__ (situation) in the most (1) _____ (picture) landscape you can imagine. Most rooms overlook the Silver Lake, whose (2) _____ (deep) is estimated to be more than 10 km. The lake, always (3) _____ (mystery) misty in the morning, is surrounded by granite peaks which look so (4) _____ (approach) that you can hardly believe there is a path to the top of each. The place is completely (5) _____ (touch) by the tourist industry so you can (6) _____ (occasion) see an eagle hovering above the lake or a wild goat looking for grass between the rocks.

The hotel's unusual (7) _____ (attract) is doubled by the fact that you can only reach it on foot. The walk up from the bottom of the valley requires some (8) _____ (fit) but we can guarantee that the view from the hotel's terrace will leave you (9) _____ (speech). (10) _____ (understand), the place is meant to offer accommodation to climbers and backpackers, rather than motorists and (11) _____ (experience) hikers.

The hotel offers comfortable, spacious bedrooms and delicious (12) _____ (special) of the local cuisine. Grilled trout and home-made bread rank among visitors' favourites. The staff are competent, (13) _____ (help) and always available. Most important, however, is the unique atmosphere of this place (14) _____ (special) in the evening, when the guests gather around the fireplace in the (15) _____ (style) dining hall, so different from those (16) _____ (personal) lobbies of modern hotels. The prices are, (17) _____ (predict), quite high but you are very (18) _____ (like) to be disappointed by the quality of what is on offer. You will certainly enjoy the (19) _____ (close) to nature and the (20) _____ (simple) and charm of this unusual place.

READING

1 Read the article from the *New Scientist*. Are the statements true (T) or false (F) or is there no information (NI)? (10 marks)

1 Networked cars will be common in the future. ☐

2 Signposts will send music to passing cars. ☐

3 Music files will be sent by satellite through a wireless network. ☐

4 People in Internet cars will be able to talk to other people in Internet cars close to them. ☐

5 Drivers will be able to listen to the conversations of people in other cars. ☐

6 Karaoke could cause accidents on long drives. ☐

7 Sensors on cars are two-way – they can give and send information. ☐

8 Networked cars have sent information about air quality. ☐

9 You will be able to download information at traffic lights by tapping your foot. ☐

10 The new traffic lights in Japan use about a third of the power of ordinary ones. ☐

	10

In the next few years you'll be riding the digital highway in a networked car. *Ian Sample reports*

Music on the Move

A good car journey needs decent music. But how do you know which tunes you'll want to hear a hundred miles down the road? With the Internet car it's not a problem – whatever you want will be waiting for you at the next signpost. Just get it as you
10 go by.

Turning signposts into drive-through jukeboxes is the brainchild of Hiroyuki Morikawa at the University of Tokyo. He's looking forward to the day when drivers will be able to request files on the move and receive them just a few minutes later over a wireless network.
20 The music will be requested by mobile phone and sent to 'hot spots' which are on the car's route. When the car passes a 'hot spot', the music will be sent to it.

Karaoke Cars

Singalong Jam

Thanks to Internet technology, Tokyo's traffic jams are going to be transformed into raucous karaoke parties. According to
30 Masao Nakagawa of Keio University in Yokahama, high speed radio links aren't just for connecting cars to the Internet. They could also let drivers share information with vehicles nearby. 'You could have a very good data link between a few cars,' says Nakagawa. 'You could arrange it so that people in the middle car

2 Work out the meaning of these words in the text from the context. (10 marks)

1 A *jukebox* (line 12) is
   a digital music service.
   b a machine providing music.
   c a part of a signpost.

2 A *brainchild* (line 13) is
   a a brilliant idea.   b someone's idea.   c a suggestion.

3 *Raucous* (line 28) means
   a noisy.   b organised.   c small.

4 *Road rage* (line 47) is
   a boredom from being in traffic jams.
   b hatred of anything to do with cars.
   c anger with other road users.

5 *Windscreen wipers* (line 74) are
   a useful for knowing if it is raining.
   b useful when driving in the rain.
   c the window on the front of a car.

Roving Reporter

The networked car isn't only about getting information to the driver. Hideki Sunahara and his colleagues at Keio University say that vehicles should be talking back to the Internet.

60 'Information-flow must be two-way,' says Sunahara. Cars could use sensors to collect information about weather or traffic and send them to the Internet. There are eighty million cars in Japan and they could generate up-to-the-minute weather and traffic reports.

In a test this April, Sunahara's 70 group fitted cars with equipment which fed back information on its position, speed and the state of its windscreen wipers. 'With this information you can work out where the traffic is moving and where it's not moving at all.' The windscreen wipers show clearly where it is raining and where it is not.

Light Bytes

A red traffic light isn't usually a welcome sight but other Japanese researchers have been working on something to keep you busy while you wait for the lights to change. Because they are very common and within easy view of cars, traffic lights would make 90 ideal information points for Internet cars. Instead of tapping your foot while you wait, you'll be downloading data – Web pages or music files.

Ordinary traffic lights wouldn't work but in Japan local councils are installing new traffic lights which are capable of transmitting vast amounts of 100 information in a fraction of a second. These traffic lights could transmit data at around 110 megabytes per second – around 10,000 times faster than current WAP mobile phones.

40 hear the people in front through their front speakers and the people behind through their rear speakers.'

Being in radio contact with other drivers might make it easier for people to express their road rage, but Nakagawa sees a far more entertaining use for the technology. 'We have this thing 50 called karaoke. You could have everyone joining in,' he says. 'It'd be very good for keeping you awake on a long drive.'

WRITING

Use the notes below to write an article about football in your notebook. Or use the plan to write an article about a sport that you are interested in (120–180 words). (20 marks)

1 Introduction
Football – the most popular game/millions play it all over the world/popularity of competitions, e.g. World Cup

2 History
First played in ancient China, Greece and Rome/medieval football = very violent/rules decided in 19th century in Britain/first clubs founded at end of 19th century

3 Now
Extremely popular/most important competitions = World Cup/European Champions' League/South American Liberators' Cup

Much money in modern game/large transfer fees/very rich clubs, e.g. Manchester United/increasing violence on and off field – fans and players

4 Future
Improved performance of African teams/robot referees/world league of major clubs/increased popularity of robot football

5 Conclusion
Summarise main points – advantages and disadvantages of football (e.g. violence) – football's huge social importance

20

6 Soft Machine

21 Vocabulary

1 Parts of the body

Which of these parts of the body do you use when doing the things below? Write them in your notebook.

> brain, eyes, feet, hands, heart, knee, legs, lungs, mouth, ribs, stomach, teeth, throat, tongue

Check your answers below.

2 Collocation

Two out of the three choices in each sentence below are correct. Cross out the words which are not correct.

1. I *picked up/got/took* a stomach bug when I was on holiday.
2. A lot of people *suffer from/bear/have* back pain.
3. People can *catch/get infected/contract* malaria from a particular kind of mosquito.
4. Vaccines can *cure/prevent/stop* you from getting diseases like smallpox.
5. There was a bad flu *epidemic/disorder/outbreak* last winter.
6. If you eat badly, you are more *probable to have/likely to have/at risk from* heart disease.
7. He was diagnosed as having a *fatal/deathly/ deadly* disease.
8. Doctors are finding new ways of *helping/treating/ curing* many diseases.

1 brain, eyes, legs, feet, knees 2 brain, mouth, throat, heart, lungs, ribs, hands 3 brain, eyes, hands, mouth, teeth, tongue, stomach

3 Synonyms

Complete the crossword. Use a good dictionary to help you with the synonyms

Across

1. say formally *(8)*
4. a clinical test *(5)*
5. evening (short form) *(3)*
6. organ for breathing *(4)*
8. part of the human body *(3)*
9. workforce *(5)*
10. employ *(3)*
12. related to food *(7)*

Down

1. very surprised *(10)*
2. on toes and fingers *(5)*
3. changes (verb) *(8)*
7. result *(6)*
10. rays that are ultraviolet (abbreviation) *(3)*
11. a European institution (abbreviation) *(2)*

4 Dictionary work

Use a good dictionary to work out the meaning of the multi-part verbs in the sentences.

> In most monolingual dictionaries, you can find the meaning of multi-part verbs under the main part of the verb (e.g. *get/take*). Good learner dictionaries (e.g. *The Longman Active Study Dictionary*) will give separate entries for each meaning, with definitions and examples.

1. Her skin problem eventually *cleared up* after weeks of treatment. _____
2. I *went down with* flu last week. _____
3. Her cold was *brought on* by getting soaked in the rain. _____
4. It looks like the bad weather *has* really *set in*. _____
5. I confess I was *taken in* by the way he apologised. _____
6. He was *run over* and taken to hospital. _____

Remember

1 ★ Zero conditional

Write sentences using the zero conditional based on the cues below.

1 drive a car/pollute the air

If you drive a car, you pollute the air.

2 exercise regularly/keep fit _____

_____

3 drink plenty of water/help the body function properly _____

_____

4 eat too much salt/risk high blood pressure _____

_____

5 boil cherries/colour changes to pink _____

_____

6 sit in front of the computer screen for long periods/eyes get sore _____

_____

2 ★ First conditional

Claire is finishing school and planning her future. Write sentences about her, using the first conditional.

1 go abroad to study → meet a lot of interesting people *If she goes abroad to study, she'll meet a lot*

of interesting people.

2 do well in her final exams → get a place at university _____

_____

3 get a job → earn some money _____

_____

4 go to university → have better career prospects in the future _____

_____

5 go abroad → learn some new languages _____

_____

6 take a year off → go travelling for a few months

_____

3 ★★★ Second conditional

What would you do in these situations? Write sentences using the second conditional.

1 You get lost in London.

If I got lost in London, I would ask someone to tell me the way.

2 You win £200,000 in a lottery.
3 You are elected President of your country.
4 Your family move to Britain.
5 You fall in love with someone your parents don't approve of.
6 You find a valuable bracelet on the pavement.

4 ★★ Third conditional

Read the notes about Sam and write in your notebook a chain of sentences about him, using the third conditional.

Sam went to Italy for a holiday – met a beautiful Italian girl – didn't return to Britain – started to teach English in Florence – found out he loved teaching – started his own school – became very rich and successful

If Sam hadn't gone to Italy, he wouldn't have met a beautiful Italian girl.

5 ★★ Conditionals

Put the verbs in brackets in the correct forms.

1 If Brazil __wins__ (win) the next World Cup, the whole country _____ (celebrate).

2 If Marion Jones _____ (not be) on a proper diet, she _____ (not be able) to run so fast.

3 Nobody _____ (be able) to drive without refuelling unless new technology _____ (be) developed.

4 If ancient Greeks _____ (not invent) the Olympics, someone else _____ (come up with) the idea later.

5 If an athlete _____ (win) a race, they usually _____ (get) a financial reward.

6 The world _____ (be) a boring place if there _____ (not be) any sports competitions.

22 Grammar

MIXED CONDITIONALS

1 ★ Mixed conditionals
Use the cues to write mixed conditionals.

Ricky is very handsome …

1 → lots of girls fell in love with him *If Ricky wasn't so handsome, lots of girls at school wouldn't have fallen in love with him.*

2 → he became a model _____

3 → got a part in a soap opera _____

4 → his photo appeared on the cover of a popular magazine _____

5 → he married a pop star _____

Sara got a scholarship to Cambridge University …

6 → she is a scientist *If Sara hadn't got a scholarship to Cambridge University, she wouldn't be a scientist.*

7 → she is a professor there now _____

8 → she is a world expert in genetics _____

9 → various companies and organisations ask her advice _____

10 → she is invited to scientific conferences all over the world _____

2 ★★★ Conditionals with present consequences
Finish the sentences to say what the situation would be now.

1 If Europeans hadn't colonised the Americas, *we could learn more about American Indian culture.*

2 If people hadn't invented money, _____

3 If Americans hadn't landed on the moon, _____

4 If electricity hadn't been discovered, _____

5 If humans had colonised space 100 years ago, ___

3 ★★★ Conditionals with past consequences
Finish the sentences to say what would have happened in the past.

1 If there were no seas or oceans on Earth, *life would never have developed.*

2 If everybody on Earth spoke the same language, _____

3 If the human race was less aggressive, _____

4 If there was life on all the planets in our solar system, _____

5 If all people were vegetarians, _____

6 If animals were as intelligent as humans, ____

4 ★★ Mixed conditionals
Write mixed conditionals about the situations below.

1 Tim didn't see the film so he can't tell you about it.
If _____

2 Jamie is so good at maths that he passed the test without revising at all.
If _____

3 I don't know about your party because I never got your message.
If _____

4 Our parents used to be very good friends. That's why we are good friends as well.
If _____

5 Paul failed his exam so he has to take it again.
If _____

6 Lucy rejected their help because she's very proud.
If _____

7 I'm not very fit so I didn't go mountain climbing.
If _____

5 ★★★ Mixed conditionals

Finish these conditional sentences so that the second part refers to the time given in brackets.

1 If Mike didn't have such a nice voice, _he wouldn't have become a radio announcer._ _____ (past)

2 If Tom had watched the morning news, _____ _____ (past)

3 If Sara wasn't so selfish, _____ _____ (past)

4 If Peter hadn't lost his passport abroad, _____ _____ (past)

5 If Mark hadn't the lost chess competition, _____ _____ (present)

6 If Jonathan didn't have a lot of friends, _____ _____ (present)

7 If Steve hadn't sold his old car, _____ _____ (present)

8 If Linda wasn't so talented, _____ _____ (past)

Prepositions

In phrases

Look at these examples.

- *If records fall, it is usually **due to** better equipment, training and diet.* (2 words)
- *My flat is **in front of** the new Olympic stadium.* (3 words)
- *Ben Johnson lost his gold medal in the 100 metres **as a result of** taking drugs.* (4 words)

Complete the prepositions in the sentences below with words from the box.

to, of, from, with, for

1 Last Sunday I went to watch the race *along* _____ a few friends.

2 She is one of the best young runners, *according* _____ the newspapers.

3 At this point in the race, Smith is slightly *ahead* _____ the other runners.

4 *Next* _____ him, in the outside lane, is the Australian swimmer, Ian Thorpe.

5 His time of 9.83 seconds was *close* _____ a world record.

6 All of the swimmers have finished the race, *except* _____ Eric Moussambani – Eric the Eel.

7 *Instead* _____ winning the gold as expected, he only came fifth.

8 She stood *on top* _____ the podium and received a gold medal.

9 He kept on trying *up* _____ the last moment but his legs had no strength left.

10 Some runners continue to take performance-enhancing drugs *in spite* _____ the risks.

11 She has won all of the Grand Slam tennis competitions *apart* _____ Wimbledon.

12 The British athletics team did quite well *in comparison* _____ the previous World Championships.

13 A new coach has been appointed to be *in charge* _____ the 100 metre relay team.

14 She did very well in the race, *thanks* _____ months of preparation and training.

15 Some sports, like cycling, are *in need* _____ a change in attitude towards doping.

16 The national team are *in search* _____ a new manager after the resignation of the previous one.

17 She was disqualified from the race *on the grounds* _____ tripping up an opponent.

18 Some athletes have been *in contact* _____ the newspapers over the latest doping scandal.

19 The race was called off, *owing* _____ the torrential rain.

20 She gave me a ticket for the match *in return* _____ that new T-shirt.

21 *Because* _____ her height she is an extremely good highjumper.

22 *As* _____ me, I don't like watching a lot of Olympic events like weightlifting.

23 *Together* _____ Mercx, Hinault and Anquetil, Indurain is one of the greatest cyclists of all time. They have all won the Tour de France five times.

24 *In addition* _____ winning the 400 metres, she won the long jump.

25 The charity football match was *in aid* _____ UNICEF and other organisations working with children.

▷ **Lexicon, Students' Book, pages 165–169.**

23 Communication

1 Giving advice
Read the dialogues and match them with the descriptions. Then complete each dialogue with the words from each box.

a a formal dialogue between a doctor and a patient ☐

b an informal dialogue between two friends ☐

c a television interview ☐

Dialogue 1

> ought, you'd, should, I were you

A: I'm feeling really awful. I only slept four hours last night.

B: It's not surprising, when you're always stuck in front of that computer.

A: What do you mean?

B: Well, you (1) _____ go out a bit more. And if (2) _____ I wouldn't drink so much coffee. Caffeine is bad for you, you know.

A: Yes, I know. But it keeps me awake when I'm playing games.

B: Mmmm, and you (3) _____ to do some exercise. (4) _____ feel much better. Why don't you play football with us on Saturday?

A: I'd like to but ... OK, what time is it?

Dialogue 2

> ...'d advise you, mustn't, must, ...'ve got, need

A: I'm afraid you (5) _____ to change your diet.

B: What do you mean?

A: Well, you (6) _____ to eat more fruit and vegetables and you (7) _____ eat so much fast food like pizzas and hamburgers.

B: But I don't like vegetables and I've hardly got any time to cook.

A: I'm afraid you (8) _____ make sure you eat properly. Your cholesterol level is much too high. I (9) _____ to go on one of the cookery courses organised by the local authority.

Dialogue 3

> there's no point, it's important, advice, ...'d advise, be counter-productive, could, should, what tips

A: So, (10) _____ for jogging have you got for our viewers?

B: Well, (11) _____ to start slowly. Trying to do too much all at once can (12) _____ .

A: Do you think people (13) _____ join a club?

B: Not necessarily. You can go jogging on your own or with friends. (14) _____ in joining a club unless you feel you need to have the discipline of a group.

A: And (15) _____ you give us some advice about trainers?

B: Well, there are lots on the market. My (16) _____ is to look around and talk to friends and find out which ones they find most comfortable. And I (17) _____ you not to worry too much about the label. A lot of the time you are just paying for the name!

2 Giving advice
Read about the two people's lifestyles.

Elvis Presley For breakfast, at 5 p.m., he had half a kilo of fried bacon and a quarter of a kilo of sausages (3,000 calories). For lunch, at midnight, he had two 'fool's gold' sandwiches – each made from a jar of peanut butter and a jar of strawberry jam, plus half a kilo of bacon (8,400 calories). For dinner he had five double hamburgers and a lot more sandwiches (2,000 calories). At the time of his death from a heart attack in 1977, he was taking 14 different kinds of drugs.

Monsieur Mangetout His diet has included bicycles, a supermarket trolley, television sets, a vacuum cleaner, two beds, and a Cessna four-seater plane! He once ate a coffin. And at a restaurant in Normandy he ate a whole table including plates,  knives, forks, glasses and bottles, as well as the tablecloth and napkins. Recently, he said he had heart disease, but believes it is not due to his diet or the fact that he smokes sixty cigarettes a day.

In your notebook, write advice for the people in the texts.

1 Imagine you are Elvis Presley's doctor. Use expressions from Dialogue 2 in Exercise 2.

2 Imagine you are a close friend of M. Mangetout. Use expressions from Dialogue 1 in Exercise 2.

MULTI-PART VERBS

1 Multi-part verbs
Read the book review and complete the multi-part verbs with these words.

off, up (x3), out (x3), down, through (x2)

TONY BUZAN is a world famous expert on ways of developing the mind and intelligence. His latest book is called *Head First – 10 ways to tap into your natural genius*. A few years ago, Buzan started to think about the topic of intelligence but couldn't (1) **work** ___out___ why some so-called 'intelligent' people did not seem very bright, while others who failed to (2) **get** _____ exams appeared much more intelligent. Buzan (3) **got** _____ **to** work on this and eventually (4) **came** _____ **with** the ideas in his book.

His starting point is that everyone can do well if they get rid of the barriers put up by the way they were educated and (5) **brought** _____ . The first step is to boost your belief in yourself. Buzan's performance in maths (6) **went** _____ a lot when he (7) **found** _____ he was in the top 1 percent of all mathematicians. Secondly, it is important to realise that ability is not something only for the talented few. For example, we are (8) **put** _____ singing because we feel we haven't got the 'gift' but in fact we 'sing' all the time when we speak a language. His third lesson is that all of us are intelligent. 'There is only one intelligence test,' he says, 'and that is life on planet Earth. Every day we are faced with new problems that we learn to handle.'

In the book, you can (9) **go** _____ a series of activities which will change your perception of how intelligent you are. Personally, I (10) **got a lot** _____ **of** this book and would recommend it to anyone.

2 Multi-part verbs and style
Read the information below.

- Multi-part verbs are more common in conversation than in written language.
- They appear more often in informal letters, fiction and newspapers than in academic writing.
- Some multi-part verbs (e.g. *carry out*) are exceptions and are more formal in written language than in conversation.

Replace the inappropriate expressions in the dialogue with the correct forms of these multi-part verbs.

shut up, listen to, look at, hurry up, pay back, talk to, get out of, put on, go off, get on with, get at, come on, go on, look for

Tina: ~~Please do what I ask~~. (1) ___Come on!___ We're going to be late. And ~~clothe yourself with~~ (2) _____ that coat. It's going to be cold.

Joe: ~~Stop talking~~! (3) _____ You're always telling me what to do and criticising (4) _____ me!

Tina: ~~Observe~~ (5) _____ yourself. Your shoes are really dirty. You're trying to ~~avoid~~ (6) _____ going to the party aren't you? (pause)

Joe: Continue talking. (7) _____

Tina: Well, it's just because you don't ~~have a good relationship with~~ (8) _____ Ross. You've ~~stopped liking~~ (9) _____ him recently.

Joe: Well, he still hasn't ~~reimbursed me~~ (10) _____ for those match tickets I bought for him last month.

Tina: OK, why don't you ~~communicate orally with~~ (11) _____ him? Oh no! We're going to be late. ~~Go faster please~~! (12) _____

Joe: I'm ~~searching for~~ (13) _____ my keys. Have you seen them?

Tina: You never ~~hear~~ (14) _____ me ~~with attention~~ do you? I put them in your pocket!

⇨ Lexicon, Students' Book, pages 170–176.

24 Focus on Writing

1 Linking

Complete the second sentence so that it has a similar meaning to the first sentence. Use the cue given and up to four more words.

1 She won the race even though she had a cold. (despite)

   Despite having a cold, she won the race.

2 I arrived late but did not miss the start of the concert. (even though)

   I did not miss the concert _____ .

3 I passed the exam despite making a mess of one question. (although)

   I passed the exam _____ of one question.

4 I'm against human cloning, except for medical reasons. (whereas)

   I'm against human cloning _____
   of cloning for medical reasons.

5 Although it was raining heavily we completed the race. (in spite of)

   We managed to complete the race _____ .

6 I don't like the Olympics apart from the swimming events. (though)

   I quite like the swimming events _____
   most of the Olympics.

2 Style

Rewrite the sentences formally. Use the cues in italics.

1 'A lot of people think smoking is bad for you – but they don't want it banned.' *on the one hand/considered dangerous/on the other hand/not in favour of*

   On the one hand, smoking is considered dangerous by a lot of people.
   On the other hand, they are not in favour of it being banned.

2 'Many scientists feel that cloning could be great – but they also think it's dangerous.' *whereas/see potential/aware of/dangers*

   _____
   _____

3 'Scientists have done lots of work on cancer – but they still haven't cured it.' *despite/carry out research/ways of curing/not found*

   _____
   _____

4 'Smoking causes lots of illnesses and kills thousands a year – but that doesn't make people give up.' *many diseases caused/thousands of deaths/however/knowledge/stop*

   _____
   _____

5 'You can't smoke on most buses or planes – but it's OK to do it in some places on trains.' *smoking not allowed/whereas/permitted*

   _____
   _____

3 Linking

Complete the sentences with linking words and expressions.

Scientists have used cloning (1) _in order to_ save endangered species (2) _____ the gaur. The gaur is a species of ox-like animal (3) _____ comes from India. (4) _____ November a baby bull gaur named Noah was born (5) _____ 'mother' was an ordinary cow from Iowa. (6) _____ the cloning process requires a lot of time and investment, in the future it is hoped that cheetahs can be cloned (7) _____ their number can be increased. In southern Africa there are only 12,000 cheetahs, (8) _____ need large areas to breed in. (9) _____ to this, there are plans for experiments on the giant panda (10) _____ there are only 1,000 left in the wild in China.

4 Editing
Some of the sentences in the text have missing words. Write the missing word on the right, or tick (✔) if correct.

SMART MICE

A team headed by Dr Tsien, from Princeton University, has	1	✔
produced a breed of mice, called 'Doogie Mice', are smarter	2	*that*
and learn more quickly than those born in wild. The team has	3	_____
identified a gene, NR2B, which is related the way we form	4	_____
associations. In the experiment, a group of mice were given extra	5	_____
copies of the gene help improve their memories. Then, tests	6	_____
were given to the Doogie mice and to another group normal mice.	7	_____
The Doogie mice learnt more quickly the other group and adapted	8	_____
lot more quickly to changes in their environment. For example,	9	_____
in one the experiments carried out by the team, the mice had to	10	_____
find a way of getting out a tank of water. The Doogies quickly learned	11	_____
to get out, whereas the other mice took twice long. 'The	12	_____
transgenic mice are learning things much better,' said the head of	13	_____
team, Dr Tsien. 'They are much smarter.' The results show that	14	_____
is possible to make animals more or less intelligent by manipulating	15	_____
their genes. Humans possess genes in common with mice and opens up	16	_____
a lot possibilities for the future, though very little is known about	17	_____
the impact of the gene on human intelligence. One these is	18	_____
gene therapy for illnesses such dementia, which affects	19	_____
people's memory and learning ability.	20	_____

5 Style
Replace the informal words and expressions with formal ones.

(1) *Kids* are healthier at birth, they get fewer infectious diseases and they are taller than in the (2) *old days*. However, Britain's teenagers are (3) *messing up* their health with a diet of junk food according to a new survey. Many teenagers are fatter than before and they take less exercise than their (4) *mums and dads* did. Teenagers today eat (5) *loads and loads* more fast food and sweet things than in the past: (6) *burgers*, pizzas, crisps, chocolate, chips, biscuits and cakes. They spend (7) *a real fortune* on sweets every year and eat too much fatty food. Doctors (8) *tell us* that fat should be less than 35 percent of our diet, but for many teenagers this figure is (9) *way over* 40 percent.

1	_Children_	6	_____
2	_____	7	_____
3	_____	8	_____
4	_____	9	_____
5	_____		

6 Guided writing
When you are writing a 'for and against' essay, it is a good idea to brainstorm your main points using a table. Tick (✔) the correct column.

	What are the arguments for and against genetic engineering?	For	Against
1	might cause new diseases		✔
2	might reduce diversity of plants		
3	could help to cure diseases like cancer		
4	could allow bad people to clone themselves		
5	could increase agricultural production		
6	might lead to control by big pharmaceutical companies		
7	might help to produce special animals to use as organ donors		
8	might help infertile people to have children		
9	could make laboratory animals suffer more in experiments		
10	could help to produce anti-ageing drugs		

7 Guided writing
Use the information in Exercise 6 to write one paragraph in your notebook about the advantages and one paragraph about the disadvantages of genetic engineering.

Word Power

1 Confusing words
Circle the correct word to complete the sentences.

1 Many experts think that tuberculosis is *probable/likely/possible* to increase in the next few years and there have already been serious *bursts/outbreaks/breakthroughs* in some parts of the world.

2 No *effective/affective/suitable* treatment is *disposable/possible/available* for many neurological diseases such as Parkinson's disease or multiple sclerosis.

3 In the accident, the car suffered serious *injury/damage/hurt* but luckily nobody in it was *injured/wounded/damaged*.

4 Vaccination has *avoided/cured/prevented* many infectious diseases such as smallpox.

5 Yesterday, a young girl was *checked into/admitted/entered* to hospital with a serious *hereditary/parental/inheriting* disease.

6 Doctors *could/managed/achieved* to cure the boy's disease which had meant that the *smaller/least/slightest* infection could be deadly.

7 This area of the brain controls emotions *such/for example/like* fear and love.

8 When we *discussed/argued/talked* the subject, some people did not find my argument very *persuading/convincing/winning*.

9 Our next guest has been *on the news/in the news/at the news* a lot in the *latest/recent/last* few days because of her recent *breakthrough/setback/outcome* in the treatment of cancer.

10 It is a bad thing to *pass/stay/spend* hours and hours in the library. I would *council/advise/advice* you to take regular breaks.

2 Fixed expressions
Complete the fixed expressions below. Then decide which are used in informal situations and which in formal ones. Write I (informal) or F (formal) in the box.

1 I __*bet*__ you'd like to live to a hundred and fifty if you could. ☐

2 There's no _____ that medical research will improve our life expectancy. ☐

3 What you're saying is completely _____ map. ☐

4 Let's _____ it. Human cloning is totally unacceptable. ☐

5 Come _____ it! That's not true! ☐

6 Just _____ at how cloning is used to help endangered species. ☐

7 I'd like to _____ that your figures are wrong. ☐

8 The _____ thing is to improve the quality of people's lives. ☐

9 I wouldn't touch that food with a _____ . It's full of artificial additives. ☐

10 I don't care two _____ about what other people think of me. ☐

11 The first _____ I'd like to say is that I'm afraid I disagree. ☐

12 This has been a big problem from the word _____ . ☐

3 Homophones
Some words sound the same but are spelt differently and have different meanings. Match the words that sound the same.

1 scene		a	site
2 weight		b	way
3 cell		c	fare
4 flaw		d	sore
5 genes		e	seen
6 weigh		f	floor
7 caught		g	sell
8 sight		h	jeans
9 saw		i	court
10 fair		j	wait

4 Homophones

Complete the sentences with words from Exercise 3.

1 I don't think it's ___fair___ that my bus ___fare___ has gone up by 25 percent.

2 My finger is still a bit _____ because I cut it with a _____ when I was cutting some wood at the weekend.

3 One _____ of making sure you get the right quantity is to _____ the vegetables yourself, using the scales in the supermarket.

4 It's an interesting design but I can see several _____ in it. For example, why are there so many stairs going up to the second _____ ?

5 I've never _____ such a bad accident in my life. But luckily, several ambulances came to the _____ of the accident almost immediately.

6 There must be something in my _____ . I'm just like my mum because we both hate wearing formal clothes and spend most of our time in _____ .

7 The Health Minister has just chosen the _____ for a new hospital specialising in problems related to people's _____ , such as cataracts and blindness.

8 I am starting to put on _____ because I have to spend most of the day sitting around while I _____ for the phone to ring.

9 New biotech companies are starting to _____ a range of new products, including vitamin supplements which they say help to regenerate every _____ in our brain.

10 I think I must have _____ that cold when I was playing tennis. There was a really cold wind blowing on to the _____ .

5 Homonyms

Some words are spelt in the same way but have different meanings, and some are pronounced differently. Translate the words in *italics* into your own language. Are the words the same or different in your language?

1 The *point* is that it can be dangerous. _____

2 The *point* of the needle wasn't sharp enough. _____

3 We scored two *points* in the first half. _____

4 It's rude to *point* at people. _____

5 She has a *mark* on her skin. _____

6 I lost a *mark* for making a bad mistake. _____

7 The heart *beats* thousands of times a day. _____

8 She sometimes *beats* the carpet with a stick. _____

9 Lying on a beach *beats* doing homework! _____

10 She is not very honest and told me a *lie*. _____

11 After lunch I *lie* down and have a siesta. _____

12 I'd like to *own* a flat when I'm older. _____

13 I gave her my *own* pen. _____

14 I am going to discuss the *matter* with my boss. _____

15 *Matter* can't escape from a black hole. _____

16 What's the *matter*? You look upset. _____

17 Metal objects *contract* when it is very cold. _____

18 We still haven't signed the *contract* yet. _____

6 Extension: Pronunciation

Choose the correct symbol for the <u>underlined</u> sounds.

1 I w<u>ou</u>nd up the clock.
   a) /uː/   b) (/aʊ/)

2 He had a bad w<u>ou</u>nd in his leg.
   a) /uː/   b) /aʊ/

3 That w<u>i</u>nd is very cold.
   a) /ɪ/   b) /aɪ/

4 In the morning I w<u>i</u>nd down the blinds.
   a) /ɪ/   b) /aɪ/

5 Michael Schumacher is in the l<u>ea</u>d.
   a) /e/   b) /iː/

6 You can only buy l<u>ea</u>d-free petrol nowadays.
   a) /e/   b) /iː/

7 She b<u>a</u>thed the baby.
   a) /ɑː/   b) /eɪ/

8 We b<u>a</u>thed in the sea every day.
   a) /ɑː/   b) /eɪ/

9 I've always lived in the same hou<u>s</u>e.
   a) /s/   b) /z/

10 There are tents to hou<u>s</u>e the refugees.
   a) /s/   b) /z/

11 He didn't b<u>o</u>w when the Queen arrived.
   a) /əʊ/   b) /aʊ/

12 I don't like b<u>o</u>w-ties.
   a) /əʊ/   b) /aʊ/

⇨ Lexicon, Students' Book, (inside back cover).

Language Awareness

1 ★ Modal verbs

Write what the person with the speech bubble is saying, using these modal verbs.

shall, must, could, may

1 '_____
   _____,'

2 '_____
   _____,'

3 '_____
   _____,'

4 '_____
   _____,'

2 ★★ Modal verbs

Use the verbs in brackets to rewrite these sentences in your notebook.

1 It's a pity you didn't visit Florence when you were in Italy. (should)

   You should have visited Florence when you were in Italy.

2 I'm sure Mark arrived on time – he always does. (will)

3 It's possible that he isn't as clever as he looks. (may)

4 I advise you to take some antidepressants. (ought)

5 She wore her evening dress unnecessarily; formal clothes weren't required. (need)

6 Don't touch this bottle – there's poison in it. (must)

7 I'm sure he didn't accept any bribes – he's too honest for that. (can)

8 Look at him. It's obvious that he's suffering. (must)

9 He was forced to work during his holidays to earn his university fees. (had)

10 She's likely to come up with a solution. (might)

11 I didn't call a taxi because I had enough time to get to the station by bus. (need)

12 It was impossible for us to come to the meeting. (could)

13 It's possible that the trains were delayed. (may)

14 She is probably waiting for us and getting furious – I know her. (will)

15 There was no need to buy the tickets – the museum was free on Sunday. (have)

3 ★★ Modal verbs

Circle all the suitable modal verbs and expressions in the text. There may be more than one correct choice.

Mark Stewart and Jonathan Pierce, candidates for this year's Nobel Prize in chemistry, announced today that they (1) *may/could/need* give up their research on a new generation of antidepressants. Professor Pierce said: 'We (2) *can't/have to/mustn't* bear the thought that our work (3) *must/should/might* be used to harm, rather than help people. This is what we fear happened with our research on anaesthetics. We (4) *could/were able to/may* produce a chemical substance that (5) *shall/could/might* alleviate migraine pain by 80 per cent. However, we've now been informed that the results of our research (6) *may/can/could* have been used to produce a poison gas. This shows how careful scientists (7) *ought/have/must* to be with disclosing their work. We probably (8) *shouldn't/needn't/couldn't* have published the results of our research. In future, we (9) *must/will/can* be more careful because it's our duty to think about how scientific data (10) *should/must/can* be used.'

Check Your Grammar

1 Complete the sentences with the correct forms of the verbs in brackets.

1 We'll let you know as soon as the Personnel Manager ___has taken___ (take) her final decision.

2 If he _____ (speak) Chinese, he could have negotiated a better contract with the Hong Kong company.

3 Don't bother calling me on Saturday – I _____ (lie) on the beach and _____ (listen) to Greek folk music.

4 He's a good player, so I'm sure he _____ (win) a few tournaments by the time he's twenty-one.

5 They _____ (not feel) offended if you had accepted their invitation.

6 If your immune system _____ (not work) properly, your life can be threatened by a common infectious disease.

7 Dad, if you really cared about money, you _____ (choose) to study business rather than philosophy when you were young.

8 When the guests _____ (arrive), ask them to wait in the lounge.

9 If we all _____ (live) on the moon, it _____ (be) terribly crowded.

10 _____ (you go) to the post office this afternoon? Could you buy me some stamps?

Floods in Central Europe

Following a period of very heavy rainfall, water levels have risen dramatically. Mountain rivers have already flooded hundreds of villages and the big rivers of the region (1) ____ the same any minute. The moment water levels (2) ____ above 'danger level', the people from the areas bordering the rivers (3) ____ .

Tonight, an emergency task force set up by five countries of the region (4) ____ a possible aid plan for the flooded areas. They have been co-ordinating all rescue operations: 2,500 rescue teams have been sent to the most affected regions so far and at least 500 more rescue teams, including psychologists, (5) ____ by the end of this week. The psychologists (6) ____ the most distressed families to offer counselling and help develop effective stress-coping strategies.

However, the most important things now are food and water. The rescue operation co-ordinator said today: 'Fresh water (7) ____ be provided to the flooded areas to prevent water-borne diseases from spreading. If we (8) ____ people safe water and food, we (9) ____ be facing an epidemic very soon.'

Experts say that the flood (10) ____ prevented after the disaster that struck this part of Europe in 1997. An anonymous expert said today: 'The flood (11) ____ predicted – it was clear from meteorological evidence that very heavy and long-lasting rain (12) ____ over central Europe. I think people (13) ____ warned and it was certainly possible to introduce more protection measures. If this (14) ____ done, we (15) ____ at least some of the tragedy.'

2 Read the text above *Floods in Central Europe* and choose the best option (a–d) for each gap.

	a	b	c	d
1	may do	may have done	must do	must have done
2	rises	rise	will rise	will be rising
3	will evacuate	will have evacuated	will be evacuated	will be evacuating
4	will be discussing	will have discussed	discuss	have discussed
5	will be sending	will have sent	will send	will have been sent
6	will be meeting	will have met	will be met	are meeting
7	might	must	may	could
8	aren't giving	won't give	don't give	wouldn't give
9	will	must	have to	should
10	could be	should be	could have been	must have been
11	should have been	can't have been	must have been	will have been
12	is going to fall	was going to fall	was falling	will be falling
13	should have been	should be	may have been	will be
14	will be	had been	was	is
15	would avoid	will have avoided	will avoid	would have avoided

7 Journeys

25 Vocabulary

1 Key words
Read the text and (circle) the best words to complete this description of Istanbul.

When you walk through its (1) *breathtaking/bustling /striking* streets you can just feel the vitality of this (2) *ancient/ antique/historic* city. It was built on several hills and so from different parts of the city there are (3) *breathtaking/exotic/ romantic* views. The setting is (4) *unspoilt/perfect/scenic*, with the Bosphorus dividing the city's western and eastern sides. When you cross one of the (5) *magnificent/powerful/ breathtaking* bridges you can often see the old city with its beautiful, (6) *good-looking/ bustling/historic* buildings like the Haga Sofia mosque or Topkapi palace. The people are extremely (7) *exotic/magnificent/friendly* and there is (8) *delicious/elegant/ graceful* food. What more could you ask for?

⇨ Lexicon, Students' Book, page 154.

2 Wordbuilding
Read these sentences and write the opposites of the words in brackets.

1 They are so __impatient__ (patient), and they __disagree__ (agree) with everything I say.

2 Is it _____ (legal) to park here?

3 The beach was _____ (crowded) and _____ (spoilt) by tourism.

4 I'll _____ (pack) my bags later.

5 He's a _____ (loyal) and _____ (responsible) worker.

6 Are you going to _____ (wrap) the present now?

7 You always seem to _____ (understand) me.

8 I've never met such _____ , _____ (honest, helpful) and _____ (friendly) people.

9 She's very _____ (sensitive) and _____ (tolerant).

10 We were _____ (lucky) – the hotel was _____ (comfortable) and very _____ (convenient) for the beach.

11 Our postal service is very _____ (reliable) and _____ (efficient).

12 I've never seen such an _____ (interesting) programme.

13 Is it _____ (visible) without a microscope?

14 The magician made the rabbit _____ (appear) in a hat.

15 I think it's _____ (possible) to do this _____ (correctly).

⇨ Lexicon, Students' Book, page 156.

3 🄰🄕 Dictionary work
Read the information in the box. Then add a prefix to each of the words below. Use a good dictionary to help you.

- Entries beginning *un-*, *in-*, *im-*, *ir-* or *il-* are usually adjectives.
- Entries beginning *dis-* or *mis-* are usually verbs (v).

_in_ accurate	___experienced	___necessary	___satisfactory
___active	___fortunate	___obedient	___suitable
___approve (v)	___human	___perfect	___successful
___calculate (v)	___hurt	___place (v)	___sympathetic
___conventional	___important	___pleased	___treat (v)
___common	___judge (v)	___popular	___usual
___competent	___kind	___practical	
___credible	___like	___regular	
___equal	___like (v)	___relevant	

Remember

1 ★ Infinitive and -ing
Match the halves to make logical sentences.

1	We can't afford	a	driving in crowded streets.
2	If you don't take an umbrella, you risk	b	to spend all our holidays abroad.
3	The suspect denied	c	playing tennis.
4	I'm learning	d	getting wet on the way home.
5	I invited him to the meeting but he refused	e	to come.
6	The head teacher threatened	f	to introduce strict measures against smoking.
7	To pass my driving test, I should practise	g	selling stolen goods.
8	If you want your knee to mend, you must give up	h	to play chess but it's hard.

2 ★ Infinitive or -ing?
Complete the sentences with the infinitive + *to* or the *-ing* form of the verbs in brackets.

1 Many people can't afford ____*to send*____ (send) their children to private schools.

2 I've never really enjoyed _____ (visit) other countries.

3 I didn't manage _____ (meet) anyone famous when I was in Hollywood.

4 We're looking forward to _____ (see) Egypt and the Middle East.

5 I'll have to consider _____ (take up) a job away from the city.

6 He offered _____ (organise) our trip to Mexico.

7 During the trek in Nepal I sometimes couldn't stand _____ (sleep) in a tent.

8 We threatened _____ (call) the police if they didn't stop _____ (make) a noise.

9 They suggested _____ (have) a cup of tea before we left.

10 I don't regret _____ (go) to Asia as it was a fascinating journey.

3 ★★ Verb patterns
Match the verbs with the verb patterns given.

agree, admit, avoid, consider, finish, decide, enjoy, imagine, manage, offer, not mind, plan, promise, put off, refuse, want, would like

agree	to do something
admit	doing something

4 ★★ Verb patterns
Choose verbs from Exercise 3 to complete these sentences. Use the correct form of each verb.

1 I never _____ to do the washing-up. I could even say I like it.

2 The student union _____ to call off the rally because of the weather.

3 After a few questions from the teacher that he couldn't answer, Tom _____ being unprepared for the lesson.

4 If you don't want your breathing problems to get worse, you should _____ passive smoking at all costs.

5 She's always _____ eating – that's why she's so plump.

6 Frankly, I can't _____ living in another country. I've lived here all my life.

7 After a lot of effort he _____ to change his lifestyle completely after his first heart attack.

8 Some people were so keen to listen to the concert live that they _____ sitting on the floor.

81

26 Grammar

1 ⋆⋆ *be used to* and *get used to*
Complete the sentences with *(not) be used to, (not) get used to* or *used to/didn't use to.*

1   When I started living in the forest I gradually
    got used to the complete silence at night and
    birds singing at dawn.

2   My granny _____ make up fairy
    tales for me when I was a little girl.

3   Be careful! The dog _____
    being touched by strangers.

4   Farmers in this area _____ buy
    chemical fertilisers until the 1970s.

5   Don't worry! You will slowly _____
    our working hours and even if you _____
    _____ getting up so early,
    you'll soon find finishing work early a great
    advantage.

6   Travelling _____ be much
    slower and less comfortable in the old days.

7   We have never been to Africa before and I _____
    _____ the hot and humid
    climate at all.

8   When you start a new job, it can take some time to
    _____ the different routine.

2 ⋆ Completed or in progress?
Tick (✔) the sentence that best describes what you
see in the picture.

1   a I heard a Dutch singer perform
       'An Englishman in New York'. ☐
    b I heard a Dutch singer performing
       'An Englishman in New York'. ☐

2   a I saw Gina read a letter. ☐
    b I saw Gina reading a letter. ☐

3 ⋆ Verb patterns
Circle the verbs that could complete the gap.

1   He was so scared of the storm that he .... to hide
    under the table.
    tried   attempted   risked   wanted

2   Tessa _____ her children cook lunch on Sunday.
    allows   lets   makes   prepares

3   We _____ to finish the exam before 11 a.m.
    hoped   wanted   expected   tried

4   The girl _____ losing the money on her way home.
    happened   seemed   admitted   regretted

5   Harry couldn't _____ listening to the director's
    speech.
    stand   afford   remember   refuse

6   We finally _____ to go on a short holiday to the
    mountains.
    arranged   considered   managed   suggested

7   When I am abroad, I always _____ tasting the local
    food.
    enjoy   offer   decide   avoid

8   People nowadays _____ to use a lot of cosmetics.
    seem   tend   admit   risk

4 ⋆⋆⋆ Infinitive or *-ing*?
Put the verbs in brackets into the infinitive with to
or the *-ing* form.

Jenny Adams, an 11-year-old girl travelling from San
Diego to Philadelphia by Western American Airlines
ended up in Miami instead.

    Jenny first flew from San Diego to Denver, where she
managed (1) _to get_ (get) to the Philadelphia gate just
in time. However, the airline staff rushed her through
the adjacent gate of the Miami flight, convinced that
this was her destination. Seeing that she was being put
on a wrong flight, Jenny tried (2) _____
(protest) but the airline staff chose (3) _____
(ignore) her desperate attempts to change flights.
    'When I heard the pilot (4) _____
(announce) the estimated landing time in Miami I knew
it was too late, there was no point in (5) _____
(say) anything to the cabin staff, so I decided
(6) _____ (call) my mother from Miami and
ask her what to do,' said Jenny.

In Miami, a passenger who had been sitting next to her, agreed (7) _____ (lend) her his mobile so that she could call her parents, who, in the meantime had not seen her (8) _____ (get) off the plane in Philadelphia and were seriously worried.

'We deeply regret (9) _____ (trust) the Western American Airlines. We only let our daughter (10) _____ (fly) alone after carefully (11) _____ (check) that the airline would take care of her properly. Jenny isn't used to (12) _____ (travel) on her own, so we were quite anxious. Ironically, we paid an additional $100 for this service,' said Marilyn Adams, Jenny's mother.

The airline spokesperson admitted (13) _____ (make) a serious mistake and offered (14) _____ (refund) the extra $100 charge the parents had paid.

Prepositions

Position/order and direction

Look at these examples.

*I was strolling **through** the town.*
*Salmon swim hundreds of miles **up** rivers and streams.*
*Monarch butterflies fly 3,000 km south **to** California.*

Circle the correct prepositions.

Sometimes I get interested in people who I've never even met. For example, it happened the other day when I was (1) *at/in* the city of Hamville. I was (2) *in/on* my way (3) *at/to* Hamville in the early morning. I was reading the newspaper (4) *by/on* the train when I noticed a man sitting (5) *at/in* the seat (6) *opposite/over* mine. The man was middle-aged and looked quite ordinary but had a strange scar (7) *above/on top of* his left eye and (8) *down/underneath* his chin there was a tattoo of a very small dragon. The man was sitting (9) *in/next to* the window and from time to time looked (10) *from/out of* it anxiously, occasionally taking an old watch (11) *of/out of* his pocket.

When we arrived (12) *at/to* the station, the man took his bag (13) *down/from* the luggage rack (14) *above/on* the seats and got (15) *from/off* the train. There was something mysterious about him, so I decided to follow him. He did not get (16) *in/on* a taxi, but walked slowly (17) *among/between* the people in the station and went (18) *out/out of* the railway station carrying his bag. He then went (19) *across/through* the road and started to walk (20) *along/around* the river.

He crossed (21) *over/through* a bridge and then went to the main square and sat (22) *in/on* a bench in the old square (23) *in front of/opposite* the cathedral. I waited and stood (24) *at/behind* a tree in the square.

After five minutes two men went up (25) *by/to* him and started talking. He started to run away (26) *by/from* them but they ran (27) *after/at* him and one of them took (28) *from/out* a gun. Two minutes later police cars and vans came screeching (29) *at/into* the square. Heavily armed police officers jumped out and put the man (30) *in/on* one of the vans before leaving again at high speed. The next day, in the newspapers, I found out that the police had captured one of the most important leaders of organised crime in the whole country.

➡ Lexicon, Students' Book, page 165.

27 Communication

1 Polite requests
Match the two parts of the requests.

1	If you'd like to	a	could have another cup of coffee, please?
2	Is it all right if	b	possibly give me a map of the city, please?
3	I was wondering if	c	all right if I had my meal in my room?
4	Where can I	d	sign here, please.
5	Could you	e	if you could help me, please?
6	Do you think I	f	I come ten minutes late?
7	I wonder	g	you could give me a leaflet, please?
8	Would it be	h	make a phone call, please?

2 Polite language
Rewrite the dialogues using more polite language.

Man: (1) ~~Hey there!~~ _____Excuse me._____

Waiter: Yes, sir. How can I help you?

Man: (2) ~~I want another bottle of water.~~

_____

Waiter: Certainly, sir. Still or sparkling?

Man: (3) ~~Give me a big bottle of still.~~

_____

Sue: (4) ~~Hey, you there! Chris!~~

_____

Chris: How's it going, Sue?

Sue: Fine. I've left my dictionary at home. (5) ~~Lend me yours.~~ _____

Chris: (6) ~~No, I can't.~~ _____

_____ , I haven't got mine either.

Woman: (7) ~~What time's breakfast?~~

_____

Receptionist: From seven till nine-thirty, madam.

Woman: (8) ~~Well, I need a wake-up call.~~

_____

Receptionist: At what time, madam?

Woman: (9) ~~Eight o'clock. On the dot.~~

_____

Receptionist: Certainly, madam.

Woman: Oh, and one more thing. (10) ~~I want a newspaper. The Telegraph~~.

_____

Receptionist: Of course, madam.

3 Asking permission
Write suitable requests for permission. Use the cues given and a variety of expressions.

1   borrow/pen
    Can I borrow your pen, please?
    Of course you can. Go ahead and take it.

2   make/phone call

    _____
    Of course. The phone's on the left.

3   leave early

    _____
    I'm afraid you must stay till the end of the class.

4   have time/go for a coffee

    _____
     Of course, but don't be late – the bus is leaving at four o'clock.

5   stay in/hotel room/another two hours

    _____
    Yes, sir. That's no problem. But the cleaners have to come in before three.

6   stay out late

    _____
    Well, as long as you're back by one.

MULTI-PART VERBS

1 Multi-part verbs
Replace the words in brackets with these verbs in the correct form.

> check in, catch up with, fill in,
> get back, get to, get up, go out, keep to,
> pick up, set off, stay over, stop off

It was an amazing journey. We didn't have to (1) __check-in__ (register our arrival) as you do in airports, though my boyfriend had to (2) _____ (complete) a form, because he's American and not from the European Union. Well, we (3) _____ (started our journey) at about one o'clock and we (4) _____ (arrived at) Austerlitz Station in Paris in under three hours.

We wanted to (5) _____ (spend the night) in Paris so we went to a hotel and booked a room. Then we (6) _____ . (left our hotel) and had dinner together. The next morning we (7) _____ (rose) early and got the TGV south. It's really punctual and always (8) _____ (follows) the timetable, not like trains here! Anyway, in Nice we (9) _____ _____ (joined) some friends who'd gone down there a few days earlier. They (10) _____ (collected us) from the station and we went to their villa.

It was a marvellous holiday. On the way back, we (11) _____ (interrupted our journey) for two hours in Paris. We (12) _____ (returned) to London last night!

2 Multi-part verbs in fixed expressions
Complete the sentences with these verbs in the ⌐

> bring, bump, come, get (x2), make (x2), run, take, turn (x2)⌐

1 I _____ *time off* work next July to go campi⌐
2 When we set off it was cloudy, but later it _____
3 We went hitchhiking round France, but _____ o⌐ after a week!
4 I _____ *into an old friend* while I was in London; w⌐ seen each other for ages.
5 _____ *out!* The drivers are crazy in this country.
6 I spent all day in the museum. It was worth it; I really _____ *a lot out of it.*
7 She _____ *down with* a cold on holiday after she'd been swimming in the lake.
8 I don't want to _____ *up the subject*, but how are we going to get home?
9 This map isn't very clear; I just *can't* _____ *it out.*
10 I suppose after the long holiday we'll have to _____ *down to some work.*
11 He _____ *up an excuse* for being late for the bus.
12 They said we could stay an extra two days but we _____ *down their offer.*

⇨ Lexicon, Students' Book, pages 170–176.

3 🄰🄯 Multi-part verbs in fixed expressions
Complete the expressions with these words. Use a good dictionary.

> against, into, of (x2), up, with

Amy: We couldn't (1) *make* _____ *our minds* about where to go on holiday.
Brenda: So where did you go in the end?
Amy: We decided to go to Cornwall. We took the train.
Brenda: Oh, you didn't drive?
Amy: No. You've got to (2) *take* _____ *account* that it's nearly 500 miles away, and that's a lot of driving, isn't it?
Brenda: Yes, it is. You can get a plane nowadays.
Amy: (3) *I've nothing* _____ *planes* – I'm not afraid of flying or anything like that, but I prefer the train.
Brenda: What was the weather like?
Amy: Not too bad. We (4) *made the most* _____ the sun when it came out. I even got a bit of a tan.
Brenda: So what did you get up to?
Amy: Most days we went down to the beach and (5) *made do* _____ a couple of sandwiches for lunch. Oh, once we tried windsurfing. Everybody (6) *made fun* _____ me because I kept on falling in!

28 Foc...

1 Linki...
Compl... ...so that it has the ...tence. Use between ...the cue given.

...you must bring it back
sam...

_____ *unless you bring it back*
t...

...ew CD player without a
...t)

r _____
_____ a discount.

...t not be such a good idea.

...sure _____ such a
...d idea.

If it rains, I'm certainly not going swimming.
(as long as)
I'll go swimming _____ rain.

5 I only went to see her because I wanted to help her out. (if)
I wouldn't have gone to see her _____
_____ help her out.

6 Could you possibly send me a leaflet about the hotel? (if)
I would _____ send me a leaflet about the hotel.

7 I'll help him when he gives me back that CD I lent him. (except if)
I _____ he gives me back that CD I lent him.

8 I'll do it provided that it's safe. (unless)
I _____ it's safe.

2 Linking
Complete the article using these linking words.

in order to, also, although, as long as, as well as, because of, despite, for example, however, if, in conclusion, provided that, since, unless, whether

Package Holidays

Literally millions of people leave Britain every summer (1) __*in order to*__ relax on the sunny beaches of the Mediterranean. There are (2) _____ growing numbers of tourists who travel to more exotic holiday destinations.

(3) _____ , these package holidays have many disadvantages. It doesn't matter (4) _____ you are flying or going by tour bus, it can be uncomfortable and exhausting (5) _____ delays and long journeys. (6) _____ that, many British tourists are disappointed with the resorts.

(7) _____ , the apartments are not always as big as they seemed in the brochure. And many British people only like the bars and restaurants (8) _____ they serve British food and (9) _____ the menu is in English!

(10) _____ these disadvantages, foreign travel has revolutionised the quality of life for many people. (11) _____ you live in a warm climate anyway, a couple of weeks in the sun can make all the difference to you, (12) _____ it cheers you up and gives you something to look forward to. And to be fair, (13) _____ a lot of tourists do stay in the resorts, there are many others who make an effort to get to know something about the people and country they are visiting.

(14) _____ , foreign travel is a great thing for most people. (15) _____ they didn't go abroad, many people wouldn't have the opportunity to experience cultures and lifestyles which are different from their own.

3 Editing

Read the text carefully. When a line has an extra word, circle the word and write it on the right. When a line is correct, put a tick (✔) on the right.

One of the most interesting journeys I have ever been on was in	1 _____✔_____
(the) South America. I had been working in the city of Santa Cruz in	2 ____the____
the east of Bolivia and wanted to travel to Brazil. I decided to go by	3 _____
boat down along the Amazon and one of its tributaries, then spend some	4 _____
time on the unspoilt coast of north-east Brazil. I started off of my journey	5 _____
by taking a bus from Cochabamba, a beautiful city which in the Andes	6 _____
mountains where it is permanently spring. The bus was full of country	7 _____
people going to home and there was a happy atmosphere as we wound	8 _____
our way on muddy, untarred roads down to the lowlands. While the	9 _____
further down we went, the hotter it became until when we eventually	10 _____
arrived at the town of Puerto Villaroel. In fact, to call it by a town would	11 _____
be something of an exaggeration. Even though it looked like important	12 _____
on my map, Puerto Villaroel was in fact one short street with some of	13 _____
huts on the either side, leading to a rather muddy river. This was the port	14 _____
and along the bank were several of river boats plus their barges, as well	15 _____
as was a gunboat belonging to the Bolivian navy. I went into the café	16 _____
overlooking the river and asked him about boats downriver. I was in luck.	17 _____
A well-dressed, tallish young man came just over to my table. He was the	18 _____
son of the owner of several boats and had come down from Cochabamba,	19 _____
where his family lived in, to go on a boat trip up to the northern city of	20 _____
Trinidad. He was friendly and, for a very reasonable price, he agreed that	21 _____
to take me with them on the week-long journey down by the river. That	22 _____
night I could hardly to sleep at all. Not only was I constantly attacked by	23 _____
a whole air force of mosquitoes that felt as big as bees, but I was going	24 _____
on the first of real journey of my life.	25 _____

4 Style

Below are sentences from two letters – one formal and one informal – but they are mixed up. Decide which sentences are from each letter, and then write the letters in your notebook.

1 Thanks for the letter.
2 However, there are a few points which are not clear.
3 Hi!
4 I look forward to hearing from you.
5 Take care,
6 It was really interesting.
7 In this way we could discuss the matter further.
8 Dear Ms Turner,
9 Is it OK if I give you a ring sometime?
10 Would you mind if I phoned you?
11 But there are still one or two things I'm not sure about.
12 Thank you for your letter.
13 Anyway, write back soon.
14 S. Davies (Mr)
15 Simon.
16 It contained some very useful information.
17 Then we can talk about it some more.
18 Yours sincerely,

5 Guided writing: Letters

In your notebook, write an introduction (one or two sentences) for each situation below.

1 You have seen an advert in a magazine for a summer school in England. You need more information and wonder if the school can send you a leaflet.

2 You have seen an advert for a summer job working with disabled children. You are interested. The advert asked you to send your CV.

3 You read in your local newspaper about plans for a new power station near your town. You strongly disagree.

Word Power

1 Confusing words
Circle the more suitable alternative in each sentence.

1 I had a terrible *flight*/*travel* last summer. There was a fault and the plane had to turn back only half an hour after taking off.

2 The best school *outing/voyage* that I remember was when we went to the zoo in Year 7.

3 My mum wants to go on a *cruise/voyage* around the Mediterranean, sailing to different places like Barcelona and Malta.

4 The first sea *cruise/voyage* around the world was begun by the Portuguese commander, Ferdinand Magellan and completed by the Spanish sailor, Juan Sebastian del Cano.

5 I never get bored on a long car *journey/trip*. I really love driving.

6 I love reading *journey/travel* books, because you can read about people's experiences from the comfort of your armchair.

7 On the last day of the holiday, we went on an excellent *excursion/package tour* to a nearby ruined castle.

8 My dad has just come back from a business *outing/trip* to New York.

9 Last year we went on a *package tour/travel* around Italy by coach.

10 Bye! Have a good *trip/voyage*!

2 Missing out words
Cross out the words that could be missed out in this very informal dialogue.

Ted: ~~Have you~~ finished your tea?
Ricky: No, I haven't finished my tea. I'm doing the crossword.
Ted: That sounds like good fun.
Ricky: Yes. I finished the one in yesterday's paper. Have you ever done the crossword in this paper? It's usually really difficult.
Ted: No, I don't really like them. I prefer reading. I've just finished another book by Paul Auster. It was absolutely amazing!
Ricky: Mm, I think he's great.
Ted: Are you going to be here all day?
Ricky: No, I'm just finishing! Just give me a couple of secs.

3 Colloquial expressions
Complete the expressions below with these words.

life, nightmare, nowhere, sailing, straw, track

1 We finished the project after a lot of problems. It wasn't all plain _____ , I can tell you!

2 I haven't a clue where we are. I can't see any houses. We're right in the middle of _____ .

3 She lives miles away in the country somewhere. Her house is right off the beaten _____ .

4 I lost all the money I'd won earlier in the day. But that's _____ , isn't it?

5 He stood on the table and started singing. It was awful. That really was the last _____ and we all left the party.

6 It was the worst journey in my life, I can tell you. It was a complete _____ .

4 Introducing requests
Write questions with *will be* to introduce a request.

1 You want to ask someone to take you to the centre of town.
   Will you be going anywhere near the centre of town?

2 You want to ask someone to lend you their dictionary.
   _____

3 You want someone to help you with your homework this evening.
   _____

4 You want someone to take something to school for you.
   _____

5 You want someone to come with you to a party on Saturday.
   _____

6 You want someone to give a message to your friend, Paul.
   _____

5 Proverbs

Match the proverbs (1–10) with the explanations (a–j).

1	Nothing ventured, nothing gained.	a	It is preferable to do something late than not at all.
2	There's no smoke without fire.	b	The final victory is the most complete one.
3	Better late than never.	c	You cannot achieve anything without taking risks.
4	Never judge a book by its cover.	d	What is attractive is very subjective.
5	Absence makes the heart grow fonder.	e	Too much work can make you boring.
6	Don't put all your eggs in one basket.	f	There is always a basis for rumours no matter how untrue they seem.
7	One man's meat is another man's poison.	g	Everybody has different tastes.
8	He who laughs last laughs longest.	h	Don't only think about people's appearance.
9	Beauty is in the eye of the beholder.	i	Spread your risks.
10	All work and no play makes Jack a dull boy.	j	If you don't see someone for a time, you love them more.

6 ⒶⓏ Extension: Proverbs

Match the statements (1–5) with the proverbs (a–e). Use a good dictionary.

1 I've sent him to piano lessons, but he's just not interested in music. ☐

a   Don't count your chickens before they're hatched.

2 Oh well, if everybody else is doing it, I suppose we should! ☐

b   Too many cooks spoil the broth.

3 I've studied so hard, I'm sure I'll pass the exam. ☐

c   A bad workman blames his tools.

4 This computer is useless! The keyboard is so slow. ☐

d   You can lead a horse to water but you can't make it drink.

5 Don't you think we'll get in each other's way? ☐

e   When in Rome, do as the Romans do.

USE OF ENGLISH

TIPS **for sentence transformations**

1 Try to work out what grammatical structure or fixed expression is tested in each sentence. The most common are: reported speech, conditionals, the passive, linking, verb patterns, prepositions, modal verbs and expressions.

2 Think of phrases that include the cue word provided.

   time ⟶ *it's high time*; spite ⟶ *in spite of*; were ⟶ *if I were you*.

3 Always check whether you have changed everything you were supposed to change in rewriting the sentence. Is the infinitive correct (passive/perfect)?

   Does the verb form agree with the subject? Is the word order correct?

4 Make sure you haven't omitted any information from the original sentence.

1 Rewrite the sentences using the beginnings provided, so that the meaning is the same. (20 marks)

0 Monet painted this picture in 1891.

   This picture _____ *was painted by Monet in 1891.*

1 It was a mistake not to warn him about the storm.

   We should _____

2 They won't score any goals if they don't start running faster.

   Unless _____

3 I think he doesn't like modern art.

   I don't _____

4 The college has a very good reputation but very few students choose to attend it.

   In spite _____

   _____

5 The police were questioning the shop assistant in connection with the bomb scare.

   The shop assistant _____

   _____

6 I didn't learn French and I can't understand what she's saying.

   If I _____

   _____

7 Mary talked to her mother and understood why her parents had separated.

   Having _____

   _____

8 It seems that Robert enjoys big parties.

   Robert _____

9 I regret buying this awful CD.

   I wish _____

10 Smoking in public places is forbidden here.

   It _____

11 Janet Mason is my best friend, and her father is working abroad.

   Janet Mason, _____

   _____

12 I'm sure he is going to wear a dark suit.

   He will _____

13 The pickpocket said that he had taken the man's wallet out of his pocket.

   The pickpocket admitted _____

   _____

14 We came very early although it wasn't necessary.

   We needn't _____

15 As they get richer, they spend more and more money on useless things.

   The _____

   _____

16 What will you do with this piece of evidence? I just want to know.

   I just want to know _____

   _____

17 I wish I had helped Jeremy paint his flat.

   I regret not _____

   _____

18 No one told us that this was private property.

   We _____

19 It wasn't easy but he won the scholarship.

   He managed _____

20 The book was so interesting that I couldn't stop reading it.

It was such _____

20

2 Use the word in brackets to complete the second sentence, so that the meaning is the same.
(20 marks)

0 Why didn't they play any music at the party? (should)

They ___*should have played some*___ music at the party.

1 The last time I ate seafood was at my parents' wedding anniversary. (since)

I _____ my parents' wedding anniversary.

2 It's impossible that she listened to our conversation. (can't)

She _____ to our conversation.

3 The pain made it impossible for me to walk. (because)

I couldn't _____ the pain.

4 Could you turn up the volume a little bit? (mind)

Would _____ the volume a little bit?

5 She will hire a painter to redecorate her flat. (have)

She will _____ redecorated.

6 Excessive drinking often leads to acts of violence. (results)

Violence often _____ excessive drinking.

7 I strongly advise you to look for a new job. (were)

If _____ look for a new job.

8 I'm afraid we'll have to postpone the pay rise that we promised. (put)

The manager threatened _____ _____ the pay rise they'd promised.

9 'Are you going to sell your old books?' Lucy asked. (if)

Lucy asked me _____ old books.

10 We'll wait for the taxi and leave for the airport immediately afterwards. (soon)

We'll leave for the airport _____ _____

11 Sleeping on the floor seems to be natural for him. (used)

He seems _____ on the floor.

12 It's useless to call the bank now as it's 8 p.m. (point)

There _____ the bank now as it's 8 p.m.

13 I'd prefer you to listen to this music in your room. (rather)

I'd _____ to this music in your room.

14 I'm quite sure William hates westerns, and so does his girlfriend. (nor)

I'm quite sure _____ _____ westerns.

15 I advise you to think twice before you cancel this appointment. (better)

You _____ before you cancel this appointment.

16 She was not allowed to leave the town while the investigation lasted. (let)

The police didn't _____ _____ while the investigation lasted.

17 Don't mention the tax issue during the negotiations. (must)

You _____ the tax issue during the negotiations.

18 It's probable that she will become the president of the students' union. (likely)

She _____ the president of the students' union.

19 Perhaps Olivia married him only for his money. (may)

Olivia _____ only for his money.

20 Take some money with you because you may have to pay for the bus on the way home. (case)

Take some money with you _____ _____ pay for the bus on the way home.

20

THE fire stood between us and linked us together. A boy added wood and the flames rose higher, illuminating our faces.

'What is the name of your country?'

'Poland.'

Poland was far away, beyond the Sahara, beyond the sea, to the north and the east. The *Nana* repeated the name aloud …

'They have snow there,' Kwesi said. Kwesi worked in town. Once, at the cinema, there was a movie with snow. The children applauded and cried merrily '*Anko! Anko!*' asking to see the snow again. The white puffs fell and fell. 'Those are lucky countries,' Kwesi said. 'They do not need to grow cotton; the cotton falls from the sky. They call it snow and walk on it and even throw it into the river.'

We were stuck here by this fire by chance – three of us, my friend Kofi from Accra, a driver and I. Night had already fallen when the tyre burst – the third tyre, rotten luck. It happened on a side road, in the bush, near the village of Mpango in Ghana. Too dark to fix it. You have no idea how dark the night can be. You can stick out your hand and not see it. They have nights like that. We walked into the village.

The *Nana* received us. There is a *Nana* in every village, because Nana means boss, head man, a sort of mayor but with more authority …

The *Nana* from Mpango was skinny and bald, with thin Sudanese lips. My friend Kofi introduced us. He explained where I was from and that they were to treat me as a friend.

'I know him,' my friend said. 'He's an African.'

That is the highest compliment that can be paid a European. It opens every door for him.

The *Nana* smiled and we shook hands. You always greet a *Nana* by pressing his right hand between both of your palms. This shows respect. He sat us down by the fire, where the elders had just been holding a meeting. The bonfire was in the middle of a village, and to the left and right, along the road, there were other fires. As many fires as huts. Perhaps twenty. We could see the fires and the figures of the women and the men and the silhouettes of the clay huts – they were all visible against a night so dark and deep that it felt heavy like a weight.

Poland. They did not know of any such country. The elders looked at me with uncertainty, possibly suspicion. I wanted to break their mistrust somehow. I did not know how and I was tired.

'Where are your colonies?' the *Nana* asked.

My eyes were drooping, but I became alert. People often asked that question. Kofi had asked it first, long ago, and my answer was a revelation to him. From then on he was always ready for the question with a little speech prepared, illustrating its absurdity.

Kofi answered: 'They don't have colonies, *Nana*. Not all white countries have colonies. Not all whites are colonialists. You have to understand that whites often colonise whites.'

The elders shuddered and smacked their lips. They were surprised. Once I would have been surprised that they were surprised. But not any more. I can't bear that language, that language of white, black and yellow. The language of race is disgusting.

Kofi explained: 'For a hundred years they taught us that the white is somebody greater, super, extra … only the English travelled around the globe. We knew exactly as much as they wanted us to know. Now it's hard to change.'

One of the elders asked, 'Are all the women in your country white?'

'All of them.'

'Are they beautiful?'

'They're very beautiful,' I answered.

'Do you know what he told me, *Nana*?' Kofi interjected. 'That during their summer, the women take off their clothes and lie in the sun to get black skin. The ones that become dark are proud of it, and others admire them for being as tanned as blacks.'

1 Read the story and sequence these events (a–j). Write numbers (1–10) in the boxes. (10 marks)

a The writer greeted the *Nana*. ☐

b Kofi introduced his friend as an African. ☐

c The children saw snow at the cinema. ☐

d The three men went into the village. ☐

e The village headman or Nana received the three men. ☐

f The chief asked the writer about his country's colonies. ☐

g The vehicle they were in had a puncture. ☐

h It got dark. ☐

i The writer was asked about the women in his country. ☐

j They all sat down around the fire. ☐

☐ **10**

2 Read the story again and answer these questions. (2 marks each)

1 Why did the children applaud the snow?

a It was a funny film.

b It was like cotton.

c They had never seen it before.

2 Why did the travellers have to stop in the village?

a There were no spare tyres.

b It was too dark to put on a new tyre.

c They had had bad luck with their tyres.

3 How did the writer react to their question about colonies?

a He was tired but it made him nervous.

b He let his friend answer the question.

c He was surprised by their question.

4 What attitudes did the Africans have towards the British?

a They resented being colonised.

b They still thought the British were great.

c They did not know about other Europeans.

5 Why did Kofi mention the fact that the women in the writer's country sunbathed?

a The sun in Africa would be too hot.

b The women were white.

c To have dark skin was admired.

☐ **10**

WRITING

You are interested in spending a week in the countryside. You have seen an advert for a hotel but would like more information. Read the advertisement and the notes. Then write your letter (about 150 words) covering the points in the notes and any relevant information. (20 marks)

Claremont Manor Hotel
Come to our beautiful 16th century manor house set in beautiful countryside near the Cornish coast. We offer superb accommodation, delicious food and a wide range of leisure activities for all the family including aerobics, swimming, walking, sailing and canoeing.
Prices from **£100** per room.

How far from the coast? Near a town or village?

How large are the rooms? Do they have 'en suite' bathrooms?

Does the price include breakfast? What is the price for a double room? Are there any special offers for families?

Has the hotel got a swimming pool? Is there a gym?

Do they offer sailing lessons? How much are they?

How can you get to the hotel without a car?

☐ **20**

8 Global Issues

29 Vocabulary

1 Confusing words
Circle the most suitable word.

1 Experts *expect*/hope/consider temperatures to rise by at least three degrees.

2 The floods have *effected/ affected/damaged* an area of three hundred square kilometres.

3 The *effect/affect/influence* of the rise in temperature is still unknown.

4 The earthquake *affectively/ totally/effectively* wiped out the town so that only a few districts were left standing.

5 The government is *presently/ currently/actually* sending aid to the disaster area and has so far sent 300 tons of food and medicine.

6 It was thought that numbers would go down but *presently/ currently/actually* they have gone up.

7 The Prime Minister will *presently/currently/actually* visit the area affected by the floods.

8 The population is growing at the *speed/rate/number* of 10,000 people every hour.

9 There are several species in *danger/threat/risk* of extinction, such as the gorilla.

2 Wordbuilding
Use the correct form of the words in brackets to complete the text.

The (1) ____unusual____ (usual) golden lion tamarin, a beautiful squirrel-sized primate, was nearly extinct in the 1970s. Its numbers had gone (2) _____ (hill) rapidly and there were only 200 left, due to loss of habitats from (3) _____ (forest). However, the World Wildlife Fund began a programme to (4) _____ (place) the numbers of the tamarin. This involved (5) _____ (plant) large areas of forest, linking together isolated areas of forest and the (6) _____ (introduce) of animals born in zoos into the wild. There are now over 1,000 tamarins in the wild and the tamarin is on the road to recovery.

➡ Lexicon, Students' Book, pages 156–157.

3 Ⓐ Ⓩ Dictionary work
Replace the words in *italics* with words beginning with the prefixes in brackets.

1 That CD player is *too expensive*. (over)_____overpriced_____

2 She *went through* an operation which took ten hours. (under)_____

3 American society is *a mixture of different cultures*. (multi)_____

4 The children *behaved very badly* in class. (mis)_____

5 I am *given too much work to do* and *I am paid too little*. (over/under)_____

6 She promised to *pay me back* soon. (re)_____

7 He was *not at all thankful* for what we had done. (un)_____

8 Another volcanic eruption is *improbable*. (un)_____

9 My name was *spelt wrongly* in the newspaper article. (mis)_____

10 A car *passed* us at over 180 kph on the motorway. (over)_____

Remember

1 ★ Indirect questions
Change these questions into indirect questions using the beginnings provided.

1 What time does the next coach to Canterbury leave?

   Do you know what time the next coach to
   Canterbury leaves?

2 Has this novel been translated into Spanish?

   Can you tell me _____

   _____

3 How long did it take you to cook this meal?

   I'd like to know _____

   _____

4 Where can I find the children's clothing department?

   Could you tell me _____

   _____

5 Do they realise what they have done?

   I wonder _____

   _____

2 ★ Reported orders and requests
Report these orders and requests using the verbs in brackets.

1 'Close the door, please.' (tell)

   The head teacher told me to close the door.

2 'Will you hold these books for a moment, please?' (ask)

   The librarian _____

   _____

3 'Please don't tell anyone about what happened.' (beg)

   Miriam _____

   _____

4 'Don't talk!' (tell)

   The teacher _____

   _____

5 'Could you give me lift?' (ask)

   Jack _____

   _____

6 'Why don't you stop nagging me?' (want)

   Mark _____

3 ★★ Reported statements and questions
Report these statements and questions. You must decide if you have to change the original tense.

1 'Mike hasn't come to school today.'

   The teacher says that Mike hasn't come to school today.

2 'Are you going away for the weekend?'

   Tom asked me _____

   _____

3 'I'm really angry with you for what you've done.'

   Hannah said that _____

   _____

4 'How long has Paul Shorter been living in this street?'

   The police officer asked _____

   _____

5 'The police will probably want to question me.'

   The director thought that _____

6 'I was in love with Judith once.'

   He confessed that _____

   _____

7 'I have a lot of pets at home: a dog, a cat and some budgies.'

   Anna says that _____

   _____

8 'Have you met Kylie before?'

   Mike wanted to know _____

   _____

4 ★★ Reporting a conversation
Report the conversation below in as much detail as possible using verbs such as *ask*, *say* and *tell*. Write it in your notebook.

Teacher: Sit down, Katie. I want to talk to you about that accident in your chemistry lesson.

Katie: I don't know anything about it, sir.

Teacher: Who brought the tear gas to school?

Katie: I don't know, sir. I never bring anything dangerous to school.

Teacher: Is Mark Connors interested in chemistry? I've heard he likes to experiment with chemicals.

Katie: Yes, sir.

Teacher: Well, he's been kept in hospital after the accident, but I'll have to talk to him when he gets back. He's coming out in a day or two.

30 Grammar

REPORTING

1 ★★ Reporting verbs
Complete the sentences with the correct forms of the verbs in the box. You will not need to use all the verbs.

> promise, suggest, warn, add, offer, complain, announce, admit, deny, claim, agree, insist, advise, beg, refuse, threaten, regret, accuse, apologise, remind, declare

1 Judy ____promised____ not to tell my parents that I had lost the money.

2 Our neighbour _____ to call the police if we carried on fighting.

3 The old man _____ that he had a pain in his chest.

4 Frances _____ not going to the concert when she heard how good it had been.

5 Jack _____ breaking the mirror in the bathroom.

6 The police _____ the man of planning a terrorist attack on a government building in Paris.

7 The patient _____ to have a blood transfusion for religious reasons.

8 My sister _____ organising a surprise party for our parents' wedding anniversary.

9 He shouted at me but then quickly _____ for his behaviour.

10 Patrick _____ that he and Carol were getting married.

2 ★★★ Patterns of reporting verbs
Put the verbs from the box in Exercise 1 into the table below according to the verb pattern they follow. Some verbs can follow more than one pattern. Use a dictionary if necessary.

VERB + that	suggest
VERB + someone + that	
VERB + (not) doing something	
VERB + (not) to do something	
VERB + someone (not) to do something	
VERB + (someone) + preposition + (doing) something	

Now write a short news report in your notebook using five of these verbs.

3 ★★★ Reporting verbs
Report the dialogues using the reporting verbs given.
Dialogue 1

> agree, complain, suggest, insist

Bill: I'm so fed up with washing-up. Why can't we buy a dishwasher?

Claire: OK, but the washing-up will still be your job!

_____

_____

_____

_____

Dialogue 2

> advise, wonder, admit, explain

Tina: Why do you always wear black?

Jill: I think it suits me, but it's true, perhaps it's a bit dull.

Tina: If I were you, I'd wear brighter colours.

_____

_____

_____

Dialogue 3

> refuse, beg, warn, offer

David: Please, please help me revise for my biology test!

Chris: Sorry, I can't help you today, but I can tomorrow. Just don't expect me to know everything!

_____

_____

_____

_____

4 ★★ Change of tense?

All these sentences were said last night. Turn them into reports. In which sentences should you not change the tense?

1 'The first underground line will be finished in 2015,' said Peter.

   Peter said _____

   _____

2 'It's very stuffy in here,' Mary said.

   Mary said _____

   _____

3 'I love chocolate pudding,' John said.

   John said _____

   _____

4 'This film is quite boring,' Julia said.

   Julia said _____

   _____

5 'The USA is the richest country in the world,' Mike said.

   Mike said _____

   _____

Prepositions

In compound words

Look at how prepositions are used in these two examples.

*The meeting was a follow-**up** of the 1997 conference.
A lot of their employees are **under**paid.*

1 Complete the words in these sentences.

1 She's a very friendly, _____*going* person.

2 Scientists have made major *break*_____ in the field of biotechnology.

3 He's a very nice person but he's a bit too *laid-*_____ sometimes.

4 I have just bought a really _____*date* encyclopedia.

5 That area of the city is very depressed and *run*_____ .

6 The _____*look* for the economy is not very bright, I'm afraid.

7 After many *set*_____ and difficulties, I passed my driving test.

8 Eventually, the _____*come* was that he was disqualified for three games.

9 Do you think she _____*heard* us talking about her?

10 The lorry was so _____*loaded*, it could hardly get up the hill.

⇨ Lexicon, Students' Book, page 160.

2 A/Z Dictionary work

Complete the words below with these prepositions. Use a good dictionary to help you.

up, under (x2), down, out, on, in, off

1 I can't afford to pay for the _____*keep* of my car any more.

2 He wrote an _____*-depth* report about that new product.

3 There are not enough waiters in that restaurant. They are badly _____*staffed*.

4 The goal was not given because the referee said the player had been _____*side*.

5 They have just built a new _____*pass* around the town and it has made the traffic in the centre much better.

6 She is not afraid of speaking her mind. She is an _____*spoken* politician.

7 The dictator's _____*fall* came when he lost control of the army.

8 The car swerved and nearly crashed into the _____*coming* traffic.

31 Communication

1 Giving opinions and agreeing
Complete the dialogue with these words.

> think, absolutely, agree, as if, reason, why, mean, totally, should, do

Tina: Don't you (1) ____think____ we should get rid of nuclear power?

Alex: Yeah, I (2) _____ . I mean it's very dangerous, isn't it?

Tina: Another (3) _____ is the nuclear waste. I (4) _____ , it lasts for centuries.

Alex: Right. I (5) _____ .

Tina: And I think because of that, we (6) _____ invest more money in alternative energies.

Alex: (7) _____ ! Like solar and wind energy.

Tina: It's not (8) _____ there's not enough sun or wind, is it?

Alex: Sure. And we need to stop burning so many fossil fuels. That's (9) _____ there's the greenhouse effect.

Tina: I (10) _____ agree. I mean BMW have developed a new car powered by hydrogen. But it's not in the interests of the oil companies, is it?

2 Justifying arguments
Complete the justifications with these linking words and expressions.

> basically, that's why, because of, one reason, to, so that, to do with, main reason

1 I think we should use less energy, ____basically____ to reduce the greenhouse effect.

2 We live in a consumer society. _____ we use so much energy, isn't it?

3 We should plant a lot more trees. _____ for that is to restore habitats.

4 We need to reduce poverty. A lot of it's _____ discrimination.

5 It's important to conserve water. The _____ is to avoid desertification.

6 We must reduce discrimination. _____ that there's a lot of poverty.

7 I think we should give more aid _____ help underdeveloped countries.

8 We need to send food and medicine _____ the victims can survive the floods.

3 Giving opinions and reasons
Choose five of the issues below and put them in order of importance for you.

a pollution ☐
b the greenhouse effect ☐
c climate change ☐
d aid to developing countries ☐
e poverty ☐
f discrimination ☐
g endangered species ☐
h globalisation ☐
i natural disasters ☐
j) diseases like AIDS and malaria ☐

Write about your five choices. Give reasons for your opinions, like this:

> I think we should stop using such a lot of fossil fuels. That's why there's the greenhouse effect.

1 I think we should _____

_____

That's why _____

_____

2 Personally, I think _____

_____

so that _____

_____

3 Don't you think _____

_____

A lot of it's to do with _____

_____

4 I think we need to _____

_____

basically to _____

_____

5 Why don't we _____

_____

The main reason is to _____

_____

6 Governments should _____

_____

because _____

_____

MULTI-PART VERBS

1 Multi-part verbs
Complete the multi-part verbs in italics in the text.

Last year I saved up to go to Canada on holiday. I tried to (1) *put* _____ about ten pounds a week by (2) *cutting* _____ on the money I spent on bus fares and by cycling everywhere instead. However, I still couldn't save enough and I often (3) *ran out* _____ money by the middle of the week. So, I (4) *brought* the subject _____ with my dad, hoping he would (5) *put* _____ my pocket money. No chance! But he (6) *came up* _____ the idea of getting a job so I started looking around for one. I saw an advert in the paper for delivering pizzas and I (7) *turned* _____ at the pizza place that evening and got the job. Unfortunately, my first delivery was an absolute disaster. I had to deliver three family-sized pizzas to 23 Mill Lane. When I (8) *got* _____ the house everything seemed very dark. I rang the bell several times and I was just about to (9) *go* _____ when someone (10) *turned* the lights _____ and a

very old man (11) *came* _____ of the house. When I showed him the pizzas, he had a fit and started chasing me down his garden. I was just (12) *getting* _____ the fright when I saw the street sign – Mill Road. I had got the wrong address! By the time I got to the right house it was very late. I (13) *made* _____ an excuse about a problem with the oven but the woman was very angry when she saw the cold and broken pizzas. I (14) *put* _____ going back to the pizza place but when I finally (15) *got* _____ there the owner was furious. He (16) *turned* _____ me and told me to leave and never (17) *come* _____ again! When I told my family about what had happened, they completely (18) *cracked* _____ and after a while I saw the funny side of things, too. Now, every time I have a pizza, I think of that evening!

2 Verbs with different meanings: *take*
Match the definitions (a–i) with the multi-part verbs in *italics* in the sentences (1–9).

a   to remove
b   to like a person immediately
c   to begin doing an activity
d   to deceive or trick
e   to employ people
f   to invite someone out
g   to agree to do something
h   to understand
i   to be angry with someone when it is not their fault

1   I didn't *take in* much of the lecture because I was worried about my dentist's appointment and I had toothache. ☐
2   The bank manager was completely *taken in* by two men who cashed a false cheque at the bank. ☐
3   I've *taken on* too much work and I don't think I'll be able to finish it all. ☐
4   That new software company has just *taken on* thirty new employees. ☐
5   The dentist had to *take out* two of my teeth because they were in such bad condition. ☐
6   I was *taken out* for dinner by my girlfriend last week. ☐
7   When she's angry, she always *takes it out on* me and gives me a hard time. ☐
8   I *took to* her from the start. She came across as a really open, honest person. ☐
9   In the weeks before the exam I *took to* getting up early and doing revision before breakfast. ☐

⇨ Lexicon, Students' Book, pages 170–176.

32 Focus on Writing

1 Linking
Circle the most suitable linking words and expressions.

WE LIVE in an increasingly global world. (1) *According to/As a result of* statistics from the World Trade Organisation, between 1990 and 2000 international trade grew almost twice as fast as the world growth in gross domestic product. (2) *In spite of/In addition to* that, the world has become a much smaller place (3) *as a result of/despite* a revolution in global communications. (4) *Neither/Both* transport and telecommunications have become much cheaper over the last twenty years. (5) *For example/In addition*, international phone calls used to be extremely expensive but the cost has gone down dramatically in many countries.

(6) *However/On the one hand*, there are many benefits to globalisation and the standard of living of many people has gone up. (7) *Furthermore/What this means* in practical terms is that we are travelling more and consuming more products from global companies (8) *for example/such as* Coca Cola, Sony and Siemens. In terms of jobs, more and more people are working for multinational companies. Nestlé, (9) *as well as/despite* being a Swiss company, does over 94 percent of its business outside Switzerland.

(10) *Moreover/On the other hand*, there are negative aspects of globalisation highlighted by the anti-globalisation movement. (11) *Although/Because* the standard of living in developed countries has gone up, the gap between rich and poor countries has widened considerably. More and more people are living in poverty, (12) *especially/also* in Africa and parts of Asia. (13) *However/Moreover*, big multinationals now have much more power and influence than ever before and are beyond the control of many governments.

(14) *To sum up/In this way*, globalisation is a process which not only brings many benefits but (15) *in addition/also* many disadvantages. (16) *However/As a result*, it is important to realise that we cannot stop globalisation as such. What we can do, is to give developing countries a fairer deal (17) *so that/as a result* they can compete in international markets. Developed countries also need to provide much greater long-term aid in areas (18) *like/for example* agriculture, education and health (19) *so as not to/in order to* improve the lives of most of the people on the planet.

2 Synonyms
Complete the second sentences with the words below. Circle the similar word in the first sentence. Use a good dictionary to help you.

methods, birds, country, products, impact, cattle, animals, landscape, poultry

1 Modern farming techniques have increased production dramatically. However, these _____ often have a very negative effect on the environment and on farm animals.

2 The British countryside has changed in the last twenty years. The _____ now has many fewer trees and hedges than thirty years ago and there are considerably fewer people working in the _____ than before.

3 Pesticides and herbicides have also had a major effect on wildlife. The _____ of these _____ has been greatest on certain species of birds which are now in danger of extinction.

4 A few years ago, many cows lived to the age of about fifteen. Today, with modern factory farming, most _____ die after only six or seven years. The _____ also live in very cramped conditions and are given hormones to make them grow faster.

5 Factory-farmed hens have very short lives. Sometimes the legs of the _____ break because their bodies are too heavy for them. Many people now prefer to buy free-range _____ .

3 Style

For each of the situations (1–3), write two sentences expressing your interest and requesting further information using the cues in column B. Use the expressions below.

> I am writing in connection with/in response to/with regard to ...I would like to express my interest in ... I would like to apply for ... I would be grateful if you could explain/inform/specify ... I would like to know more about ... I wonder if you could .../Could you please ... send/give me more information about/regarding...

A What the advertisement offers	B What you want to know	C Your sentences
1 Relief operation in hunger-stricken areas in India/approx. 6 months' stay/poor facilities	• What specialists do they need? • Will there be running water?	_____ _____ _____ _____
2 Charity walk to support victims of globalisation/speakers of foreign languages especially welcome	• How long will the walk take? • I'm a speaker of English – how can I help?	_____ _____ _____ _____
3 A two-week stay at a farm to learn how to lead a good ecological lifestyle/some previous experience essential	• What types of activity are planned? • What kind of experience is required?	_____ _____ _____ _____

4 Guided writing

Read the advertisement and the notes (A–O). Sort the notes according to the paragraph plan. Then, write a letter of application based on the plan in your notebook.

A   course in child psychology (October-January 2000)
B   could help with accommodation
C   looking forward to hearing from you
D   writing in connection with the advertisement
E   could organise games and activities
F   where will the children be from?
G   would like to join in
H   have organised holidays for youngsters before (2001 – Hungary; 2002 – Romania)
I   how long will the holidays be?
J   languages: Hungarian, English, Russian
K   what will living conditions be like?
L   could offer some help with general problems
M   like children; help with neighbours' children on a regular basis
N   could teach children various skills such as pottery
O   can drive a car

Volunteers needed to work with children from poor countries while on holiday in Hungary. You need to be able to communicate and interact easily with children. Help may involve collecting children from the station or airport, helping them with general problems.
Applicants should:
• be 18–25 years old
• have at least one foreign language
• have good organisational skills
• have a driving licence
• have some experience working with children
Please write to Jenny Peck (Ms) for further information.

Paragraph Plan

Greeting
Paragraph 1: reasons for writing
Paragraph 2: information about you
Paragraph 3: suggestions of help
Paragraph 4: asking for more information
Formal ending
Signing off

Word Power

1 Disasters

Complete the sentences below with the correct form of the words in the box.

avalanche, drought, earthquake, flood, forest fire, hurricane, landslide, famine, disease, volcano

1 _____ have been burning for three weeks in Indonesia and have destroyed thousands of hectares of virgin forest.

2 One of the most infectious _____ is Ebola, which kills its victims extremely quickly.

3 The harvest in Afghanistan has failed four years running due to a terrible _____ which has affected most of the country.

4 Bangladesh is regularly hit by _____ caused by heavy rain in the monsoon period.

5 The small island of Montserrat in the Caribbean was almost wiped out by a _____ which erupted a few years ago.

6 Three skiers were killed yesterday by an _____ in a Swiss mountain resort.

7 A district of the capital of El Salvador was wiped out by a _____ due to heavy rain and the cutting of trees.

8 A major _____ is expected in California in the next few years and special building regulations have been introduced to minimise loss of human life.

9 The _____ in this part of Africa has been caused by drought and harvest failure as well as the continuing civil war.

10 A _____ is due to hit the coast of Florida this evening and residents are being evacuated from coastal areas.

2 Collocation

Circle the best word in *italics* to complete the sentences.

1 After days of negotiation, the two sides finally *reached/made* an agreement which is due to be formally *stamped/signed* tomorrow morning.

2 In some countries, the *vast/big* majority of women are still only involved in doing *free/unpaid* work.

3 Workers in many developing countries have very little job *safety/security* and hardly any social *benefits/profits*.

4 The future of this region is not all *gloomy/dull* and there have been *major/large* advances in the fields of health and education.

5 An improvement in *educational/school* qualifications will allow these countries to *close/finish* the gap with those of the developed world.

6 Refugees have been leaving the country on a *huge/great* scale due to the continuing *army/armed* conflict.

3 Expressing opinions

Complete the sentences below with your own opinions about the environment.

1 What I don't understand is *why we don't use more solar energy.*

2 What's ridiculous is _____

3 What we need to do is to _____

4 What we should do is _____

5 What I think is that _____

6 What's a good idea is to _____

102

4 Pronunciation: Shifting word stress

Which of the words in italics are nouns and which are verbs?
Tick the correct column in the table and underline the main stress on the words.

	Verb	Noun
1	✔	
2		
3		
4		
5		
6		
7		
8		
9		
10		
11		
12		

1 It is much easier to *contract* some diseases than others.
2 We signed the *contract* after some negotiation.
3 Those companies *produce* most of the world's computers.
4 Farmers bring fresh *produce* to the market every day.
5 Developing countries *import* a lot of manufactured goods.
6 Our biggest *import* is probably oil.
7 The *subject* of discussion was third world debt.
8 Some multinationals *subject* their workers to poor conditions.
9 The *contest* for the leadership of the party was very close.
10 That MP is not going to *contest* the next election.
11 The workers demanded a major *increase* in their salaries.
12 The company refused to *increase* their salaries.

A‑Z Check your answers in a good dictionary.

5 Extension: Wordbuilding with prefixes

These prefixes come from Latin or Ancient Greek.

anti-	Greek *(anti)*	= against
bi-	Latin *(bi)*	= two
inter-	Latin *(inter)*	= between/among
mal-	Latin *(male)*	= badly
micro-	Greek *(micros)*	= small

mini-	abbreviation from Latin *(miniatura)* = very small	
mono-	Greek *(monos)*	= alone
post-	Latin *(post)*	= after
pre-	Latin *(prae)*	= before
pro-	Latin *(pro)*	= in front of/on behalf of

A‑Z Complete the words using the prefixes. Use a good dictionary to help you.

1 He tends to be very boring. He's got a *mono* tonous voice and he doesn't listen to other people – conversation with him is just listening to his *mono* logue.

2 In the _____war period from 1945 to 1950 she was a _____graduate student at Cambridge and did her doctoral thesis on the economics of developing countries.

3 A minority of the _____globalisation campaigners are very _____social and have been involved in damaging property during demonstrations.

4 She is completely _____lingual in English and French, but she still doesn't know how to ride a _____cycle!

5 He is going for an _____view with a big _____national aid organisation.

6 Using new _____scopes which are much more effective, they have succeeded in producing an even smaller _____chip.

7 He is very _____ American and loves everything about the place. He is especially _____ Hollywood.

8 The surgeon was condemned for _____practice, though he claimed that the accident had happened due to the _____function of one of the machines in the operating theatre.

9 Some of the most important developments in the study of _____historic life in the area were made in the _____war period – between 1900 and 1914.

10 A woman with a _____skirt got into the _____bus and sat down next to me.

Language Awareness

1 ★ Impersonal reporting
Match the statements with the people or things they are about.

1 It is supposed to have been the venue of the first Olympic Games. [b]

2 It is believed to be Jesus Christ's place of birth. ☐

3 They are known to eat mainly meat and animal fat. ☐

4 They are said to have become extinct some 65 million years ago. ☐

5 It is claimed that the US navy wanted to use them to destroy enemy submarines. ☐

6 It is expected to host the 2008 Olympics. ☐

7 It is known to have been the place where convicts from Britain were sent. ☐

8 They are believed to have the most sophisticated cuisine in Europe. ☐

a	the French	e	dinosaurs
b	Olympia	f	dolphins
c	Beijing	g	Australia
d	Bethlehem	h	the Inuit

2 ★★ Impersonal reporting
Rewrite these sentences in two ways using the beginnings provided.

1 Geographers claim that Africa and Europe were once one continent.

It is claimed _____

_____

Africa and Europe are claimed _____

_____

2 People believe that Robin Hood helped the poor.

It _____

_____

Robin Hood _____

_____

3 In Ancient Egypt people thought that cats were sacred animals.

In Ancient Egypt it _____

_____

In Ancient Egypt cats _____

_____

4 Doctors say that physical exercise helps you to keep healthy.

It _____

_____

Physical exercise _____

_____

5 People believed that Mars was an inhabited planet.

It _____

Mars _____

_____

6 Historians say that Hitler committed suicide.

It _____

_____

Hitler _____

_____

7 The Chinese have proved that green tea can cure various diseases.

It _____

_____

Green tea _____

_____

8 Everyone assumes that travelling broadens the mind.

It _____

_____

Travelling _____

_____

9 We know that people drank beer in ancient times.

It _____

_____

Beer _____

_____

10 People used to believe that whales were fish.

It _____

_____

At one time, whales _____

_____

3 ★★★ Impersonal reporting
Choose an animal and complete the sentences about it.

1 _____ are known to live in _____

2 It is said that they _____

3 Their habitat is believed to _____

4 Their numbers are expected to _____

5 It is feared that _____

6 However, it is hoped that _____

Check Your Grammar

1 *-ing* form or infinitive?
Put the verbs in brackets in the *-ing* form or the infinitive.

I must say I'm not very fond of
(1) _____ (travel). I realise
that nowadays everybody is
expected (2) _____ (spend)
their weekends and holidays away
from home but I always prefer (3)
_____ (stay) at home and
enjoy family life.

   Is it worth (4) _____
(spend) your whole holiday on a
coach or in the car without
(5) _____ (be) able to
stretch your legs? What is the
point in (6) _____ (see) all
those places if afterwards you
don't remember what you have
seen?

   I used (7) _____ (travel)
quite a lot on business but once I
discovered what (8) _____
(travel) is all about, I changed my
job. I just couldn't get used to (9)
_____ (sleep) in hotel beds
and (10) _____ (eat)
restaurant food. I couldn't see
anything glamorous in
(11) _____ (spend) ten
hours in a meeting and then being
asked (12) _____ (eat) out
in a restaurant and going to bed
after midnight. I saw my
colleagues (13) _____ (live)
like this for years and I don't
think they were enjoying
themselves.

   Now, during my holidays I try
(14) _____ (relax) at home,
do some gardening and DIY, and I
never regret (15) _____
(change) my lifestyle.

2 Reporting verbs
Use the sentence beginnings to rewrite the sentences so that the meaning stays the same.

1 'The weather in England is horrible,' said Sven.
   Sven complained *that the weather in England was horrible.* _____

2 'Have you travelled abroad a lot?' Sheila asked.
   Sheila wanted to know _____

3 'I'll give it back tomorrow,' said Adam.
   Adam promised _____

4 'Don't do any exercise and sleep flat on your back for two weeks,' the
   doctor said.
   The doctor told _____

5 'Are you planning to look for a job abroad?' asked John.
   John wondered _____

6 'I can't tell you anything because it's meant to be a surprise,' said Susan.
   Susan explained _____

7 'I can do the shopping tomorrow if you don't feel like it,' said George.
   George offered _____

3 Verb patterns
Use the words in brackets to rewrite the sentences so that the meaning stays the same.

1 When I was at university I hated jazz. (use)
   I ___*used to hate jazz*___ when I was at university.

2 Everybody thinks that all Americans have a lot of money. (believed)
   All Americans _____ a lot of money.

3 The robber said he would use the gun if we didn't give him the jewellery.
   (threatened)
   The robber _____ if we didn't give him the jewellery.

4 It's nothing unusual for me to eat raw meat. (used)
   I _____ raw meat.

5 Jill doesn't sing in the choir any more. (gave up)
   Jill _____ in the choir.

6 I hate it when everybody stares at me on the tube. (stand)
   I _____ on the Tube.

7 Could you turn the volume down? I can't concentrate. (mind)
   Would _____ the volume down? I can't concentrate.

8 Scientists have shown that global warming causes natural disasters. (known)
   Global warming _____

9 If you go there alone at night you may be mugged. (risk)
   You _____ if you go there alone at night.

9 Society

33 Vocabulary

1 Social problems

Write the name of a social problem next to each statement. The first letters are given.

1 Some people move to big cities but have nowhere to live; they sleep in the streets. h_____

2 Many women get a lower salary than men for doing the same work. d_____

3 In cities you often see people asking for money on the streets. b_____

4 In some parts of town it's hard to find a phone box that hasn't been broken or a wall that hasn't been written on. v_____

5 In the USA, a murderer is five times more likely to be given the death sentence if he or she is black. r_____

6 More cases of violence in the home are reported nowadays. d_____ v_____

7 There are not enough clinics to treat heroin addicts. d_____ a_____

8 The running down of the old industries like mining and shipbuilding has led to a lot of job losses. u_____

➡ **Lexicon, Students' Book, page 155.**

2 Describing trends

Look at the graph and complete the text with these words.

> doubled, on the increase, rocketed, rose, tripled

Population increase 1990–2000 in some major cities
(Source: The World Bank)

In most countries, urban population is (1) _____ .
While the population of Rio de Janeiro (2) _____ by a modest 12 percent in the 1990s, the populations of other cities (3) _____ .
Cairo's population went up 25 percent, but the number of people in Bombay nearly (4) _____ that figure, and the population of Lagos in Nigeria almost (5) _____ it!

3 Rich language

Complete the text with these words and expressions.

> bursting with new ideas, cradle of Spanish culture, explosion of trade, flourished, golden age, magnificent, major changes, outstanding, period of transition, underwent dramatic changes

The (1) _____ of Seville

Seville has lived through (2) _____ in its long history. Originally called Hispalis, it was captured by the Romans in 45 BC. After the 4th century AD, there was a (3) _____ under the Vandals and the Visigoths until the Moors arrived from North Africa in 712. From then on it (4) _____ as a cultural centre. The Moorish influence can be seen everywhere, such as the (5) _____ Alcázar palace and the many winding streets and fountains.

In 1248 Seville was conquered by Ferdinand III of Castile and León and it (6) _____ . The (7) _____ Gothic cathedral stands on the site of a 12th century mosque. The opening of America to Spain after 1492 led to an (8) _____ and the city was (9) _____ . A university was founded in 1502, and by the 17th century, Seville had become the (10) _____ .

Remember

1 ★ wish, if only, should, ought
Complete the text with the words from the box.

have, had, wish, if, should (x2), ought

My name is Christian and I'm a student of electronic engineering. To tell you the truth, it wasn't my choice – it was my parents'. (1) _____ only I'd been more insistent! I (2) _____ have done what I wanted and studied psychology but they said I wouldn't get a good job. I wish I (3) _____ told them then that good psychologists can earn much more than bad engineers. I (4) _____ I hadn't passed my maths exam at school then I wouldn't (5) _____ been accepted to do engineering. I'm sitting in the library now and I (6) _____ to be doing some physics problems but instead I'm reading Erich Fromm's *Escape from Freedom*. I think my parents (7) _____ read this as well, so they would understand better how I feel.

2 ★★ Expressing regret
Rewrite the sentences using *I regret* or *It's a pity that*.

1 I wish I had learned to drive when I was a teenager.
I regret _____

2 If only my parents were a bit more tolerant.
It's a pity that _____

3 I shouldn't have put so many things into my backpack.
I regret _____

4 I wish I was slimmer.
It's a pity that _____

5 I should be learning another foreign language as well.
It's a pity that _____

6 If only I had known the deadline for the application.
I regret _____

3 ★★ Expressing regret
Rewrite the sentences using the beginnings provided.

1 It's a pity Tom didn't remember your birthday.
Tom should _____

2 Why on earth did I leave my passport at home?!
If only _____

3 It's a shame Sandra isn't revising with us.
I wish _____

4 It was a mistake to tell John that we had seen Kate with another boy.
We should _____
_____

5 It's a pity I haven't got a dog.
I wish _____

6 I'm sorry I didn't return the books.
I should _____

7 I'm so unhappy that Naomi isn't in my class.
If only _____

8 It wasn't a good idea to watch that horror film last night.
I wish _____

4 ★★★ Expressing regret
Read the description of Paul Davis's life. Use the cues below and the expressions in the box to write his possible thoughts.

Paul Davis is 73. He lives in a council flat, with no garden or balcony. He has no family or close friends. He has never been married and doesn't have any children. His life hasn't been very exciting: he left school at fourteen and worked as a postman all his life. His main form of entertainment was gambling and he lost most of the money he earned. He has never been outside Britain. He used to have a car but he sold it to bet on a horse. He is not very healthy, either – he has a serious heart problem.

I wish ..., If only ..., I should ..., I shouldn't ...

I wish I wasn't living in a council flat.

1 council flat	6 university
2 garden	7 health
3 married	8 car
4 children	9 see the world
5 lonely	10 gamble

34 Grammar

1 ★★ Persuasion: Spoken English
Complete the conversation with the expressions in the box.

> I'd rather you ..., I'd rather ..., You'd better ...,
> You ought ..., If I were you, I ...

Mum: Kate, (1) __I'd rather you__ stopped watching TV and helped me a bit. They'll be here soon.

Kate: (2) _____ wouldn't make so much food. They won't eat even half of it.
(3) _____ to take it easy – relax, have a bath and just enjoy yourself. It's your birthday, after all.

Mum: (4) _____ lay the table. We haven't got time to take it easy!

Kate: Oh Mum, you know I hate doing that.
(5) _____ make the salad.

Mum: OK, but do it now!

2 ★★ Persuasion: Informal
Rewrite the advice to a friend using the words in brackets.

1 Lose some weight. (better)

   You'd better lose some weight.

2 Wear more fashionable clothes. (why)

   _____

   _____

3 Give up eating sweets. (should)

   _____

   _____

4 Have a haircut. (time)

   _____

   _____

5 Ride a bike or go swimming every day. (were)

   _____

   _____

6 Don't drink too much coffee. (better)

   _____

   _____

7 Drink a lot of mineral water throughout the day. (should)

   _____

   _____

3 ★★ Persuasion: Informal
Complete the sentences with the words from the box.

> better, ought, should, rather, had, would, insist, time

1 You'd ___better___ hurry up if you want to catch the train.

2 It's about _____ the council did something about all the stray dogs in town.

3 I _____ rather you paid more attention to spelling.

4 You _____ really be more helpful at home.

5 You _____ better stop reading and get down to work.

6 They _____ to plan their future more carefully.

7 I _____ that you return the money by the end of this week.

8 I'd _____ you didn't call me Piggy.

4 ★★ Persuasion: Formal
Rewrite the sentences more formally, using the words in brackets.

1 I think that Mark should apologise to Helen. (better)

   Mark had better apologise to Helen.

2 Don't make spaghetti for dinner again! (rather)

   I _____

3 Let's paint the whole flat white. (suggest)

   I _____

4 Don't you think you should finally decide what you want to study at university? (time)

   It _____

   _____

5 You must write in pencil. (insist)

   We _____

6 If I were you, I wouldn't worry so much about your appearance. (ought)

   You _____

   _____

7 The university made all the students pay their fees at the beginning of the year. (demand)

   The university _____

   _____

8 I'd really like Jamie to help me with the decorations. (would)

   I _____

5 ★★ Persuasion: Formal and informal
Complete the sentences with the correct form of the verbs in brackets.

1 I'd rather you _____didn't think_____ (not think) so much about the past.

2 I suggested _____ (have) a picnic.

3 It's about time you _____ (start) treating life more seriously.

4 The government ought _____ (invest) more money in public transport.

5 You'd better _____ (work) harder if you want a pay rise.

6 The director insists that Jackson _____ (be) fired at once.

7 If I were you, I _____ (not ask) Jennifer out to dinner.

8 I think you should _____ (spend) more time reading and less time watching TV.

6 ★★★ Persuasion: Written English
In your notebook, write a formal letter to your local authority suggesting what should be done to improve your local park. Use the cues below and the verbs and expressions from the box. Provide arguments for each suggestion.

I suggest that the grass is mown more frequently; it often grows too high to walk on.

should, ought to, it's high time, insist, suggest, demand

bicycle routes
more benches
safe playgrounds
public toilets
better maintenance (removal of rubbish, broken glass, dead leaves, etc.)
a fence around the pond
ban dogs

Prepositions

In sentences

In English, a clause or sentence can end with a preposition.

Examples:

*It was an exciting period to live **in**.*
*Who is that music **by**?*
*This is exactly what I'm looking **for**.*
*What do you spend your money **on**?*

1 Translate the examples into your own language.

2 Complete the letter with the prepositions in the box.

about (x2), in, of, on (x2), with (x2)

Dear Sir/Madam,

At last I have found an article I agree (1) .... 'Spend, Spend, Spend', in last week's magazine, shows what a terrible consumer society we live (2) .... and highlights many of the issues I myself am angry (3) ....

It is high time people realised there is more to life than material things. It is the younger generation I am particularly concerned (4) .... I suppose advertising is a part of modern life that we have to put up (5) .... but adverts aimed at young people just encourage them to waste their money and this is something they don't seem to be aware (6) .... More control over advertising is what we should insist (7) ....

Does any reader know of an 'anti-advertising' group I could join, because the government certainly cannot be relied (8) .... !

Yours,

K. Jordan (Mr)

➡ Lexicon, Students' Book, pages 166–176.

35 Communication

1 Suggestions
Complete the dialogues below with suitable expressions from the box.

let's, I'd, it'd be a good idea, it'd be better, it's about time, I wish, ought, should, there could be, what about, what we need, why don't

Dialogue 1
Ann: (1) __Let's__ go out tonight.
Bob: OK. (2) _____ a disco?
Ann: Yeah. (3) _____ we try that new club in town?

Dialogue 2
Mike: There's nothing to do in the school holidays round here. (4) _____ they did something for us.
Sue: I know. (5) _____ is a place to meet.
Mike: They (6) _____ build a sports centre.
Sue: (7) _____ to have a club, you know, with other activities, not just sports.
Mike: Mmm, (8) _____ a place to play music.
Sue: And (9) _____ if they organised trips to other places.
Mike: Yeah. (10) _____ they'd do something.

Dialogue 3
Andy: Do you think there's more vandalism these days?
John: Yes, I do. They (11) _____ to do something about it. If I had my way, (12) _____ put more police officers on the streets.

2 Suggestions
Look at the picture and complete the suggestions for improvements to the town.

1 What they need _____
_____

2 They ought _____
_____

3 It's about time _____
_____

4 They should _____
_____

5 Why don't they _____
_____

3 Strong and tentative suggestions
Write strong (S) or tentative (T) suggestions for reducing some of these social problems.

1 domestic violence (S)
_____
_____

2 drugs (T)
_____
_____

3 homelessness (S)
_____
_____

4 racism (T)
_____
_____

5 unemployment (S)
_____
_____

6 vandalism (T)
_____
_____

MULTI-PART VERBS

1 Multi-part verbs
Match the sentences (1–10) with the responses (a–j).

1	Our house looks a bit run-down.	e	a	Yes, but you mustn't *give up*.
2	Oh, look at this mess.	☐	b	Why don't you just *make up* an excuse not to go?
3	What are you wearing for the cocktail party?	☐	c	I'll help you to *clean* it *up*.
4	This crossword is really hard.	☐	d	Why don't you *set up* your own business?
5	Have you seen the latest figures?	☐	e	Why don't you *do* it *up*?
6	Sorry I'm late.	☐	f	Oh, I don't feel like *dressing up*.
7	I don't feel like seeing Mark tonight.	☐	g	Yes, prices have really *gone up*.
8	You're early!	☐	h	Did you get *held up* in the traffic?
9	I need to do more exercise.	☐	i	Yes, Sue *picked* me *up* at the station.
10	I'm fed up with working for this company.	☐	j	Why don't you *take up* golf?

2 Verbs with *down*, *up*, *on* and *off*
Complete the sentences with verbs from the box.

> brighten, bring, cut, get (x3), go (x3), hang, keep, pick, put, set, show, sit, turn (x3), wrap

1 Don't let the exams _____ you *down* – they'll soon be over.

2 You should _____ *down* on sweets.

3 I couldn't _____ *down* his offer.

4 We must _____ *down* to some work.

5 Would you _____ *down* and wait here a moment?

6 I finally had to _____ *up* the subject of payment.

7 You don't want to _____ *up* a virus – get vaccinated.

8 The artist has plans to _____ *up* the Eiffel Tower!

9 You could _____ *up* your room with a coat of paint.

10 Try not to _____ *up* late for the next meeting!

11 We saw the bomb _____ *off* on the news.

12 What time do you _____ *off* for school?

13 There's no need to _____ *off* – I know you can speak English well!

14 You're very moody. You can _____ *off* someone very suddenly.

15 You have to _____ *off* the main road just before the lights.

16 My brother would like to _____ *on* to study law.

17 We don't _____ *on* well with our neighbours.

18 It's hard, but you must _____ *on* trying.

19 That comedian can _____ *on* lots of funny voices.

20 You want to speak to Dan? _____ *on* a minute, I'll get him for you.

3 Suggestions with multi-part verbs
Make responses to the comments below using multi-part verbs from this page.

1 Someone has spilt a drink on the floor.

   Shall I clean it up? _____

2 I can't go to the party because there aren't any buses.

   _____
   _____

3 My dad is a heavy smoker.

   _____
   _____

4 I get really bored at weekends.

   _____
   _____

5 We really need a centre for the homeless.

   _____
   _____

6 I don't know the answer to this question.

   _____
   _____

⇨ Lexicon, Students' Book, pages 170–176.

36 Focus on Writing

1 *as* and *like*

Look at the examples in the table. Then match the words and expressions (a–f) with the different uses of as and like in sentences 1–7.

a because			
b in the same way as	*like*	+ noun	1 I wouldn't want to live in a place *like* Utopia. [c]
c similar to			2 There were great painters *like* Botticelli and Donatello. [ ]
d such as		+ pronoun	3 My friend is a football fanatic, *like* me. [ ]
e the same as		+ -ing	4 It was so boring – *like* watching paint dry. [ ]
f what			
	as	+ subject + verb	5 I didn't like his idea of Utopia *as* it was too organised. [ ]
			6 Treat other people *as* you would like to be treated. [ ]
			7 We did *as* you suggested. [ ]

2 *as* and *like*

Complete the sentences with *as* or *like*.

1 I agree with last week's article _____ it condemned 'soft' prison sentences.

2 When a person has killed somebody they deserve to suffer exactly _____ their victim has done.

3 The government hasn't done _____ it promised.

4 Prisons have become _____ luxury hotels with televisions and gyms.

5 I think that violent criminals, _____ murderers or rapists, should be given life sentences.

6 I don't agree with him, _____ I think that we should see prison _____ a way of reforming people.

7 The problems of our society are _____ yours.

8 We need to eliminate social problems _____ drugs and poverty.

9 Young people have ideas too – they shouldn't treat us _____ idiots.

10 They never do _____ we want.

3 Linking

Complete the second sentence so it has a similar meaning to the first. You will need to use the words in brackets and some words of your own.

1 Most people in Britain live longer than people did twenty years ago, and they are also better educated. (as well as)
Most people in Britain live longer than twenty years ago _____ better educated.

2 Life expectancy has increased because health care and diet have improved. (due to)
Life expectancy has increased _____ _____ health care and diet.

3 People are more worried about crime but there is no proof that the streets are more dangerous. (in spite of)
People are more worried about crime _____ _____ no proof that the streets are more dangerous.

4 Students need to get a good job because they have to pay back the government for their education. (so that)
Students need to get a good job _____ pay back the government for their education.

5 More women work than ever before but they still earn only 80 percent of men's wages for the same jobs. (despite)
_____ than ever before, they still earn only 80 percent of men's wages for the same jobs.

4 Editing

Read the text. When a line has an extra word, circle the word and write it on the right. When a line is correct, put a tick (✔) on the right.

Buenos Aires, the capital and most populous city in Argentina, is
located on the western bank of the River Plate, a little of inland from
the Atlantic Ocean. The city, it founded in 1580, has become one of
the world's greatest cities. In the 1990s, about 11 million of people
lived in the large area of greater Buenos Aires. The city's greatest
period of an expansion started in the 1860s. European emigrants,
especially from Italy and Spain, entered into the city and Argentina's
coastal area. The literature flourished in the 19th century. 'Martín
Fierro', a narrative poem by José Hernández, is considered by many
to be the national epic of Argentina. Writers such as like Manuel Puig
and Jorge Luis Borges gained any international recognition in the 20th
century. In the art world, Argentina is the best known for the painters
Pettoruti and Soldi, and the works of sculptor Rogelio Yrurtia are also
well known of. Perhaps Argentina's most famous contribution to
modern music is the tango, which developed in Buenos Aires
and became a favourite ballroom dance throughout as much of the
world. Classical music and opera are also too important. The Colón
Theatre, was built in 1908, and the Colón Opera company have
been achieved an international reputation for excellence. Alberto
Williams, founder of the Buenos Aires Conservatory, was the best
known most of all Argentine composers, and Alberto Ginastera's
music remains popular all over of the world.

1	✔
2	*of*
3	
4	
5	
6	
7	
8	
9	
10	
11	
12	
13	
14	
15	
16	
17	
18	
19	
20	
21	
22	

(Source: *Encarta*[1])

5 Paragraphs in essays

Look at this essay title and read the notes. Then put each note into the correct paragraph.

Most people in Britain are better off than they have ever been. Do you agree?

a   only top 20% of society very rich

b   average family spends £550/week (2005) vs £326 (1981) – inflation?

c   bottom 20% of society poorer than ever

d   Britain – one of the richest countries in the world

e   increase in begging and homelessness

f   British people – more material possessions than people in most countries – better off?

g   74% households with cars (2005) vs 62% (1981)

h   in general, most people are better off – but still gap between rich/poor, or has gap widened?

i   90% houses – central heating (2005) vs 61% (1981)

j   over 50% of households – computers (2005) vs 3% (1981)

Paragraph 1: Introduction [d] [ ]

Paragraph 2: For [ ] [ ] [ ] [ ]

Paragraph 3: Against [a] [ ] [ ]

Paragraph 4: Conclusion [ ]

6 Now use the notes in Exercise 5 and the cues below to write the essay in your notebook.

Paragraph 1 Britain is _____ . British people have _____ but are they _____ ? This essay will examine this question.

Paragraph 2 Statistics can be used to show that the standard of living in Britain has risen. For example, _____ . Moreover, _____ . Not only _____ but also _____ .

Paragraph 3 However, there is still a lot of inequality. On the one hand _____ , while on the other hand _____ . Furthermore, _____ .

Paragraph 4 All things considered, _____ , although _____ .

[1] *Encarta* is a registered trademark of the Microsoft Corporation.

Word Power

1 Idiomatic language

Look at the pictures and complete what the people are saying, using idiomatic expressions.

1 It's .... in here.

2 Yes, my feet are .... of ....

3 I'm .... for a cup of coffee.

4 If you're homeless you can't get a job; if you can't get a job, you can't pay rent. It's a ....

5 House prices have .... this year.

FOR SALE

2 Confusing words

(Circle) the correct word in each sentence.

1 House prices have *raised/risen* steadily this year.
2 The thief *robbed/stole* the local bank.
3 I need to *borrow/lend* some money to buy a car.
4 She *assisted/attended* a meeting for unemployed people.
5 I explained the problem but he wasn't very *comprehensive/understanding*.
6 Air *contamination/pollution* is our biggest problem.
7 He gets very *angry/nervous* when there are a lot of adverts on TV.
8 Governments should *pass/spend* more time helping homeless people.
9 Many *foreigners/strangers* visit London every year.
10 I'll get a holiday job to *earn/win* some money.

In your notebook, write sentences using the other words.

3 Synonyms

Cross out the word which cannot go in the gap.

1 The number of crimes has ____ in the last two years.
   a gone up   b increased
   c ~~raised~~   d risen

2 Unemployment has been ____ steadily.
   a decreasing   b falling
   c going down   d lowering

3 A new ____ class led to an expansion of the arts.
   a fortunate   b rich
   c wealthy   d well-off

4 St Paul's Cathedral is a(n) ____ example of Wren's architecture.
   a flourishing   b magnificent
   c outstanding   d superb

5 A programme of public works is ____ for the economy.
   a essential   b major
   c necessary   d vital

6 I'm ____ about living in such a consumer society.
   a concerned   b annoyed
   c uneasy   d worried

7 Economic conditions were ____ for a renaissance.
   a ideal   b perfect
   c just right   d utopian

8 Great literary activity ____ into the next century.
   a carried on   b continued
   c followed   d went on

4 Collocation

Complete the sentences with words from the box.

> consumer, human, insatiable, major, prison, severe, social, technical, violent, vital

1 Society is undergoing _____ changes. There is more _____ mobility.
2 There seems to be an _____ demand for new gadgets nowadays. The shops are full of products with _____ innovations.
3 We are living in a _____ society and there is no doubt that advertising plays a _____ role.
4 Whenever there is a _____ crime, many people call for _____ punishments or longer _____ sentences. That's understandable – it's part of _____ nature.

114

5 Exaggeration and understatement
Match the exaggerated statements (1–10) with the understated replies (a–j).

1 The church is huge.	☐	a I'm a bit peckish myself.
2 This will take ages.	☐	b I suppose he is getting on a bit.
3 I'm starving.	☐	c Yes, it is quite big.
4 He's really ancient.	☐	d It's not exactly tropical.
5 I'm dying for a cup of tea.	☐	e Yes, it could be quite a while.
6 It's freezing.	☐	f I suppose he is quite slim.
7 He's very brainy.	☐	g Mine are a bit cold, too.
8 I'm absolutely delighted.	☐	h I'm quite pleased.
9 My feet are like blocks of ice.	☐	i Mm, I wouldn't mind one, either.
10 He's very skinny.	☐	j Yes, he is quite bright.

6 Categories
Complete the diagrams by dividing the words in the box into six categories of four words each. Give each category a title, like the example.

age, borrow, century, climb, comedy, drama, earn, fine, increase, lend, painter, period, play, playwright, poet, rise, rocket, sculptor, sentence, shoplifting, spend, theft, time, tragedy

age

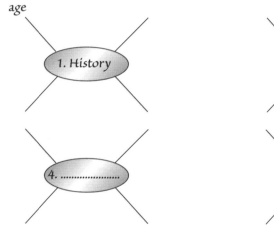

1. History

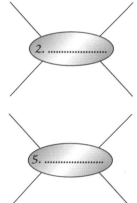

2. ....

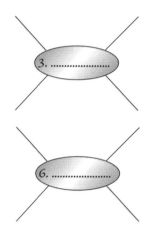

3. ....

4. ....

5. ....

6. ....

7 Extension: Crime and punishment
Write the answers to the clues in the puzzle.
What crime can you find in the shaded boxes?

1 Killing a person illegally and deliberately.
2 Violently forcing someone to have sex.
3 Dishonest behaviour in order to trick someone into giving you money.
4 Robbery with violence.
5 **and** 6 Another expression for 'capital punishment'.
7 A violent attack on someone.
8 Getting money from someone by threatening to make known something unpleasant.
9 Money paid as a punishment for a crime.
10 A punishment for a criminal who has been found guilty in court.
11 Entering a building by force and stealing things.

Exam Zone

USE OF ENGLISH

1 Decide whether the gap should be filled with a tense or another verb form, e.g. infinitive, *-ing* form.

2 Decide if the verb form should be passive, e.g. *has been made*, *to be found*, *being admired*.

3 Think about the time the verb form refers to (past, present or future) and choose the verb form accordingly, e.g. *must have been* (perfect infinitive if we speculate about the past), *he is leaving tomorrow* (Present Continuous for personal future arrangements).

4 Check that you haven't made any silly mistakes: ~~must to go~~, ~~had have~~, ~~may had been~~

1 Verbs in brackets
Put the verbs in brackets in the correct form.
(20 marks)

0 I ___am looking forward___ (look forward) to our holiday, I ___have never been skiing___ (never ski) before.

1 If I _____ (not be) so lazy, I _____ (find) a better job ages ago.

2 I've never enjoyed _____ (watch) westerns.

3 By this time tomorrow I _____ (write) two essays.

4 Peter and Mary _____ (live) together for three years before they got married.

5 The journalist is believed _____ _____ (kidnap) by the local mafia.

6 Mike found out that he _____ (have to) undergo brain surgery.

7 You're out of breath. _____ you _____ (jog)? How far _____ you _____ (run)?

8 Sorry, I'm not used to _____ (eat) oysters.

9 Jane must _____ (read) in bed – the light is on in her room.

10 We stopped _____ (have) a rest and we ate the chocolate we _____ (buy) at the village shop.

11 I'd rather Roger _____ (not spend) so much time training.

12 Any news about George? We _____ (not be) in touch with him since he _____ (go) to South Africa.

13 He was very tired because he _____ (teach) all day.

14 I didn't realise she was listening. If I _____ _____ (know), I _____ (not say) all these things about her.

15 The police watched the burglar _____ (enter) the shop and while he _____ (look) for the safe, they _____ (arrest) him.

16 If you don't like the salad, try _____ (put) some soy sauce on it.

17 There's nothing dangerous about _____ (trap) in a lift.

18 I must rush. I _____ (fly) to London tomorrow and I _____ (not pack) my suitcase yet.

19 I wish I _____ (become) a tennis player. I _____ (be) rich and famous now.

20 I don't mind _____ (look) after your son but I'll go home as soon as you _____ (get) back.

20

2 Put the verbs in brackets in the correct form. (30 marks)

Marriage can wait

By Steve Doughty

Official figures (0) _____ (show) that more and more young people (1) _____ (reject) early marriage now, e.g. the number of women (2) _____ (marry) under the age of 25 (3) _____ (fall) by half during the last decade.

It seems we (4) _____ (come) a long way since the fifties, when women (5) _____ (be) less concerned with their education and career and when (6) _____ (get) married seemed (7) _____ (be) the woman's main ambition. Many girls (8) _____ (start) families because they (9) _____ (teach) that (10) _____ (be) a wife and mother was a woman's most logical choice, at least after she (11) _____ (complete) her basic education. Most young women of that time must (12) _____ (be) convinced that marriage (13) _____ (be) their destiny.

This concept of marriage seems (14) _____ (disappear) for good. Nowadays, the average age for a woman (15) _____ (marry) for the first time is 28 and for a man, over 30. A first-time bride is now likely (16) _____ (be) in her late twenties with a career, or a woman who (17) _____ (have) children while (18) _____ (live) with her boyfriend. Bridegrooms (19) _____ (get) older too: only one in six being under 25 now, compared with four in ten in 1989. Young people often choose (20) _____ (live) together without (21) _____ (get) married at least for some time before they (22) _____ (decide) if they want (23) _____ (legalise) their relationship.

Marriage (24) _____ (hit) its peak in 1972 as babies born during the post-war boom went to the altar. Since the early eighties it (25) _____ (decline) in popularity, a trend helped by the removal of tax benefits and legal privileges from married couples by successive governments.

Interestingly, divorce numbers (26) _____ (fall) in recent years to follow the declining marriage figures. However, about one in four marriages still (27) _____ (end) in divorce, after an average of nine years.

It is not easy to predict the future of marriage. On the one hand, family bonds (28) _____ (believe) to play a less important role in most societies, which (29) _____ (become) increasingly liberal. On the other hand, though, the youngest generation may turn out (30) _____ (be) much more conservative, in opposition to their parents' values and beliefs.

30

READING

1 Matching extracts with gaps
Read the text and complete the gaps (1–6) with these extracts (a–g). There is one extra extract.
(12 marks)

a At first Laura only saw the good things

b They are put on a three-meals-a-day diet based on fruit and vegetables

c I want to leave my drug life behind and never, never be tempted back.

d They come to visit her every weekend.

e and that meant I had to shoplift, or steal from people in the street.

f But he came to visit me the other day

g They had no idea their daughter was abusing drugs

A second chance of childhood

As Britain's drug addicts get younger and younger, a unique rehabilitation centre in the heart of the English countryside is helping children come off heroin.
Report by **Angela Neustatter**.

Laura Hardiman*, 16, is sitting on a sofa in Middlegate Lodge, a unique drug rehabilitation centre which takes the youngest addicts in the country. They live there like a family in a converted farmhouse. Alongside the detoxification programme, the centre focusses on building up both physical *and* psychological health – a lot of the children are maladjusted after years of drug abuse and mistrust people who try to help them. They are given help
10 with how to communicate, make relationships and deal with conflict. Homeopathic remedies, massage, yoga and relaxation are part of the daily routine. Because people on drugs often don't eat, they tend to arrive very skinny or even suffering from malnutrition. (1) _____ , and are taught about nutrition, food hygiene and how to cook.

Laura has just completed the first stage of the programme to free her from her heroin addiction. She sits looking out at fields as far as the eye can see.
20 Tossing shiny, blonde hair from her shoulders, she remembers Sunday walks in the countryside with her mum and dad; meals in the dining-room where an open fire blazed; curling up on the sofa in the sitting-room to watch a video with her mother and brother; the celebrations when she passed her exams to go to a grammar school; and the time when her parents were proud of their pretty, healthy daughter.

Three years ago her happy childhood disappeared. 'All I had in my mind was getting the heroin I
30 needed for the day,' she explains, '(2) _____ It's like having the devil inside you; you do anything to get the stuff.'

Laura is one of the lucky ones to have a place at Middlegate Lodge. She tells how she came to be here. At the age of 13 she began mixing with a group of teenage dropouts who spent their time in a disused block of flats where heroin dealers did their business. It all happened so easily: 'I was offered some heroin to smoke and I wanted more. I didn't use other drugs,
40 I went straight on to heroin.' (3) _____ , but later, she says, 'I began to see the horrors. But it was too late to get out by then. I needed the drugs.'

It still horrifies Laura's mother, Juliet, a social worker, and her father, Bob, the manager of a machinery business. (4) _____ . Juliet says, 'Someone else's mother phoned and said my daughter was on heroin. I listened in disbelief. Heroin is a word you've heard from another world, but you never dream it will come into your world. It shouldn't
50 happen if you have a stable family, a nice home, firm values.' Juliet never stops blaming herself because she didn't realise what it meant when Laura got thinner, her pupils shrank, her clear rosy skin turned pallid and her once shiny hair became dull.

Laura has been at Middlegate for six weeks, and she is only now beginning to realise how her addiction caused problems in her family. 'My parents started arguing more. And my brother was very, very angry with me. He used to cry and say "I hate you for
60 what you've done to this family." (5) _____ .'

Laura knows she can recapture her happy memories. 'I'm learning self-discipline.
(6) _____ . It's only in the past couple of weeks that I have really seen what an unhappy existence I was leading as an addict.' If she can hold on to this memory, Laura may be able to avoid returning to drugs.

The names of the girl and her family have been changed.

2 Multiple choice
Choose the correct answer according to the text. (4 marks)

1 The young addicts need to be built up psychologically because
a they are undernourished when they arrive.
b they need to keep to a fixed routine.
c they have problems trusting other people.
d they are following a detoxification programme.

2 Before she started taking heroin, Laura
a passed exams to go to Middlegate Lodge.
b watched videos all the time.
c lived in a farmhouse with her family.
d led a happy life with her family.

3 Laura's mother blames herself for what happened because
a she didn't know who Laura's friends were.
b she didn't understand why her daughter looked unhealthy.
c she never took Laura to the doctor.
d she had heard of heroin before.

4 Laura's addiction affected her family because
a there was a lot more conflict at home.
b they had to pay a lot for her to go to the centre.
c the parents thought they had a nice home.
d they had no happy memories.

4

3 Vocabulary
What do these words from the text mean? Choose the best answer – a, b or c. (4 marks)

1 *skinny* (line 14)
a very lonely
b very thin
c very tired

2 *straight* (line 40)
a directly
b gradually
c painfully

3 *stable* (line 50)
a healthy and safe
b secure and steady
c small and rich

4 *pallid* (line 53)
a cold and dry
b red and shiny
c pale and unhealthy

4

WRITING

An essay question

'The government should do more to help drug addicts.' Do you agree? Write an essay of about 150 words.

1 First read these comments about the drug problem. Decide which are for or against the essay title.

- Addicts should be able to register with a chemist to get their drugs. In this way they wouldn't have to depend on drug dealers.
- Taking drugs is a crime. Drug addicts should be put in prison.
- These people are just criminals. They rob people to pay for their drugs.
- We need to have special rehabilitation centres where we can help addicts to rebuild their lives. Prison is not a solution; these people need help, not punishment.
- Drug addiction is just a habit, like smoking or biting your nails. Drug users can give up if they want to.

2 Plan your paragraphs. Read the ideas below and make notes.

1 **Introduction** – the drug problem in your town or country

2 **Arguments 'for'** – how some people think the government should help addicts

3 **Arguments 'against'** – why some people think the government should not help addicts

4 **Conclusion** – give your own opinion

3 Write your essay. Remember to use linking words, especially in paragraphs 2 and 3.

20

10 Conflict

37 Vocabulary

1 Conflict words

Circle the most suitable alternatives to complete the newspaper extracts (1 and 2).

1

More Riots in Oldham

There has been more gang (1) *friction/warfare* in the streets of Oldham. (2) *Arguments/Clashes* between rioting (3) *fights/gangs* of youths and the police culminated late last night in a full-scale (4) *battle/row*. One police officer said, 'The (5) *violence/quarrel* is getting out of control.'

2

Gnome War Ends

The Hardcastles and the Sweeneys, two families from Huddersfield, have not spoken to each other for two years, but they finally made peace yesterday. Mr Hardcastle said, 'You could say there's been long-standing (6) *friction/violence* between us. But it's over now.' Mrs Sweeney added, 'It all began with a petty (7) *argument/clash* when I started putting garden gnomes in our front garden. We had a big (8) *battle/row* about them one day, and our husbands even had a (9) *feud/fight* in the garden.' The (10) *feud/violence* ended when the Sweeneys agreed to move the gnomes into their back garden.

2 Abstract nouns

Complete the quotations with an abstract noun.

1 'One person with a b_e_l_i_e_f is equal to a force of ninety-nine who have only interests.'
John Stuart Mill, 1806–73

2 'F _ _ _ has many eyes and can see things underground.'
Miguel Cervantes, 1547–1616

3 'H _ _ _ _ _ is like fire – it makes even light rubbish deadly.'
George Eliot, 1819–80

4 'There is enough in the world for everyone's need but not for everyone's g _ _ _ _ .'
Frank Buchman, 1878–1961

5 'A _ _ _ _ _ _ _ is so powerful a passion in the human breast that, however high we reach, we are never satisfied.'
Niccolo Machiavelli, 1469–1527

⇨ Lexicon, Students' Book, page 155.

3 Verb families

Replace the words in *italics* with these verbs in the correct form.

beg, chat, recall, reply, shout, stagger, stroll, whisper

A soldier from the Second World War (1) *tells* one of his war memories ...

During the war I had to work on an air base in South Africa. I remember once we had 24 hours off duty, and me and my friends had a night out in the town. We were (2) *walking slowly* back to the base at about midnight. We were (3) *talking in an informal way* when suddenly my friend, Bob, (4) *asked us anxiously* to be quiet. 'Be quiet yourself!' somebody (5) *said*. Then I heard them. 'No, everyone be quiet,' I (6) *said softly*. And then we all could hear the lions. 'Quick, run!' someone (7) *said very loudly*. We all ran towards our base. Everyone made it back, except me – I fell into a trench! I stayed there until morning. Then I climbed out and (8) *walked unsteadily* back to the base.

1 _____	5 _____
2 _____	6 _____
3 _____	7 _____
4 _____	8 _____

Remember

1 ★ Present Perfect

Explain what has happened in each picture using the Present Perfect and the verb in brackets. You may need to use the passive.

1 (break) *The boys have broken the window.*

2 (knock over) _____

_____

3 (crash) _____

_____

4 (cut) _____

_____

5 (tear up) _____

_____

6 (eat) _____

_____

2 ★ Present Perfect

Answer the questions using the cues and the Present Perfect.

1 Do you know Venice? (be there twice) ___*Yes, I've been there twice.*___

2 Why are you so angry? (lose key) _____

3 Are you hungry? (have a big lunch) _____

4 Where's Dave? (go Brazil) _____

5 Have you got any teaching experience? (teach in Spain and Greece)

_____

6 Does your dad know London well? (work there) _____

_____

3 ★ ★ Present Perfect and Past Simple

Match the questions (1–6) with the answers (a–f).

1 How do you know so many of your neighbours? ☐
2 Did you see the match on Wednesday? ☐
3 Will you be OK? ☐
4 Is this your house? ☐
5 How did you manage to finish the exam? ☐
6 Is the match nearly over? ☐

a Yes, I live here.
b I've lived here all my life.
c Yes, it was very boring.
d Yes, I've taken a painkiller.
e I took a painkiller.
f Yes, it's been extremely boring.

4 ★ ★ Present Simple, Present Perfect and Past Simple

Complete the sentences with the Present Simple, the Present Perfect, or the Past Simple tense of the verbs in brackets.

1 Your bike isn't ready yet. I _*haven't pumped*_ (not pump) up the tyres.

2 I know Chris. We _____ (meet) during my last visit.

3 I _____ (not see) *Guernica*. I've heard it's a very powerful painting.

4 Mmm, lemon sorbet. I _____ (love) lemon sorbet.

5 Where exactly _____ (you see) Van Gogh's *Sunflowers*? In Amsterdam?

6 Tchaikovsky _____ (always be) my favourite composer.

7 I don't have to worry about the car. Joe _____ (look) after it.

8 Becky is so unhappy – she _____ (love) Allan all her life and now he's marrying Jill.

9 How many holidays _____ (you have) since 1999?

10 Do you think the ancient Romans _____ (drink) beer?

11 She won't get the job because she _____ (not speak) any foreign languages.

12 Isn't this cake nice? My children _____ (help) me make it.

38 Grammar

1 ★ Emphasis
Rewrite the sentences to make them more formal and emphatic.

1 The river flooded the street immediately after everyone had been evacuated.

No sooner _had everyone been evacuated than the_ _river flooded the street._

2 The government doesn't often attempt to inform the public about its decisions.

Seldom _____

_____

3 He didn't just smoke fifty cigarettes a day, he also drank several cans of beer.

Not only _____

_____

4 If the warning had been given in time, there would have been less damage.

Had _____

_____

5 He wasn't allowed to get out of bed, either.

Neither _____

_____

6 You hardly ever see these animals in the daytime.

Hardly ever _____

_____

2 ★★ Emphasis: Formal
Complete B's responses using the cues given.

1 A: Europe would be much more prosperous if more countries were members of the EU.

B: Never _have I heard such a ridiculous theory._
(hear such a ridiculous theory)

2 A: The Minister had a heart attack last night.

B: Had _____
(know/call off today's meeting)

3 A: The government regularly receives offers of help from international aid organisations.

B: Hardly ever _____
(know how to make use of this)

4 A: This contract will be really profitable for us.

B: Not only _____
(profitable/open up new opportunities)

5 A: The company never informs the public about how it's financed.

B: Neither _____
(publicise its plans for the future)

6 A: Did the rescue team manage to find any survivors?

B: No sooner _____
(approached the building/it collapsed)

3 ★ Emphasis
Rewrite the sentences to emphasise the words and phrases in *italics*.

1 Rob didn't fall in love in Rome, he fell in love in Venice.

It was in Venice that Rob fell in love.

2 I had cheesecake for dessert, not ice cream.

It _____

3 I usually get my fruit from the market, not the supermarket.

It _____

4 They didn't give me money but a free ticket to London as compensation.

It _____

5 He didn't go to Australia in September, he went to the States.

It _____

4 ★ *All ...* and *What I ...*
Rewrite the sentences using *All ...* or *What I ... .*

1 I only had toast and coffee for breakfast.

All _____

2 I didn't ask for much – just a few pounds.

All _____

3 He doesn't drink anything except water.

All _____

4 A: I enjoy holidays in hot countries.

B: What I _____

5 A: I can't stand people smoking in public places.

B: What I _____

6 A: I like Irish music, especially the Corrs.

B: What I _____

5 ★★★ Emphasis: Formal

Make the letter more emphatic by rewriting the sentences in italics with the opening words and phrases from the box. Write them in your notebook.

> Seldom, neither, it was, What I, all he, Not only, Never

Dear Sir,

I am writing to complain about my recent stay at your guesthouse. *I have never stayed in a more incompetently run place before. It was not only dirty and untidy but there was a horrible smell, too.*

I was disappointed with the quality of the room: it was too small, the bathroom did not have a shower and the air-conditioning did not work.

I have seldom had such terrible food. It was not fresh, *and it was not carefully prepared either.* The waiter was wearing a dirty apron and *he wasn't interested in anything except the receptionist.*

However, *I was most shocked by the bill which I was presented with on my departure.*

I shall expect financial compensation of £300. Otherwise, I intend to turn to your national tourist authorities for assistance.

Yours sincerely,

Michael Grant

Prepositions

After verbs and nouns

In English, verbs and nouns are often followed by prepositions that affect the meaning, or which are important for the meaning.

Examples:

*They complained **to** the police **about** the noise pollution.*
*The reason **for** the argument is the loud bagpipe music.*

1 Translate the examples into your language.

2 Read these letters from a magazine and choose the correct preposition for each gap.

> about, against, at, for (x2), in (x3), of (x2), on (x2), to (x6), with (x2)

→ Lexicon, Students' Book, pages 167–169

Since the government introduced new laws to fight (1) _____ anti-social behaviour, there has been a rise (2) _____ the number of complaints (3) _____ the police. We asked you to tell us about your NEIGHBOURS FROM HELL!

My neighbour lives in a flat above mine. She has a lot of plants on her balcony and waters them every day – but the water comes into my flat. I have complained (4) _____ her and she has apologised (5) _____ me, but she says it isn't her problem. I don't want to argue (6) _____ her (7) _____ it any more. Can I take her to court about the damage (8) _____ my ceiling? Should she pay (9) _____ it?

Ms E. Hill, Leicester

I believe (10) _____ the saying 'live and let live', but our relationship (11) _____ our neighbours has gone from bad to worse. The cause (12) _____ the bad feeling is their dog. They bought it two months ago and it barks all day and all night. When we complain, they just laugh (13) _____ us and say it's only a puppy. Do I have to wait (14) _____ it to grow up? Or is there another solution (15) _____ our problem?

Mr & Mrs Fenton, Bristol

My neighbours belong (16) _____ a dance club and have recently started to take part (17) _____ disco dancing competitions. They practise at home. A typical evening now consists (18) _____ loud Abba music, clapping and feet stamping on the floor. We don't want to insist (19) _____ silence, of course, but is there anything we can do? We've spent a lot of money (20) _____ our house, so don't suggest that we move!

T. Davis, Blackburn

39 Communication

1 Arguing
Complete the dialogue between two brothers with these expressions.

oh, stop getting at me	why don't you
don't be ridiculous	I don't see why I should
I'll tell Dad about	I wish you wouldn't
no, I didn't	no, I'm not
why do you always	why should I
yes, I do	yes, you did
you never let	you're always
you're the one who	

Rob: Hey, Pete. I scored two goals in today's match.
Pete: Brilliant. When are Manchester United signing you?
Rob: (1) _Oh, stop getting at me_ , will you?
(2) _____ telling people about how you always win at chess.
Pete: (3) _____ . Anyway, I'm watching this film. (4) _____ interrupt me all the time.
Rob: Well, I wouldn't mind watching the match. I don't want to miss it. (5) _____ turn over and see if it's started?
Pete: No, (6) _____ turn over? I'm watching this film.
Rob: You're just selfish, aren't you?
(7) _____ other people watch anything.
Pete: (8) _____ . I let you watch *Big Brother* yesterday.
Rob: Yeah, but you wanted to watch it, too.
Pete: (9) _____ . I can't stand that programme! (10) _____ have to twist the truth?

Rob: That's great, coming from you!
(11) _____ always lies. I did the washing up yesterday and you told Mum you'd done it.
Pete: I did not!
Rob: (12) _____ . Anyway, come on, turn the telly over.
Pete: (13) _____ .
Rob: Because if you don't, (14) _____ what you did yesterday.
Pete: Oh, come on, (15) _____ .
Rob: I will.
Pete: OK, watch your stupid match!

Why does Ricky Martin always sing the same sort of songs?

2 Criticism
Write criticisms of famous people you know.

1 Why does _____ always _____
_____

2 I wish _____ wouldn't _____
_____

3 _____ is always _____
_____

3 Sarcasm
Write a sarcastic comment after each statement.

1 John has just passed his driving test.
Oh, Michael Schumacher must be really worried!

2 Sue is cooking the dinner tonight.
_____
_____

3 Roger won the chess competition at school.
_____
_____

4 Mark decorated the house himself.
_____
_____

5 The council is building a new shopping centre.
_____
_____

MULTI-PART VERBS

1 Multi-part verbs
Complete the text with these verbs and expressions in the correct form.

> go off, get to, get your own back, give back, give in,
> go off with, kick up a fuss, put forward, put up with,
> talk over

I'm seventeen and my little brother is eleven. He used to be cute, but I've really (1) _gone off_ (stopped liking) him recently. He really (2) _____ (annoys) me. He goes into my room when I'm not there and (3) _____ (takes) my things – and he never (4) _____ (returns them). I've tried everything. I've tried (5) _____ (starting a row), but he just laughs. I've tried (6) _____ (getting revenge) by taking his things, but I feel childish. I've (7) _____ (discussed it) with my parents – they say he'll grow out of it. I've even (8) _____ (suggested) a plan where he can borrow things and return them. But the situation hasn't changed. I can't (9) _____ (tolerate) it any longer but I don't want to (10) _____ (say OK). Help!

2 Review
Complete the sentence for each picture with a multi-part verb in the correct form.

1 She _____ malaria while she was in the Far East.
2 She's always _____ trouble.
3 I _____ an old friend yesterday.
4 He _____ me _____ at the station.
5 Could you _____ a minute, please?

3 Review
Circle the best alternative in each sentence.

1 I take *after/from/like* my dad. We're both musical.
2 We don't have much money, but we get *about/by/in*.
3 He made *like/out/up* he was lost, but he knew where he was.
4 I came *across/on/out* this letter when I was tidying up.
5 She always turns *in/off/up* late for meetings.
6 The doctor has put *by/down/off* my operation until next week.
7 I set *away/off/up* for school at half past eight.
8 The weather turned *in/out/up* quite nice.
9 The doctor recommended I should take *for/up/with* jogging.
10 Please don't give *away/out/up* our secret.

4 Review
Complete these sentences with verbs in the correct form.

1 I feel terrible. I think I'm _____ down with 'flu.
2 I'm sorry I forgot your birthday. I'll _____ up for it, I promise.
3 I've been ill for two weeks. I need to _____ up with my studies.
4 My bathroom needs decorating, but I can't seem to _____ round to it.
5 Oh no, we've _____ out of petrol. Is there a petrol station near here?
6 Sugar's bad for your teeth. You should _____ down on sweets.
7 We didn't know what to do. Then Paula _____ up with this great idea.
8 How long have you been _____ out with Simon?
9 I'm really _____ forward to my holidays.
10 I have always _____ on with my neighbours really well.

⇨ Lexicon, Students' Book, pages 170–176.

40 Focus on Writing

1 Linking review

Complete the second sentence with between two and five words including the word in brackets, so it has a similar meaning to the first sentence.

1 They won the war although they lost the early battles. (despite)

They won the war _____ _____ the early battles.

2 They waited until it was dark to attack in order to surprise the enemy. (so)

They waited until it was dark to attack _____ surprise the enemy.

3 The First World War was so terrible that people said wars must never happen again. (such)

The First World War was _____ _____ that people said wars must never happen again.

4 There was a truce on Christmas Day and also Boxing Day. (only)

Not _____ a truce on Christmas Day but there was also one on Boxing Day.

5 We'll get married when the war is over. (soon)

We'll get married _____ _____ the war is over.

6 You can resolve the conflict provided that you keep calm. (long)

You can resolve the conflict _____ _____ you keep calm.

2 Sentence building

Rewrite the simple sentences as one longer sentence using the words in brackets. Be careful with punctuation and use pronouns instead of nouns. You may need to change some words.

1 I took the watch back to the shop. The manager said the guarantee was useless. I had not signed the guarantee when I bought the watch. (when, because)

_____
_____
_____

2 I am writing to complain about the Timeright watch. I bought the watch last week from Watches R Us. (which)

_____
_____

3 The watch is obviously faulty. I would like you to refund my money. (as)

_____
_____

4 I read your advert. I decided to buy the watch. You claimed it worked in all conditions. You claimed it worked in water and extreme heat. (after, since, such as)

_____
_____

5 I enclose a copy of the guarantee. I enclose a copy of the receipt. (as well as)

_____
_____

6 I expect a satisfactory reply. Otherwise I will take legal action. (unless)

_____
_____

7 It doesn't work when I go jogging. It doesn't work in the shower. (however, either)

_____
_____

3 Paragraph building

Put the sentences in Exercise 2 in the correct order for a letter of complaint and write the numbers of the sentences next to the correct paragraphs.

Paragraph 1 Introduction [2] [ ]

Paragraph 2 Reasons for complaint [ ] [ ]

Paragraph 3 Reaction to your complaint [ ]

Paragraph 4 Your demands [ ] [ ]

4 Editing

Each of these sentences has the wrong word order.
Write the sentences correctly using *exactly the same words*.

1 They often arguments have with their next-door neighbours.

   _____

   _____

2 They had known about their visit, they wouldn't have gone out for the day.

   _____

   _____

3 They put forward a solution and talked over it at the conference.

   _____

   _____

4 Where did the UN have built its headquarters?

   _____

   _____

5 Do you know why have complained the neighbours?

   _____

   _____

6 They were having a noisy big argument.

   _____

   _____

7 Never we have seen anything like it.

   _____

   _____

8 My sister borrows a lot my things.

   _____

   _____

9 They have been since April at war.

   _____

   _____

10 Why do always you have to twist the truth?

   _____

   _____

5 Writing under pressure

Match the four stages of writing a composition in an exam (1–4) with the advice (a–d).

1 Get down your ideas   ☐
2 Plan your paragraphs   ☐
3 Write neatly   ☐
4 Check carefully   ☐

a You should:
   • think about the layout
   • decide on the order of your ideas
   • write notes, not full sentences
   • decide where you can use linking words

b Make sure you leave time to:
   • read through your composition
   • correct any mistakes neatly

c Some common ways are:
   • diagrams
   • networks
   • tables

d Remember:
   • don't write a first draft – there is no time!
   • don't use a structure if you're not sure about it
   • don't use a word if you're not sure about it – try to think of an alternative

Word Power

1 Confusing words
Circle the best alternative in each sentence.

1 In the battle, over a hundred soldiers were *assassinated/killed/murdered* and hundreds more were *damaged/harmed/wounded*.
2 Many wars are unnecessary and could easily be *denied/prevented/prohibited*.
3 After *arguing/discussing/disputing* the situation, the leaders decided not to go to war.
4 The number of deaths may *expand/raise/rise* by up to 5,000 according to a *forecast/guess* by the government.
5 George Dimmack, the *actual/present/real* Minister for Defence, says the government will have to *cost/spend/waste* a further £400 million on arms.

2 Collocation review
Complete the sentences with one of the following verbs in the correct form.

do, get, have, make

1 My neighbours are always __*having*__ rows.
2 I've tried to _____ in touch with him, but I think he's changed his address.
3 We don't expect you to win the race, just _____ your best.
4 She's ambitious; she wants to _____ to the top.
5 If I were you, I'd _____ a complaint about the rubbish in your street.
6 My brother always _____ very well in general knowledge quizzes.
7 Carbon fuel emissions must _____ an effect on the temperature of the atmosphere, don't you think?
8 Could I _____ a phone call, please?
9 It took ages to _____ my homework last night.
10 I didn't like my sister's cat at first, but now I've _____ quite attached to it.
11 Eating a few sweets won't _____ you any harm.
12 I thought he _____ a good point at the meeting.
13 Sorry I'm late. I _____ lost!
14 I _____ a weird dream about you last night.
15 I can't find your watch. I _____ a clue where it can be.

3 Collocation review
Complete the sentences with a word beginning with the letter given.

1 She always dresses in the *l*_____ styles.
2 Empty houses and boarded-up shops are signs of *u*_____ decay.
3 Sadly, he caught a *f*_____ disease and died on the island.
4 I try not to buy clothes with *d*_____ labels.
5 It's stuffy in here; let's go out for some *f*_____ air.
6 There's a *b*_____ view of London from the top of the London Eye.
7 The papers are full of articles about *g*_____ warming and the *g*_____ effect .
8 I'm ashamed to live in such a *c*_____ society; we waste so much.

4 Idiomatic language
Complete the text with the following words and expressions.

a breath of fresh air, the last straw, a fuss, the four corners, all plain sailing, a complete nightmare, a stepping stone, the truth

I have been to (1) _____ of the globe and so consider myself an experienced traveller. However, my short trip to France was (2) _____ . To say my journey there was not (3) _____ would be an understatement. I wanted to go to Paris as (4) _____ to the rest of Europe, but I never got out of the hotel there. For a start, my luggage didn't arrive, but I didn't kick up (5) _____ – I kept calm. Then they put me in a tiny room – they said I had asked for this, but they were twisting (6) _____ .
I finally found someone who spoke English, which was like (7) _____ , and the manager gave me a larger room. The next day some luggage arrived, but it wasn't mine! (8) _____ was when the manager said somebody else had reserved my new room!

⇨ Lexicon, Students' Book, page 162.

5 Pronunciation

Put these words into the correct column according to the <u>underlined</u> sound.

bomb, cl<u>ai</u>m, cons<u>u</u>mer, cr<u>a</u>dle, cr<u>i</u>me, d<u>ea</u>th, d<u>u</u>ty, f<u>a</u>ll, f<u>eu</u>d, f<u>i</u>ne, h<u>o</u>meless, inv<u>a</u>de, t<u>u</u>be, m<u>ea</u>sure, qu<u>a</u>rrel, rec<u>a</u>ll, repl<u>y</u>, r<u>i</u>val, r<u>o</u>cket, sh<u>a</u>ke, s<u>o</u>cial, s<u>o</u>ldier, squ<u>a</u>t, str<u>aw</u>, str<u>o</u>ll, th<u>e</u>ft, thr<u>ea</u>ten, w<u>a</u>r

1 n<u>ew</u> /juː/	2 h<u>igh</u> /aɪ/	3 cr<u>oss</u> /ɒ/	4 m<u>ore</u> /ɔː/	5 p<u>ai</u>nt /eɪ/	6 tr<u>e</u>nd /e/	7 br<u>o</u>ke /əʊ/

6 🅰🅩 Extension: Word families

Write these words in the correct diagrams.
Use a good dictionary.

affluent, colossal, delighted, depressed, down, elated, glad, glum, immense, loaded, massive, miserable, prosperous, thrilled, vast, well-heeled

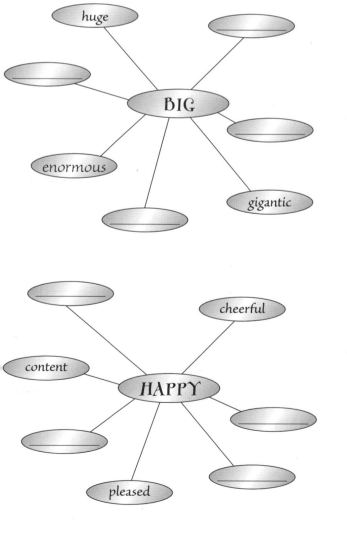

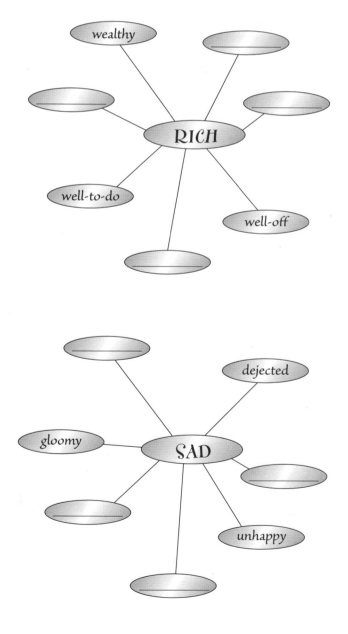

Language Awareness

1 ★ Perfective verb forms

Underline all the perfective verb forms in the text on the right. Then match them with the names of the tenses below.

a   Present Perfect
b   Present Perfect Continuous
c   Past Perfect
d   Past Perfect Continuous
e   Perfect infinitive
f   Perfective *-ing* form (gerund)
g   Perfective *-ing* form (participle)
h   Future Perfect

2 ★★ Perfective verb forms

Circle the correct verb form for each picture. How would you change each picture so that it illustrated the other sentence?

a   He's caught some fish.
b   He caught some fish.

a   I'm jogging.
b   I've been jogging.

a   When he entered the room, he took off his coat.
b   When he entered the room, he had taken off his coat.

a   They will have written four books by 2008.
b   They will write four books in 2008.

(d)

Maria came home rather late. She <u>had been working</u> hard on the school play they were going to have the following week. Having closed the door behind her, she realised that the house was completely dark and very quiet.

'Where have they all gone?' she wondered. She switched on the light and went upstairs to check the bedrooms. There was no one there, and the beds looked as if nobody had slept in them. She remembered having left her red sweatshirt on the bed but it wasn't there.

She was beginning to feel scared. And then the telephone rang. She picked up the receiver and heard her father's voice saying 'Hi, where have you been? We've been trying to contact you all evening. You must have switched off your mobile. Ted's won the school chess championship and we're celebrating in the pizzeria round the corner. Come and join us!'

'But you'll have eaten by the time I get there,' Maria said.

'No problem. We'll order another one for you.'

Maria left to join them. But she didn't forget the moment of panic she had experienced just before the phone rang.

3 ★★ Perfective verb forms

Complete the sentences with the correct perfective forms of the verbs in brackets.

1 _____ (offer) a scholarship he decided to continue his studies at Harvard.

2 By the time we come home Paul _____ (cook) dinner.

3 Clare must _____ (have) plastic surgery – she looks completely different.

4 I completely forgot _____ (put) the potatoes in the oven.

5 I'm shattered. I _____ (shop) all day.

6 _____ (live) here for twenty years, I know every inch of this street.

7 Brian couldn't come because he _____ (fall) ill.

8 By the time I was thirty, I _____ (visit) every capital city in Europe.

9 Australia is known to _____ (colonise) by the British.

10 John is not here yet. His train may _____ _____ (arrive) late.

Check Your Grammar

1 Emphasis and persuasion
Rewrite the sentences using the beginnings provided.

1 I advise you to stop worrying about your weight.

  If _____

  _____

2 The robbers killed three people for only $100.

  It was _____

  _____

3 I only really enjoy old Charlie Chaplin comedies.

  What _____

4 The government should reduce taxes as soon as possible.

  It's high time _____

5 You must change your attitude to customers.

  I insist _____

6 The President hardly ever attends these meetings.

  Hardly _____

  _____

7 Why do you always leave a mess in the kitchen?

  I'd _____

  _____

8 Nick spilt red wine on my best suit and then said it was my fault.

  Not only _____

  _____

9 Paul is interested in nothing but sport.

  All _____

10 It's the best performance I've ever seen.

  Never _____

11 You should get a taxi or you'll be late.

  You'd _____

12 Why don't we start saving for a new car?

  I suggest _____

13 We reached the mountain shelter seconds before the storm broke out.

  No sooner _____

  _____

14 He didn't realise that the house was on fire so he didn't run away.

  Had _____

  _____

15 Our politicians are seldom concerned with the problems of the poor.

  Seldom _____

  _____

16 He invited me to the theatre, not to the cinema.

  It was _____

  _____

17 We just managed to hide the presents before the children came in.

  When the children _____

  _____

18 They weren't expecting more than a lift to the nearest town.

  All _____

  _____

19 All passengers should switch off their mobiles immediately.

  The captain demands _____

  _____

20 It's a good idea to do some sport.

  You ought _____

2 Verbs
Complete the text with one word in each gap.
Contractions (*don't, needn't*, etc.) count as one word.

Mum: Jill, (1) ___I'd___ rather you (2) _____ come home so late. I (3) _____ so worried last night.

Jill: You needn't (4) _____ worried. Adam walked me home.

Mum: If I (5) _____ you, I (6) _____ be more careful with him. He (7) _____ been arrested a few times, (8) _____ he?

Jill: No, he (9) _____ ! It's just gossip. You (10) _____ better not listen to everything people say.

Mum: (11) _____ lived so long, I know who can (12) _____ trusted and who can't. And it's (13) _____ you started learning this too.

Jill: Stop it, Mum! He (14) _____ just a friend, anyway. We (15) _____ only been to the pub a few times.

Mum: OK, but I'd (16) _____ you called next time you're going to come home late.

Mini-Grammar Index

[CAPITALS = main sections of the Mini-Grammar]

Mini-Grammar

1 CONDITIONALS

1.1 Basic conditional types

We use the **Zero Conditional** to describe situations where one event always results in the other:

*If the weather is warm and rainy, mushrooms **grow** very quickly.*

In these sentences *if = when*.

- The pattern is:

If clause	main clause
If + Present Simple,	Present Simple

We use the **First Conditional** to talk about possible future events which depend on other future events:

*If you **read** this report, you **will understand** our economic situation much better.*

*They **will sign** the agreement unless their financial situation **changes** dramatically.*

If clause	main clause
If/Unless + Present Simple,	will or other modal verb + infinitive without *to*

- We also use this Conditional to give advice or an order, and to make a suggestion or a request:

  *If you **want** to make a good impression, **remember** to smile and make eye contact.*

If clause	main clause
If + Present Simple,	imperative

We use the **Second Conditional**:

1 to talk about imagined events in the future, which are impossible or unlikely:

*If I **went** on 'Who wants to be a Millionaire?' I'**d** win a lot of money.* (The event is unlikely, and the sentence is about the future.)

2 to talk about impossible present situations:

*If people **had** more common sense, there **wouldn't be** any wars in the world.* (The situation is impossible to fulfil now, and the sentence refers to the present.)

- The pattern is:

If clause	main clause
If + past,	would/could/might + infinitive without *to*

We use the **Third Conditional** to talk about unreal situations in the past, to imagine things that did not happen:

*If **we'd been driving** faster, we **would've crashed** on that slippery road.* (We weren't driving so fast and we didn't crash.)

- The pattern is:

If clause	main clause
If + Past Perfect,	would/could/might + perfect infinitive

1.2 Mixed conditionals

We use 'mixed conditionals' to talk about:

1 imaginary past situations that could have led to consequences in the present:

*If I **had** more self-confidence,, I **would have** applied for that job.*

(... but I wasn't confident, so I haven't.)

*If the rescue team **hadn't found** him, he **would be** dead.*

(... but they found him so he's alive.)

- In such sentences we use the pattern:

If clause	main clause
If + Past Perfect,	would + infinitive.

2 unreal present situations, usually imaginary permanent states, which could have had some consequences in the past:

*If Anna **was** here, she **would've known** what to do.*

(... but Anna's not here, so she can't help us.)

*If she **didn't love** driving, she **wouldn't have become** a taxi driver.*

(She loves driving, so she became a taxi driver.)

- In such sentences the pattern is:

If clause	main clause
If + Past Simple,	would + perfect infinitive

2 DETERMINERS

- We use the following determiners before singular countable nouns:

  *a tent, **an** anorak, **the** computer, **another** person, **the other** player*

- We use the following determiners before uncountable nouns:

  *the milk, **some** money, **any** furniture, **no** time, (a) little sugar, **a lot of** affection, **much** bread, all (the) work*

- We use the following determiners before plural countable nouns:

  the people, **some** fans, **any** guests, **no** cakes, **many** children, **several** articles, **(a) few** bottles, **a lot of** flowers, **all (the)** employees, **(the) other** manager

2.1 Articles

2.1a the indefinite article *a/an*

We use *a/an*:

1 when we mention something for the first time:

*There was **a pub** next to my school. The school was new and modern and the pub was very old and traditional.*

2 when it does not matter which particular person/thing we are talking about, e.g. when we mention the person/thing as an example of a group or category:

*We need **a new computer**, the old one doesn't work anymore.*

2.1b the definite article *the*

We use *the*:

1 when the person we are talking to knows precisely which person/thing we are talking about and can easily identify the person/thing:

*Did you know that **the bakery** is closing down?.*

2 with things which are unique:

***The moon** helped us find our way home in the dark.*

3 with the names of rivers (*the Nile, the Amazon, the Rio Grande*), seas and oceans (*the Baltic Sea, the Atlantic, the Dead Sea*), mountain ranges (*the Rocky Mountains, the Andes, the Alps*), and groups of islands (*the Bahamas, the Shetlands, the Canary Islands*);

4 with names of countries if they are plural (*the Netherlands, the Philippines*) or contain a common noun (*the United Kingdom, the Czech Republic*);

5 with a singular noun to talk about the whole category or concept, or a type (of machine/animal etc.):

***The plane** is the fastest means of transport.*

***The African elephant** is an endangered species.*

- Compare the sentences:

  *We really must wash **the car** today.*
  (We are talking about one specific car.)

  *I think **the car** is the most practical invention of the twentieth century.* (We are talking about the car as a concept, cars in general.)

6 with an adjective to talk about groups of people who are characterised by one feature:

the poor, the rich, the disabled, the unemployed, the dead

The verb is always plural:

***The unemployed are** always at a disadvantage.*

2.1c No article

We don't use an article before:

1 plural and uncountable nouns when we refer to things in general:

*I think **mobile phones** have as many advantages as disadvantages.*

*Where does **coffee** grow?*

2 the names of continents (*Africa, Europe*), towns (*Budapest, New York*), lakes (*Lake Victoria, Lake Erie*), single mountains (*Mont Blanc, Kilimanjaro*), single islands (*Majorca, Sicily*), countries (*France, Turkey*), airports, stations and streets (*Tegel Airport, Paddington Station, Bond Street*)

There are some exceptions to this rule, e.g. *The Hague.*

2.1d Fixed phrases with and without articles

There are a lot of fixed phrases with and without articles, which do not follow any rules, as the following examples show.

- Phrases with *the*:
  at the office, on the radio, in the end, on the one hand ... on the other hand, on the whole, give somebody the sack, late in the day, break the ice, by the way

- Phrases with *a*:
  in a day, in a way, give somebody a helping hand, have a heart, come to a head

- Phrases without articles:
  at school, day by day, in bed, in hospital, on TV, face to face, on business, on holiday, on behalf of, from left to right

3 EMPHATIC STRUCTURES

3.1 Cleft sentences

We use cleft sentences in both formal and informal language to put more emphasis on particular words:

He wants to buy a Mercedes. ⇨ ***It's a Mercedes** that he wants to buy.* (emphasis on *Mercedes*)

We took the final decision yesterday night. ⇨ ***It was yesterday night** that we took the final decision.* (emphasis on *yesterday night*)

Peter told me the true story. ⇨ ***It was Peter (not Mike)** who/that told me the true story.* (emphasis on *Peter*)

In these sentences we use the pronoun *who* or *that* when the emphasis is on the subject/doer and we use the pronoun *that* when the emphasis is on another part of the sentence.

Similar structures are:

I'm dreaming about a cup of tea. ⇨ ***What** I'm dreaming about is **a cup of tea.*** (emphasis on *a cup of tea*)

We must talk to Jill first. ⟹ **What** *we must do first is* **talk to Jill.** (emphasis on *talking to Jill*)
I only want a glass of water. ⟹ **All** *I want is* **a glass of water.** (emphasis on *a glass of water*)
He's only after her money. ⟹ **All** *he's after is* **her money.** (emphasis on *her money*)

3.2 Inversion

3.2a After negative adverbs

We use inversion in formal/written language to make what we write or say sound stronger, more emphatic. To do this we put a negative adverb at the beginning of the sentence and use the word order of questions.

I have never felt so humiliated before. ⟹ **Never** *have I felt so humiliated.*
We seldom have a chance to witness such acts of courage. ⟹ **Seldom** *do we have a chance to witness such acts of courage.*
The man dropped to the floor just after he had drunk the wine. ⟹ **No sooner** *had the man drunk the*

wine than he dropped to the floor.
We didn't know that he was planning to sell the company. ⟹ **Little** *did we know that he was planning to sell the company.*
He didn't only give her flowers, he bought her a silver bracelet as well. ⟹ **Not only** *did he give her flowers, but he bought her a silver bracelet as well.*

Such sentences are very rare in spoken English, unless someone wants to sound very formal.

3.2b In conditionals

We can also use emphatic inversion in the Third Conditional without *if*:

If I had known how to say this in Hungarian, I wouldn't have had all these problems. ⟹ **Had I known** *how to say this in Hungarian, I wouldn't have had all these problems.*
If Mike had been there, he would've lent me the money. ⟹ **Had Mike been there**, *he would've lent me the money.*

4 MODAL VERBS AND EXPRESSIONS

Meaning/Use	Examples
Obligation and necessity • obligation that comes from the speaker • obligation/necessity that results from external circumstances or rules • past obligation or necessity	• *You* **must** *tell me all about your new boyfriend.* • *I* **have to** *wear a tie at work.* • *We* **had to** *change all the locks after the robbery.*
Lack of obligation/necessity • lack of obligation that comes from the speaker • lack of obligation/necessity that results from external circumstances or rules • lack of obligation/necessity in the past • when someone did not do something because it was not necessary • when someone did something although it was unnecessary	• *You* **needn't** *do anything, we'll arrange everything.* • *You* **don't have to** *carry your ID card with you all the time.* • *We* **didn't have** *to carry our school books when we were in primary school.* • *He* **didn't need to drive** *himself, he had a chauffeur.* • *I didn't know the classes were cancelled – I* **needn't have got up** *so early.*
Permission • formal permission that is given by the speaker • neutral permission • request for permission (from the most to the least formal)	• *Hotel guests* **may** *use the pool from 7 a.m. to 9 p.m.* • *You* **can** *use your notes during the test.* • **May** *I sit here? /* **Could** *I have a look at your notes?* **Can** *I leave my luggage here for a moment?*
Prohibition • very formal prohibition that comes from an authority • prohibition that comes from the speaker • neutral prohibition	• *Passengers* **may not** *smoke on board the aircraft.* • *We* **mustn't** *say anything that could hurt her.* • *You* **can't** *smoke here.* *We* **are not allowed** *to eat in the computer room.*

Meaning/Use	Examples
Advice/weak obligation • asking for advice • giving advice and stating obligations/expectations	• *What **shall** I do now? / What **should** I do with this?* • *You **should** think before you speak. / She **shouldn't** smoke so much. / They **ought to** drive more carefully.*
Ability • ability in the present • lack of ability in the present • ability in the past • lack of ability in the past	• *Their daughter **can** speak English, Polish and Chinese.* • *I **can't** drive.* • *I **could** talk when I was two.* • *My grandfather **couldn't** pronounce 'r' correctly.*
Possibility • theoretical possibility in the present/future • lack of possibility in the present/future • possibility in the past • lack of possibility in the past • past achievement • possibility in the past that was wasted • possibility in the future	• *The weather in autumn **can** be very unpleasant.* • *It **can't** snow in summer.* • *They **could** afford all they wanted.* • *The meeting **couldn't** be cancelled.* • *We **were able to** get an exclusive interview with Clark Gable's daughter.* • *I **could've** gone to the seaside with some friends.* • *I **could** talk to her on your behalf, if you like. We **might** arrive there earlier than we thought.*
Predictions for the future (from the most to the least certain)	• *He'll expect us to wait for him, I'm sure.* *The film **is bound to** get good reviews.* *They **may** not find us if they don't know the place well.* *Hugh **might** bring his new girlfriend.* *Jenny **could** get scared of the dinosaurs.*
Speculations about the present and the past • based on the speaker's knowledge or experience • based on observable evidence • speculations which involve the speaker's uncertainty • the speaker's expectations	• *She **will** be reading her e-mail in the office.* • *I **must** have left my gloves on the bus.* *He **can't** be a United Nations interpreter.* • *Mark **may have** changed his job. / She **might** work too hard. / She **could** be talking to Chris now.* • *They **should** be at home now, if the train arrived on time.*
Intentions/spontaneous decisions • making decisions/stating intentions (promises, threats/warnings, refusals) • requests	• *I'll phone you back in a minute. / You'll be sorry you did that. / I **won't** listen to that anymore.* • ***Will** you pick Mary up on the way home?*
Typical behaviour or habit in the present	• *She **will** smoke even though she knows it's dangerous.* • *Friends **will** always support one another.*
Typical behaviour or habit in the past	• *We **would** always eat tons of chocolates when we were kids.* • *I **used** to live in a very quiet and friendly neighbourhood.*

5 PARTICIPLES

Form

1 The present ('active') participle describes what the person/thing is or was doing:

*She is **looking** into the mirror.*

*the man **sitting** at the bar, a **travelling** salesman*

2 The past ('passive') participle usually says what is/was done to the person/thing:

*He was **robbed** on the way home.*

*the **lost** key, a **forgotten** Hollywood star*

Uses

1 In tenses:

*They have been **working** very hard.*

(present participle + continuous tenses)

*I've **talked** to John this morning.*

(past participle + perfective tenses)

2 In the passive (past participle):

*He has been **interviewed** by the BBC.*

3 As adjectives:

*a **smiling** shop assistant, a **fascinating** story, a **broken** heart, an **injured** man*

4 In participle clauses used instead of full relative clauses (reduced relative clauses):

*I saw two men **trying** to break into my car. (= I saw two men who were trying to break into my car.)*

*It's the wreck of a ship **sunk** during the Second World War (= It's the wreck of a ship which was sunk during the Second World War.)*

5 In participle clauses used as adverbial clauses:

***Knowing** I would be late, I phoned home.*

***Handled** with care, this car can serve you for many years.*

***Having reached** the summit, they saw a breathtaking view of the valley.*

6 THE PASSIVE

Uses

1 When the doer (person or thing performing the action) is unknown:

*The building **has been** completely **refurbished**.*

2 To focus on the action rather than the doer:

*The new policy **will be introduced** step by step.*

3 To avoid a very long subject in an active sentence:

*Princess Diana's dress **was bought** by a famous fashion designer, who wants to open a museum of celebrity clothes. (= A famous fashion designer, who wants to open a museum of celebrity clothes, **bought** Princess Diana's dress.)*

4 When we want to put emphasis on the doer:

*The project **is going to be sponsored** by UNESCO.*

The passive is used mainly in formal and written language. It is very typical of newspaper language.

Form

To form the passive we use the appropriate form of *be* + third form of the verb:

*The room **is cleaned** daily.* (Present Simple)

*I think we **were being observed**.* (Past Continuous)

*When we arrived at the auction, the painting **had** just **been sold** for half a million dollars.* (Past Perfect)

*He's **going to be defeated** this time.* (*be going to*)

*We **will be offered** a contract for building the new shopping centre in town.* (Future)

Apart from passive forms of tenses we can use some other passive forms:

Passive infinitive: *It's nice **to be taken** seriously.*

Passive gerund: *We liked **being praised** by the teacher.*

Passive perfect infinitive: *The train may **have been delayed** by the storm.*

⇨ Passive report structures in **Reporting, 10**

7 PRONOUNS

We use the following pronouns in English.

1 Personal (subject) pronouns *I, you, he, she, it, we, they*:

***She's** my best friend.*

***They** can't go there without me.*

2 Personal (object) pronouns *me, you, him, her, it, us, them*:

*I've never met **her** before.*

*Let's tell **them** what we think.*

3 Indefinite pronouns e.g. *someone, something, anywhere, nobody, nothing*:

*We didn't see **anyone** in front of the building.*

***Nothing** will make her happier.*

4 Possessive pronouns *mine, yours, his, hers, ours, theirs*:

*This umbrella isn't **mine**, it must be **hers**.*

5 Demonstrative pronouns *this, that, these, those*:

***This** is the kind of music I can't stand.*

*I like **these** more.*

6 Reflexive pronouns *myself, yourself, himself, herself, itself, ourselves, yourselves, themselves*:

*She cut **herself** very badly.*

*I like **myself** better than anyone else.*

7 Emphatic pronouns *myself, yourself, himself, herself, itself, ourselves, yourselves, themselves*:

*I cooked all this **myself**.*

*The ceremony was opened by the Queen **herself**.*

8 Reciprocal pronouns *each other, one another*:

*They've always been in love with **each other**.*

*In my family we often give presents to **one another**.*

9 Relative pronouns *who, which, that, whose, whom, where, when*:

*We should do something **that** would cheer her up.*

*They spent their honeymoon in the mountain resort **where** they had met for the first time.*

10 The pronouns *one* and *you* (= *anyone*). These are used to say things about people in general. *One* is used in formal language, whereas *you* is less formal:

***You** can be robbed anywhere in the world.*

***One** should always consider various options before taking a decision.*

⚡ Possessive adjectives (*my, your, his, her, its, our, their*) are not pronouns because they cannot replace a noun. Compare the sentences:

*This is **her** mug. This mug is **hers**.*

8 PERSUASION

When we want to tell other people what they should do, we use different forms in formal and informal language.

1 In formal language we use:
- *ought + to* infinitive:

  *The media **ought to devote** more attention to the issue of homelessness.*

- *demand/insist/suggest that* + subject + *should do something*/present tense/subjunctive (same form as infinitive):

  *I **insist that the student** who did this **should be** severely **punished**.*

  *I **suggest that we postpone the meeting** until next week.*

  *We **demanded that they move the nightclub** to a safer area.* (the most formal pattern of the three)

- *It's high time* + subject + past tense (formal, usually used by someone in higher authority):

  ***It's high time the local authorities** started listening to the voice of the community.*

2 In informal language we can use *If I were you, I'd* + infinitive:

***If I were you, I'd take up** a sport.*

I'd (I would) rather + subject + past tense:

***I'd rather you didn't play** that music here.*

You'd/You had better + infinitive:

***You'd better concentrate** now.*

It's about time + subject + past tense:

***It's about time you started** helping at home.* (This form sounds rude unless you use it when addressing a close friend or a family member.)

I'd sooner you + past tense (This is rather formal and indicates the speaker's clear preference):

***I'd sooner they didn't use** the park for skateboarding.*

3 In both formal and informal language we can use *should* + infinitive:

*We **should get to know** each other better.*

9 RELATIVE CLAUSES

9.1 Defining relative clauses

We use defining relative clauses to identify the person or thing we are talking about:

*I know a lot of people **who've stopped eating meat**.*

*We must trace the person **whose ticket was issued on Saturday morning**.*

In defining relative clauses we can use the following relative pronouns.

- *who* to refer to people:

  *I've a friend **who** has more than ten different pets.*

- *which* to refer to things, places, etc.:

  *I've come across an old photograph of my grandmother **which** was taken in Monte Carlo.*

- *that* to refer to animals, things, places, etc. (instead of *which*) and sometimes people (instead of *who*):

  *The building **that** you can see on the other side of the river is the town hall.*

- *whose* to talk about possession:

  *They have a dog **whose** barking drives me mad.*

- *where* to refer to places:

  *Do you know a place **where** we could have a cheap meal?*

- *when* to refer to time:

  *I remember the moment **when** I found out I'd won the scholarship.*

We can omit the relative pronoun *who, which* or *that* in defining relative clauses if the pronoun is not the subject of the relative clause, i.e. if the relative pronoun is not immediately followed by a verb:

We all agreed that the club (that) we went to on Saturday wasn't worth recommending.

They are looking for a person (who) they can rely on.

9.2 Non-defining relative clauses

We use non-defining relative clauses to give extra information about a person or thing:

*The Tate Modern, **which is the newest museum in London**, has excellent facilities for children.*

*My father, **who's a wonderful cook**, promised to make a cake for my eighteenth birthday.*

Non-defining relative clauses are always separated from the rest of the sentence by commas. We can use the same pronouns as in defining relative clauses, but NOT *that*:

*My flat, **which/that I only bought last month**, is spacious and full of light.*

⚡ We can never omit the relative pronoun in a non-defining relative clause.

9.3 Co-ordinate relative clauses

We use co-ordinate relative clauses (sentential relatives) to add a comment to what was said in the first part of the sentence:

*The new buses are extremely fast and reliable, **which makes travelling to work much easier**.*

*I learned three foreign languages at school, **which helped me to get an interesting job**.*

In these clauses we always use a comma and the relative pronoun *which* (NOT *what*).

9.4 Reduced relative clauses

Instead of a full relative clause we can sometimes use a participle clause with a present or past participle :

*We'll come back to some of the issues **that have been discussed during today's meeting**.* ⇨

*We'll come back to some of the issues **discussed during today's meeting**.*

*We didn't notice the man **who was following us**.* ⇨
*We didn't notice the man **following us**.*

 **Participles, 5**

10 REPORTING

10.1 Reported speech

1 When we report what someone has said, we change the pronouns:

John: '*I love **you**.'* ⇨ *John said (that) **he** loved **her**.*

John: '***You** promised **us** a lift to the cinema.'* ⇨ *John said (that) **we**'d promised **them** a lift to the cinema.*

2 When we report a request or command, we use the pattern *ask/tell/order someone (not) to* + infinitive:

*Susan **asked Mike to help** her.*

*The pilot **told us not to panic**.*

10.1a Reported statements

When we report a statement that was made in the past we change the tense in the reported statement:

Mike: *'I'm thirsty.'*   *Mike said he **was** thirsty.*

Original tense	Tense in reporting
Present Simple	Past Simple
Present Continuous	Past Continuous
Present Perfect	Past Perfect
Present Perfect Continuous	Past Perfect Continuous
Past Simple	Past Perfect
Past Continuous	Past Perfect Continuous
will	*would*
be going to	*was/were going to*
First Conditional	Second Conditional

The Past Perfect, and the Second and Third Conditionals do not change in reported speech.
We leave the original tense if we report

- a general truth:
  'The Earth is round.' ⇨ *Galileo said that the Earth is round.*

- something that is still true because the context hasn't changed:
  'Russia is the largest country in the world.'
  The minister explained that Russia is the largest country in the world. ⇨

- a future event that hasn't happened yet at the moment of reporting:
  'Tony and Louise are getting married next year.'
  She told me that Tony and Louise are getting married next year. ⇨

- a past event that happened at a time specified in the sentence:
  'My grandmother was born in 1908.' ⇨
  Mary said her grandmother was born in 1908.

We change some time and place expressions if the context has changed:
Mike (on 26 April 2000): *'I'll do it tomorrow.'* ⇨
*Mike said he would do it **the next day**.*

Original statement	Reported statement
now	*then*
at the moment	*at that moment*
today	*on that day*
yesterday	*the day before*
last week/month/year	*the week/month/year before, the previous week/month/ year*
tomorrow	*the next day, the following day*
next week	*the next week/month/year, the following week/month/year*
here	*there*

We can leave out *that* before the reported statement.

10.1b Reported questions

In reported questions we use *asked, wanted to know* + *when, where, how, what, why, who*. We use the same word order as in statements:

Where do you live? ⇨ *She asked me **where I lived**.*

How old are you? ⇨ *He wanted to know **how old I was**.*

If the reporting verb is in the past we change the tenses in the same way as we do when we report a statement. If there is no question word, we add *if* or *whether*:

Do you speak English? ⇨ *She wants to know **if** I speak English.*

Have they been to Rome? ⇨ *She wanted to know **whether** they had been to Rome.*

10.2 Reporting verbs

We can use the following verbs when reporting what someone said.

- Verb + (somebody) *that*:
  add, admit, agree, announce, believe, boast, claim, complain, declare, deny, explain, insist, remind, suggest, warn
  *He **added that** his country was preparing for war.*

- Verb + somebody *to do* something:
  advise, beg, forbid, order, promise
  *They **advised** me **to consult** a lawyer.*

- Verb + *to do* something:
  agree, offer, promise, refuse, threaten
  *She **agreed to sponsor** the charity concert.*

- Verb + *doing* something: admit, deny, suggest
  *The boy **admitted lying** to his parents.*

- Verb + *if/whether*: inquire, wonder
  *I **inquired whether** the train was on time.*

10.3 Impersonal report structures

1 When we report what people generally believe or say, we can use the subject *It* and the passive of certain verbs (*say, know, believe, claim, suppose, think, fear, predict*). This sentence structure is formal and is mainly used in written English.

***It is believed** that elephants have a very good memory.*

***It was supposed** that the prisoner had already escaped.*

2 We can also start the sentence from the person/thing that the information concerns and use the pattern, subject + passive + infinitive:

It is known that bears like honey.
 = *Bears **are known to like** honey.*

- We use an ordinary infinitive if the opinion reported is about something that happened at the time of reporting:

  It was believed that Humphrey Bogart was similar to the characters he played.
  = *Humphrey Bogart **was believed to be** similar to the characters he played.*

- We use the perfect infinitive if the opinion reported is about something that happened before the time of reporting:

  It is thought that the reporter was kidnapped.
  = *The reporter **is thought to have been** kidnapped.*

11 TENSES AND VERB FORMS

11.1 Present tenses

11.1a Present Simple

We use the Present Simple to talk about

- general truths:

*Ice **melts** when it's heated.*

- activities that are repeated regularly:
  *I **drink** six cups of coffee every day.*

- permanent situations and states:
  *We **like** our neighbourhood.*

- future facts:
  *The concert **starts** at 7 p.m.*

11.1b Present Continuous

We use the Present Continuous to talk about:

- activities in progress at the time of speaking:
  A: Where are you?
  *B: **I'm having** a shower.*

- temporary routines or habits:
  *These days we**'re getting up** at 6 a.m. to go jogging on the beach.*

- arrangements for the future:
  *We**'re flying** back home on Friday.*

11.1c Present Perfect

We use the Present Perfect to talk about things that happened in the past when we look back on them from the present perspective.

- past events with consequences in the present:
  *The match **has been cancelled**. (We can't watch it.)*

- single or repeated events in the past when it doesn't matter when they happened:
  *I **have driven** a lorry. (at some time in my life)*

- past situations that continue up till now:
  *I**'ve lived** here all my life.*

11.1d Present Perfect Continuous

We use the Present Perfect Continuous to talk about:

- a repeated or continuous activity that started in the past and isn't necessarily finished:
  *Who **have** you **been going out** with recently?*

- an activity from the recent past which has consequences in the present:
  *She's **been peeling** onions. (... that's why she's got tears in her eyes.)*

11.2 Past tenses

11.2a Past Simple

We use the Past Simple to talk about single/repeated events in the past when we know when they happened:

*We **talked** to Peter after the prize-giving ceremony.*

*I **went** to the cinema a lot when I was at university.*

11.2b Past Continuous

We use the Past Continuous tense to talk about:

- activities that continued for some time in the past:
  *We **were dancing** all night.*
- activities that form a background to past events:
  *I **was thinking** about what I was going to do next when someone put their hand on my shoulder.*

11.2c Past Perfect

We use the Past Perfect to talk about an event or situation in the past which happened before another past event:

*We couldn't open the door because the caretaker **had put** a new lock on it.*

11.2d Past Perfect Continuous

We use the Past Perfect Continuous to talk about longer activities in the past that happened before another past event:

*I realised he **had been cheating** since the beginning of the game.*

11.3 Future

11.3a Present Simple

We use the Present Simple to talk about future facts, especially officially arranged events and timetables:

*My train **leaves** in twenty minutes and **arrives** in Paris at 10.30 a.m.*
*The UN Secretary-General **arrives** in Bucharest at 18.00 hours.*

11.3b Present Continuous

We use the Present Continuous to talk about future events that we have arranged:

*I'm **leaving** tonight.*
***Are** you **going** to school tomorrow?*

11.3c *to be going to*

We use *to be going to* + infinitive to express an intention:

*I'm **going to** relax more this year.*

or a prediction based on something we can observe:

*The meeting **is going to** take more time than expected.*

11.3d *will* + infinitive

We use *will* + infinitive to express a sudden decision made at the moment of speaking:

*I'll **get** in touch.*

to make a prediction based on our beliefs:
*They'll probably **forget** to bring the food.*
to make a request:
***Will** you **get** me 'The Independent' from the newsagent's?*

11.3e Future Continuous
(*will* + progressive infinitive)

We use the Future Continuous to talk about activities that will be in progress at a certain time in the future:

*At this time on Saturday I'll **be dancing** at your wedding.*
*We'll **be decorating** the Christmas tree in the morning.*

11.3f Future Perfect

We use the Future Perfect to talk about actions that will be completed before a certain time in the future:

*By the end of the month we **will have done** ten exams.*
***Will** you **have eaten** something by the time you get here?*

11.3g Time clauses

In time clauses referring to the future, after *when, as soon as, until, before* and *after*, we do NOT use *will*.

- We use the either the Present Simple:
  *When you **see** her, you'll see how much she's changed.*
- or the Present Perfect, if we want to emphasise the fact that this action will be finished before the other one happens:
  *When you'**ve finished**, I'll show you something.*
  *I'll finish this as soon as I'**ve made** myself a cup of tea.*

11.4 Progressive (continuous) tenses
and verb forms

We use the progressive/continuous rather than non-progressive aspect:

1 when we want to say that an activity is/was in progress at the moment of speaking and is/was not finished:

*The man **was buying** a newspaper.*
(He was in the process of buying it.)
*The man **bought** a newspaper.*
(He paid for it and walked away.)
*I've **been thinking** about your offer.*
(I'm still thinking about it.)
*I've **thought** about your offer.*
(I've finished thinking about it and I know what to do.)

2 when we want to suggest that an activity is temporary rather than permanent:

*My grandfather **was working** in this company during the war.* (only for some time)

*My grandfather **worked** in this company.* (permanently)

*We**'re playing** a lot of football this week.* (temporary activity)

*Michael Owen **plays** football.* (That's his permanent job.)

3 when we refer to a prolonged or repeated action rather than a single event:

*She **was nodding** throughout his speech.* (repeatedly)

*She **nodded** when I asked if she was OK.* (once)

*She**'s spoken** to me.* (once)

*She**'s been speaking** to me.* (for some time)

Apart from progressive (continuous) tenses (Present Continuous, Past Continuous, Present Perfect Continuous, Past Perfect Continuous, Future Continuous), we also use the progressive infinitive to express similar meanings:

*He seems **to be working** very hard.* (ordinary progressive infinitive) – describes an activity in progress at the time of the action expressed by the main verb.

*They were supposed **to be listening** to Mozart on the radio.* (ordinary progressive infinitive)

*He might **have been smoking** too much.* (perfective progressive infinitive) – describes a prolonged activity before the moment of speaking.

11.5 Perfective tenses and verb forms

We use the perfective aspect to say that something happened **before** a certain point in time:

*They**'ve been working** on this new type of engine for some time.* (before/until now)

*He **had left** before we managed to say goodbye to him.* (before a moment in the past)

*I **had been studying** English literature but I did my MA in Irish history.* (before a moment in the past)

*We **will have finished** this job by 10 p.m.* (before a moment in the future)

***Having walked** more than ten miles, I felt hungry and exhausted.* (before a time in the past)

*She must **have learned** her French in France.* (before now)

Apart from perfective tenses (Present Perfect, Present Perfect Continuous, Past Perfect, Past Perfect Continuous, Future Perfect), we also use other perfective verb forms.

1 Perfect infinitive (describes something that happened before the action expressed in the main verb):

*They seemed to **have lost** their way.* (ordinary perfect infinitive)

*She must **have been invited** by Jonathan.* (passive perfect infinitive)

2 Perfective *–ing* forms (describe actions that happened

before the action expressed in the main verb):

*I forgot **having eaten** all the strawberries.* (perfective gerund)

***Having parked** the car he took out the map of the area.* (perfective participle – written English)

12 VERB PATTERNS

12.1 *used to, be used to, get used to*

1 We use *used to* + infinitive to talk about things that happened regularly in the past and do not happen any more:

*I **used to watch** TV a lot.* (But now I don't.)

2 We use *be used to* + *-ing* form of the verb or a noun to say that we are very familiar with something:

*We**'re used to working** at night.*

*She**'s not used to standing** for so long.*

*We**'re used to the noise** of aeroplane engines above our house.*

3 We use *get used to* + *-ing* form of the verb or a noun to describe the process of becoming familiar with something:

*During the expedition we **got used to drinking** only boiled water.*

*I **couldn't get used to eating** a big breakfast when I first came to Britain.*

*When we moved to Australia, it took me some time **to get used to** the Australian accent.*

12.2 *see, hear, watch, notice*

1 We use the pattern *see/hear/watch/notice* somebody *do* something when we want to say that we witnessed the completed action and we know how it ended:

*I **watched** the burglars **enter** the house.* (I saw them inside the house.)

*We **heard** John **scream** 'Help' and then he disappeared.* (We heard the whole scream.)

2 We use the pattern *see/hear/watch/notice* somebody *doing* something when we want to say that we witnessed the action in progress:

*We **heard** him **singing** some old Frank Sinatra hits.*

*I **noticed** them **holding** hands in the cinema.*

CHECK YOUR GRAMMAR
Answer key

Module 2 page 27, 4

1 ⇨ Mini-grammar 11.2
2 worked/used to work 3 saw/had seen 4 used to watch
5 was performing 6 thought 7 had toured 8 had been
working 9 formed 10 made 11 appeared
12 accused/had accused 13 emigrated 14 lived

2 ⇨ Mini-grammar 11.1
1a 2b 3a 4b 5b 6a

3 ⇨ Mini-grammar 2
1 their 2 all 3 another 4 Such 5 Many 6 a 7 all 8 this
9 an 10 other 11 an 12 other

Module 4 page 57

1 ⇨ Mini-grammar 9
2a/b 3b/c 4a 5c 6a/b 7b/d 8a/b 9b 10c 11b
12a/b 13a/b 14b

2 ⇨ Mini-grammar 6, 7, 9
2 isn't anything that can
3 which I find most annoying
4 has been invited
5 that has
6 must be arrested
7 one takes regular exercise, one is
8 is being addressed

Module 6 page 87

1 ⇨ Mini-grammar 1, 11
2 spoke 3 (I)'ll/will be lying, listening 4 will have
published 5 wouldn't have felt 6 doesn't work
7 would have chosen 8 arrive 9 lived, would be
10 Will you be going/Are you going

2 ⇨ Mini-grammar 11
2b 3c 4a 5d 6a 7b 8c 9a 10c 11a 12b 13a 14b 15d

Module 8 page 117

1
1 travelling 2 to spend 3 to stay 4 spending 5 being
6 seeing 7 to travel 8 travelling 9 sleeping 10 eating
11 spending 12 to eat 13 living 14 to relax
15 changing

2 ⇨ Mini-grammar 10.2
1 (Sven complained) that the weather in England was
horrible.
2 (Sheila wanted to know) if I/we had travelled abroad a lot.
3 (Adam promised) to give it back tomorrow/the next/the
following) day. (Adam promised) that he would give it back
tomorrow,/the next/ the following day.

4 (The doctor told) me not to do any exercise and to sleep
flat on my back for two weeks.
5 (John wondered) if/whether I was planning to look for a
job abroad.
6 (Susan explained) that she couldn't tell me/us anything
because it was meant to be a surprise.
7 (The priest in Orvieto) was thought to be a saint.
8 (George offered) to do the shopping the next day if I didn't
feel like it.

3 ⇨ Mini-grammar 10.3, 11, 12
1 used to hate 2 are believed to have 3 threatened to use
the gun 4 (I)'m used to eating 5 has given up singing 6
can't stand everybody staring at me 7 you mind 8 has been
shown to cause natural disasters 9 risk being mugged

Module 10 page 143

1 ⇨ Mini-grammar 3, 8
1 If I were you, I'd stop worrying about your weight.
2 It was for only $100 dollars that the robbers killed three
people.
3 What I really enjoy are old Charlie Chaplin comedies.
4 It's high time the government reduced taxes.
5 I insist that you change your attitude to customers.
6 Hardly ever does the President attend these meetings.
7 I'd rather you didn't always leave a mess in the kitchen.
8 Not only did Nick spill red wine on my best suit, but he
(also) said it was my fault.
9 All Paul is interested in is sport.
10 Never have I seen a better performance.
11 You'd better get a taxi or you'll be late.
12 I suggest we start saving for a new car.
13 No sooner had we reached the mountain shelter than the
storm broke out.
14 Had he realised that the house was on fire he would have
run away.
15 Seldom are our politicians concerned with the problems of
the poor.
16 It was the theatre he invited me to, not the cinema.
17 When the children came in we had just managed to hide
the presents.
18 All they were expecting was a lift to the nearest town.
19 The captain demands that all passengers (should) switch
off their mobiles immediately.
20 You ought to do some sport.

2 ⇨ Mini-grammar 1, 8
2 didn't 3 was 4 have 5 were 6 would/'d 7 has/'s
8 hasn't 9 hasn't 10 had/'d 11 Having 12 be
13 time 14 is/'s 15 have/'ve 16 rather

Pearson Education Limited
Edinburgh Gate, Harlow
Essex CM20 2JE England
and Associated Companies throughout the world.

www.longman.com

© Pearson Education Limited 2006

First published 2002
Second edition 2006
Third impression 2007

Set in ITC Officina Sans 10.5/15.5pt

ISBN: 978-0-582-85422-2

Printed in Malaysia, LSP

Prepared for the Publishers by AMR Design Ltd
www.amrdesign.com

Illustrators
Jean de Lemos of GCI, Illustrated Arts, Maureen and Gordon Gray

Acknowledgements
We are grateful to the following for permission to reproduce
copyright material:

Atlantic Syndication Partners for an extract adapted from
'Marriage can wait' by Steve Doughty published in the *Daily Mail*
20th July 2001; Guardian Newspapers Limited for extracts
adapted from a speech by Robin Cook published on the *Guardian
Unlimited* website 19th April 2001, and 'Mice given extra gene
become smarter' by Tim Radford published in *The Guardian* 2nd
September 1999; Independent Newspapers (UK) Limited for an
extract adapted from 'Revealed: Darwin's grief over death of girl
destroyed his faith' by Anna Whitney first published in *The
Independent* 29th May 2001; Reed Business Information Limited
for extracts adapted from 'Karaoke cars' by Ian Sample published
on the *New Scientist* website June 2001, and 'Spinning a yarn for
miniature electronics' by Catherine Zandonella published on the
New Scientist website May 2001; Telegraph Group Limited for
extracts adapted from 'If you want to keep the traffic moving,
ban buses (and bicycles)' by Minette Marrin published in *The
Telegraph* 6th January 2001 © Telegraph Group Limited 2001, 'A
second chance of childhood' by Angela Neustatter published on

the *Electronic Telegraph* website 1st April 2000 © Telegraph Group
Limited 2000, and 'Mobile mania spreads as phones become the
must-have gadget' by Robert Uhlig published in *The Telegraph* 6th
January 2000 © Telegraph Group Limited 2000; Times Newspapers
Limited for an extract adapted from 'Let elephant live, say
victim's family' by Richard Duce published in *The Times* 9th
February 2000, © Times Newspapers Limited 2000; unit[e] for an
extract adapted from their Positive Futures leaflet published in
association with *The Guardian* Summer 2000; and The World Bank
for a graph showing population increases drawn from World Bank
data.

Acknowledgements
We are grateful to the following for permission to reproduce
copyright material:

Guardian Newspapers Limited for extracts adapted from 'Egypt
angered at artists' use of Nefertiti bust' by Jeevan Vasagar
published in *The Guardian* 12th June 2003 © The Guardian 2003
and 'Identity on the line' by Gary Younge published in *The
Guardian* 11th June 2003 © The Guardian 2003; Independent
Newspapers (UK) Limited for extracts adapted from 'Want to be
height of fashion? Then think cheap and go downmarket' by
Wayne Hemingway published in *Independent on Sunday* 8th June
2003, 'Taming the tortoise' by Jason Nissé published in
Independent on Sunday 6th April 2003 and 'It's a great theory,
but is it what nature had in mind?' by Laurence Phelan published
in *Independent on Sunday* 23rd February 2003; and Telegraph
Group Limited for extracts adapted from 'Japanese fall in love
with this little piggy' by Colin Joyce published in *The Weekly
Telegraph* issue no.597 © Telegraph Group Limited, 'How a posting
can change your outlook forever' by Joanna Parfitt published in
The Weekly Telegraph issue no.619 © Telegraph Group Limited and
'400,000 mobiles are disabled in battle against the muggers' by
John Steele published in *The Weekly Telegraph* issue no.607 ©
Telegraph Group Limited.

In some instances we have been unable to trace the owners of
copyright material and we would appreciate any information that
would enable us to do so.

Photo Acknowledgements
We are grateful to the following for permission to reproduce
copyright photographs:

AFP for page 32; Aldridge Press for page 50; John Birdsall Photo
Library for pages 40 and 76; Bubbles Photo Library for page 117
(photograph Peter Sylent); Bruce Coleman Collection for page 94
(photograph Werner Layer); Corbis for pages 60 and 72 (top,
photograph by Lynn Goldsmith); FLPA for pages 62 (photograph
D. and E. Hosking) and 74 (photograph M. Ranjit); Greg Evans
International for pages 14 and 86; Hemera Photo-objects for page
10; Image State for pages 66/7; The Kobal Collection for page 48
(photograph David Appleby); Nova for pages 35, 65 and 102; The
Photographers Library for pages 80, 85; Pictor International for
pages 2 and 41; Ronald Grant Archive for page 21; Silsoe
Research Institute for page 59.

KENSINGTON & CHELSEA

Map of the Royal Borough of Kensington and Chelsea.

KENSINGTON
& CHELSEA

BARBARA DENNY &
CAROLYN STARREN

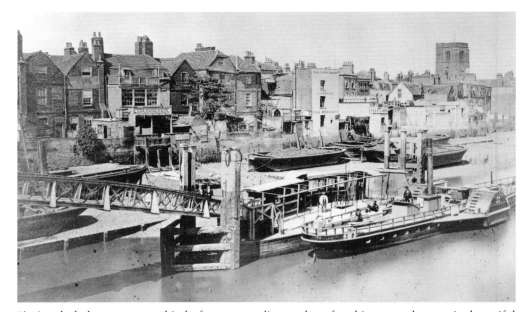

'A singularly heterogeneous kind of spot, very dirty and confused in some places quite beautiful in others' – this is how Thomas Carlyle described Chelsea in the 1830s, many years before this photograph was taken in 1870 by James Hedderley, the photographer-historian. He immortalized the Chelsea scene and particularly its riverside buildings such as the Adam and Eve inn (seen here third from the left). At much the same time the artist Daniel Maclise, describing the length of Cheyne Walk from Oakley Street to Milman Street, with its mixture of shops, houses and taverns, complained of loud-mouthed bargees, his neighbours' washing lines and crowing cocks.

First published in 1995
This edition published in 2009

The History Press
97 St George's Place,
Cheltenham Gloucestershire, GL50 3QB
www.thehistorypress.co.uk

Reprinted 2011, 2012, 2020

British Library Cataloguing in Publication Data.
A catalogue record for this book is available from the British Library.

ISBN 978 0 7524 5464 1

Typesetting and origination by The History Press
Printed in Great Britain by TJ Books Limited, Padstow, Cornwall

Contents

Acknowledgements and Bibliography

We would like to thank the following for their assistance in helping us to compile this book: the staff of Kensington and Chelsea Local Studies departments, and John Rogers for his photographic skills that made even the most faded image come alive. We would in particular like to acknowledge the contributions made by Prudential Assurance (p. 14), British Gas plc (p. 26), Kensington Housing Trust (p. 33), Mrs Thackray (p. 35), Eddie Adams (p. 38), Mrs Milne (p. 51) and Harrods (pp. 126–7). Most of all our thanks go to those, past and present, who have given their precious photographs, often anonymously, to both Kensington and Chelsea Local Studies and without whom there would be no book. In writing the captions we referred to the books listed below, most of which sadly are now out of print. However, they are available through the Royal Borough's libraries.

John Bignell, *Chelsea Seen from its Earliest Days*, Hale, 1987
Mary Cathcart Borer, *Two Villages: The Story of Kensington and Chelsea*, W.H. Allen, 1973
Harold Clunn, *The Face of London*, rev. edn, Spring Books, 1970
Barbara Denny, *Notting Hill and Holland Park Past*, Historical Publications, 1993
Sir Geoffrey Evans, *Kensington*, Hamish Hamilton, 1975
Thomas Faulkner, *History and Antiquities of Kensington*, 1820
Thomas Faulkner, *An Historical and Topographical Description of Chelsea*, 1829
William Gaunt, *Kensington and Chelsea*, Batsford, 1975
Florence M. Gladstone, *Notting Hill in Bygone Days*, Fisher Unwin, 1924
Thea Holme, *Chelsea*, Hamilton, 1972
Derek Hudson, *Holland House in Kensington*, Davies, 1967
W.J. Loftie, *Kensington Picturesque and Historical*, 1888
Survey of London, vols 37 (1973), 38, 41, 42 (1986)
Annabel Walker with Peter Jackson, *Kensington and Chelsea*, Murray, 1987

Introduction

The Royal Borough of Kensington and Chelsea, although a union born out of municipal conven-
ience, is so much more than that. It is Brompton and Notting Hill, the Boltons and Bayswater,
Holland Park, Earls Court, Campden Hill, World's End and the North Pole, St Quintin Park
and Hans Town, the Vale and all the other neighbourhoods which have grown out of either
administrative necessity, fashion or snobbery. Yet all these have come from the same beginnings,
settlements by the river, or on high ground deemed safe in Anglo-Saxon times, giving rise to the
names of Cealchythe or Celchyth – Chesil – a gravel bank, Chenesiton and Knotting Hill, after
their tribal overlords or their geographic nature, villages that expanded into 'towns' and merged
into each other yet retained something of their early identity. Even today, with no documented
or visible boundaries, they have kept their own character and are encouraged by the desire of
their residents to remain so.

If the 'birth' of an area can be dated at all, it might be by the establishment of its first place of
worship, around which the rest of it grew. For Kensington, then, it must be 1260, when the abbot
of the Benedictine Abbey of St Mary Abingdon established a church there, following the bequest
of land to his predecessors in Norman times by Aubrey de Vere. In Chelsea, the 'Old Church'
dedicated to All Saints also dated from the thirteenth century. Both original churches have, of
course, been rebuilt several times.

Change is inevitable in a living community, but the traveller who entered the district in those
days may well have journeyed by the same routes that have become our main roads. The Romans
dictated the first line from east to west, but even they had to accept the dictates of geography,
the streams and the hills, so that their highways have become ours, such as Bayswater Road and
Holland Park Avenue, with Kensington High Street as a diversion. Fulham and King's Roads
grew from the need of travellers wishing to reach a destination such as the Bishop's Palace (or
manor house) at Fulham or the royal palaces at Richmond and Hampton Court. From south to
north the ferries and fords, then the few bridges over the Thames, dictated the lines of the roads
that still cross the river.

Archaeological remains, historic buildings and artists' works are the only visual relics of the
development of the area, supported by documentary evidence. It was only in the mid-nineteenth
century that the photograph became the magic window through which the scenes of the past
could be preserved like a fly in amber. In fact the past is never easily wiped away; like a smear on
glass it may return even after the cloth has apparently wiped it clean. The fields go but the trees
live on in back gardens long after those who planted them are dead and forgotten, a road still
follows the same line because some medieval carter chose that way to ease the toil of his horse.

As little as two centuries ago, the mass of bricks and mortar which fills the 3,014 acres of the
Royal Borough today, with its contrasts and contradictions of commerce and culture, elegance
and depressing mediocrity, was a collection of rural communities set up round the houses of the
rich, aristocratic or merchant, already moving out from a noisy, polluted and crowded city centre.
First came the Tudors, Thomas More, then King Henry VIII himself, to a modest riverside palace
nearby in Chelsea, and the Earl of Shrewsbury and Lord Burleigh in Elizabethan times, before
royal favourite Walter Cope built his own 'castle' on Campden Hill which later became Holland
House, the home of the debonair turncoat Henry Rich, Earl of Holland, who lost his head in the
Civil War in 1649.

By then, the City merchant and moneylender, Baptist Hicks, later Lord Campden, had also built his stately home on Campden Hill, and by the end of the seventeenth century King William of Orange and Queen Mary set the royal seal on the area by choosing another nearby country house to be the new royal palace at Kensington.

Where the great and the good lead, the rest follow, and in the next hundred years the 'Old Court Suburb' and riverside Chelsea attracted their satellites and their servants. Although by the turn of the eighteenth century the court had left Kensington, it was still a royal residence and it was here that the young Princess Victoria lived for much of her childhood, the home she never ceased to regard with affection and on which she eventually bestowed the title of 'Royal'.

Then the railways came and with them streets lined with houses. Orchards were grubbed up, trees felled and pastures became building sites or brickfields.

When all has gone and the modern road is twice as wide (as in the case of Kensington High Street and Notting Hill Gate) it is difficult to believe that the very ground on which one is standing is the same as that where horses' hooves clattered over cobbles, carts rumbled and cattle were driven on the hoof to Smithfield Market.

Likewise, the heartland of Chelsea having moved from the riverside around the Old Church to the King's Road, it is practically impossible – even with the aid of the art works of James Whistler and the Greaves brothers – to imagine the wharves, alleys and pubs which clustered beside the water before being swept away by the construction of the embankment. 'Museumland', the proud memorial to Victoria's beloved Albert, survives almost intact, and much of Fulham Road is still strangely nineteenth-century.

In the north where the pigkeepers and scavengers, turned out from a smartening central London, had settled in Notting Dale, there came poverty and squalor as well as industry, gas works and factories, embarrassing those with plans to build mansions for the well-off on the rise of Ladbroke Hill and whose dreams have taken over a century to reach fruition.

But what really matters is people, and it is they who give life to the area, as the shades of their forebears give animation to the photographs of the past. A road sweeper stands for ever with his broom, sweeping the gutter in a high street which horse traffic could make impassable. A schoolgirl, with her violin in a case, crosses the street; a baker's boy pulls his handcart near a barrel organ long silenced; a little dog greets a Victorian lamp-post; a City gentleman goes smartly into the new station to catch a train to business.

Moments of ceremony and sorrow, the extraordinary and the mundane, are caught in the stance and expression of these people, often quite unaware that an unseen eye has focused upon them and an instant of their lives. It is they, as much as the setting in which they are playing a part, which can give this book the magic which it seeks to evoke.

Barbara Denny
April 1995

One

THE ROYAL BOROUGH

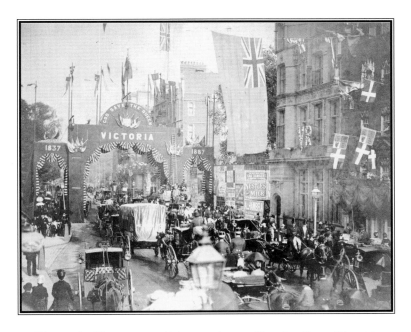

The parish of Kensington, which was to become 'Royal' at Queen Victoria's request, puts out the flags to celebrate her Golden Jubilee in June 1887. Fifty years earlier, at Kensington Palace, she had received the news that she was Queen, and she never lost her affection for the old palace which had been her childhood home. The buildings on the right of this photograph, including the Goat public house, are still recognizable today opposite the first gate into Kensington Gardens and the entrance to Palace Avenue. This section records the early years of the Royal Borough, highlighting the events and personalities which maintained its regal associations.

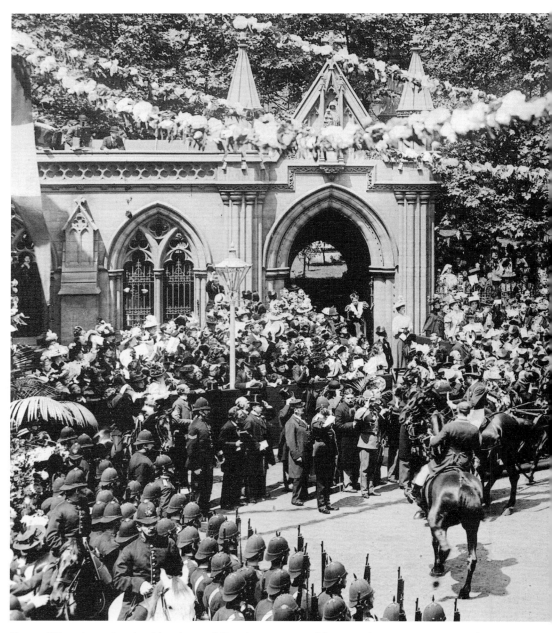

Queen Victoria maintained her love of Kensington into old age and on 28 June 1897, during the celebrations for her Diamond Jubilee, when she was seventy-eight, she paid a state visit to the place where she was born on 24 May 1819. Her carriage is seen here outside the cloistered entrance to St Mary Abbots Church on the corner of Kensington Church Street and the High Street, where the dignitaries waiting to greet her included her daughter Princess Louise and her husband the Marquess of Lorne, Lord and Lady Ilchester, West London MPs and the vicar, the Revd Canon Somerset Pennefather. Mr T. Wheeler, Chairman of the Vestry, presented an

address which a contemporary magazine described as 'slightly more original than usually is the case – to which the Queen gave a most gracious reply'. After receiving a bouquet from Princess Louise and one from Miss Beatrice Leete, daughter of Mr W. Chambers Leete, the Vestry Clerk, the Queen drove off to the chimes of the church bells and the music of military bands. The Royal carriage proceeded at a walking pace so that over 7,000 children from local orphanages, who had been allowed to watch the procession, could get a good view.

On 19 October 1904 Princess Louise unveiled the marble column erected by the people of Kensington at the junction of Kensington High Street and Church Street as a memorial to Queen Victoria. She is seen here being greeted outside St Mary Abbots Church by the Mayor, Cllr J.P. Williams, and aldermen and councillors of what had now become the Royal Borough of Kensington.

King Edward VII and Queen Alexandra driving through Holland Park Avenue on 26 May 1908 on their way to visit the Franco-British Exhibition at the White City, where they witnessed a pageant by Olympic athletes.

Queen Mary visiting Kensington on 22 April 1911 shortly before the Coronation. On her left is the Prince of Wales (later King Edward VIII) and facing them, the Earl of Shaftesbury and Prince Albert, Duke of York, who was later to become King George VI.

On 9 May 1937 Princess Louise planted a tree in the churchyard of St Mary Abbots to commemorate the coronation of her great nephew, King George VI. On her right is the vicar of Kensington, Prebendary Arthur E. Smith.

This postcard, dated 10 March 1905, shows the memorial to Queen Victoria, (designed by H.L. Florence) in more leisurely days, when policemen could stop for a chat without being distracted by traffic and small boys could lean on its base. The archway beyond remains today to the left of the church.

The widening of the High Street in 1934 necessitated the removal of the column from its original site to the northern end of Warwick Gardens. The space was originally intended to be the centre of a garden square until plans changed to give access to Pembroke Road.

King George V and Queen Mary visited Kensington as part of their Silver Jubilee celebrations on 8 June 1935 and are seen here arriving at Kensington Town Hall. Note the cavalcade of royal cars with their high roofs to accommodate the ornate millinery of royal ladies, the elaborate decorations and the fashions of the crowd (almost everyone is wearing a hat).

The east front of Kensington Palace as it appeared in 1898. On the right is the statue of Queen Victoria created by her daughter, Princess Louise, erected in 1893. The room on the lower floor, hidden by trees, was where the Queen was born in 1819; above it are the State Apartments.

View of Kensington Palace taken from the south-west across Palace Green, 1900. Behind the portico on the left is the Clock Court, one of the earliest parts of the palace, dating from the time of the alterations by Sir Christopher Wren and over the centuries the home of various members of the Royal Family up to the present day, including the late Princess of Wales, Princess Margaret and the Kents.

In 1895, at the express wish of Queen Victoria, this room in Kensington Palace where she was born, and which had been kept closed for years, was restored to its original appearance and opened to visits by special friends. Its modest, if not austere and rather dreary appearance, contrasts dramatically with the splendour of the Presence Chamber (below), as it appeared a few years later in 1898.

The talent of Princess Louise as a sculptress is evident from this 1900 photograph of her most permanent memorial, the statue of her mother, Queen Victoria, which stands to the north-east of Kensington Palace on the Broad Walk. The sixth child of Victoria and Albert, the Princess was described by the Queen as a 'clever dear girl'. In 1873 she married the Marquess of Lorne (later Duke of Argyll) but the union was not without difficulties and she spent time abroad when her husband was Governor General of Canada. The Princess lived at Kensington Palace from 1873 to her death in 1939 at the age of ninety-one. She worked on her sculpture in a studio in the walled garden of her apartments in the south-west corner.

This photograph shows the statue in 1905 (note the park keeper in pill box hat and brass buttoned coat). Princess Louise became a patroness of many charitable and social concerns in Kensington, especially the Children's Hospital in St Quintin Avenue, North Kensington, which bore her name, the Memorial Playing Fields and the 13th London Regiment of which she was Honorary Colonel. On 31 July 1928 she was made a Freeman of the Borough.

The famous statue of J.M. Barrie's 'Peter Pan' by Sir George Frampton had just been erected in Kensington Gardens when the postcard above was taken in 1912. The monument was set up in secret during the hours of darkness, on 30 April 1912, as if brought there by the fairies that clamber around its base, their heads finely polished by the hands of generations of children. The figure of Peter is said to be based on the six-year-old Michael Llewellyn Davis, one of the brothers who inspired Barrie to write his immortal story and whose guardian Barrie became after their parents' death. The lower picture, taken some eight years later in 1920, shows fashions of the time on summer strollers by the Long Water (the Serpentine).

Children with their nursemaid, shading from the summer heat in the shelter by the Palace Green entrance to Kensington Gardens in 1890, are among the thousands who have similarly sought respite there from sun or rain for over a century. Little has changed but the fashions in clothing and perambulators.

The Alcove, as seen in the 1890s, designed by Christopher Wren for Queen Anne, originally stood in Dial Walk facing Kensington Palace but now stands on the Bayswater boundary of Kensington Gardens. A romantic story is told that in May 1809 a notice appeared on its wall from a love-lorn gentleman begging a young lady he had parted from after a quarrel to contact him urgently.

St Govor's Well stood about 250 yards from the south end of the Broad Walk where these little boys are playing in 1890, but is now covered over. Its waters were supposed to possess medicinal qualities and it is quite likely that its source was connected to the spa which flourished near the gravel pits to the north in the early eighteenth century, where the 'purging waters' were likened to Epsom salts. The well became famous in the 1870s when a Mrs Lacy was given the right to sell water from it for a penny a glass. In 1875 an official enquiry decided the water was unwholesome, but it remained as a drinking fountain – which these boys are enjoying. St Govor was a Welsh saint and the naming of the well is thought to have been the idea of the first commissioner of works in 1855, Sir Benjamin Hall, later Lord Llanover of Lanore, in Monmouthshire, where St Govor founded a church.

The tea rooms in Kensington Gardens in Edwardian times when it was fashionable to be seen taking tea under the elms with service by smartly uniformed waiters and waitresses. A lady's day might well begin with coffee at Fortnums, shopping in Bond Street or Knightsbridge, lunch at the Ritz and tea in Kensington Gardens before a late afternoon visit to Hurlingham or Ranelagh to watch husband or fiancé playing polo. The tea rooms, with outdoor tables, were near the Albert Gate, not far from the Flower Walk and the bandstand where military music was played every summer afternoon and evening by Guards' bands. Leigh Hunt made an impressive list of those who might be seen strolling in the Gardens in 1791. Joseph Addison wrote in *The Spectator* of his admiration of Henry Wise's gardening expertise in 'turning the unsightly hollow of a gravel pit into so beautiful an area', but Sheridan, with classic wit, realized that not all sophisticated ladies feel at home amidst rural delights and has his Woman of Fashion complaining about the trees:

> . . . the spread of their leaves such a shelter affords
> To those noisy impertinent creatures called birds,
> Whose ridiculous chirruping ruins the scene,
> Brings the country before me and gives me the spleen.

The Round Pond, known officially as 'The Basin', edged here with serious Edwardian model yachtsmen, was one of the features created by two famous royal gardeners, Henry Wise for Queen Anne and his successor, Charles Bridgeman, Royal Gardener to Queen Caroline, Consort of George II. Official records recount that in 1726 'the Bason [sic] next to the Snailery was to be enlarged for Tortices' and to be 'raised so as to hold water 30 feet deep with a fence between the snailery and the tortoise place'. One can only speculate as to whether the occupants of these places were curiosities of natural history or intended for the palace menus!

The Serpentine, also seen in Edwardian days when nursemaids and their charges made up a large proportion of the park's visitors. The creation of the Serpentine, or Long Water, in 1730–1 was an enormous and costly enterprise involving vast excavations to transform pools in the Westbourne River into a lake. The bridge in the distance was built in 1826.

The Broad Walk (looking south, *c.* 1900) was also the creation of Charles Bridgeman. Fifty feet wide, leading from Kensington Gore to Bayswater Road, it became a fashionable promenade when the Gardens were opened to the public on Saturdays in the reign of George II when the court was at Kew. By the time of William IV they were open all the year round to 'respectably dressed persons'. In the 1930s the felling of the avenue of elm trees caused a public outcry.

Sheep were a familiar sight grazing in Kensington Gardens in the years both before and after the First World War. These four-legged lawn-mowers, with a phlegmatic attitude towards dogs, gave the park a pleasantly rural atmosphere.

Two

KENSAL AND NORTH KENSINGTON

When this aerial photograph of North Kensington and Kensal Green was taken in 1935 the area had probably reached the peak of its industrialization. Only the monuments in the cemetery of All Souls (bottom left) provide a corner of tranquillity along the snaking course of the Grand Union Canal. Railway lines, sidings and engine sheds fill the foreground, with the Gas Light and Coke Company's gasometer towering above their newly-built Kensal House flats, an experiment in working-class housing using gas power, with communal facilities such as a nursery and laundry. Large-scale slum clearance had only just begun. By a curious quirk of medieval land ownership, much of the area known as Kensal Town actually belonged to the parish of Chelsea until 1900.

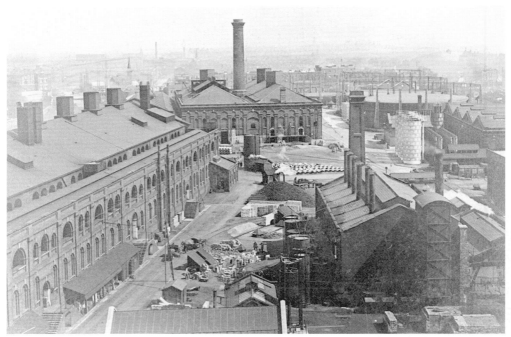

Kensal Green gas works in 1909, some half a century after the Western Gas Company had established their first works there in 1845, on land isolated by the east–west lines of the canal and the Great Western Railway. The gas works expanded westward until they occupied all the land west of Ladbroke Grove.

This gas worker with his horse and cart was photographed in 1907.

The Victorian 'North Pole' public house on the corner of Latimer and North Pole Roads, seen here in 1910. It replaced an earlier one-storey country inn of the same name, and earlier still The Globe, probably dating from about 1839 when the Hippodrome race course reached to this point. Until the 1860s the area was completely rural, first used for training horses as the Notting Hill Hunting Grounds, then for market gardens. Among the early developments was a terrace of cottages called the 'Sixteens', each with its pig sty and vegetable plot, but by the 1890s the area became known as Soapsud Island, owing to the large number of cottage laundries there. In this photo a watchful policeman and locals, with two ale delivery draymen, pose for the photographer.

Kensington Public Baths and Wash Houses on the corner of Lancaster and Silchester Roads, seen here in 1900 (above), were opened in 1888. The need for laundry facilities by a community where few homes had laid-on water is clear from the statistics – nearly 60,000 women used the laundry in 1897. Equally important was the opportunity to teach children to swim, and the London Swimming Association used the bath for their instruction programme, a session of which is shown below, *c.* 1898.

A cricket game in progress at St Charles College in St Charles Square in 1890. The college, founded in Bayswater by Dr Henry (later Cardinal) Manning in 1863 to provide a Catholic education for upper-class boys, was housed in this handsome building with its 140 foot tower. Damaged during the Second World War, it was demolished and the site used to build secondary schools.

The Oxford Gardens School cricket team with their master, c. 1892–5. The school originated in 1884 when some of the leading local tradesmen petitioned the school board to provide state-aided education for their children, but at a fee high enough to keep out poorer families! Oxford Gardens was therefore a 'sixpenny school' until fees were abolished in 1891.

Talbot Mews at the turn of the century when these backways, intended to accommodate the carriages, horses and coachmen of the wealthy residents of the area, had deteriorated due to the developers' financial failures into a squalid mixture of cramped dwellings, sheds and workshops. They would have horrified the Talbot family for whom the mews was named. They had been owners of the farmland here since the early eighteenth century, and the Misses Mary-Anne and Georgina-Charlotte Talbot found themselves in Victorian days the inheritors not of mere fields but of land highly desirable for the building of houses and the laying of railway tracks. Those railways spelt the death of the mews in places such as Notting Hill where even comparatively wealthy residents in Ladbroke Grove dispensed with carriages in favour of the train. In Inner London the 'carriage trade' lasted much longer. So for several decades, until the advent of the motor car, the mews had no purpose except to house the poor in conditions which had never been salubrious. Living in close proximity to horses, with all the attendant sanitary problems, is not as romantic or amusing as later developers might have one believe.

Silchester Road in the 1900s was a busy shop-lined highway striking west from Lancaster Circus, the junction of Walmer, Lancaster and Clarendon Roads, to Latimer Road. In the 1960s it was chopped off near to its meeting with Bramley Road (below), most of which also succumbed to the bulldozers. Both roads were named for the Hampshire associations of their developer, James Whitchurch, a lawyer from Southampton.

31

Kenley Street (formerly William Street) in its last days before redevelopment in 1904. From the 1820s the arrival of the piggeries and potteries (brick-making) made the 'Dale' a slum. In 1904 Kenley Street was the scene of one of the first improvement schemes of the newly created Royal Borough. Active in both the planning and financing was Sir Henry Seymour King, the first mayor, who actually made a large interest-free loan of his own money so that the tumbled down properties could be bought. In the lower picture, Lady King is seen performing the opening ceremony (with the Mayor, Cllr J.P. Williams, on the left) on 8 November 1904, after the buildings had been refurbished, or demolished and rebuilt.

Two photographs of Crescent Street
(now the site of Henry Dickens Court)
in the 1930s, its last days before it was
swept away in the borough's pre-war
slum clearance plan. In 1893 a journalist
writing in the *Daily News* described life
there and in adjacent streets as 'these
wretched places where life is more
hopeless and degraded and abandoned
than anything in London'. Together with
neighbouring Bangor Street (famed for its
rag fair) and Sirdar Road, Crescent Street
was massively over-occupied with families
of six or seven living in one room, or
houses let as the lowest of lodgings where
a bed on the floor cost a penny a night
and sanitation was at its minimum.

This religious street procession celebrated the opening of St Columb's, the new High Anglican church in Lancaster Road, a mission church to neighbouring All Saints, in 1900. When the two churches amalgamated in 1951 the building became the Serbian Orthodox Church of St Sava.

Golborne Road, seen here in 1900, was intended for better things in a district called Portobello Park, but plans changed: the intended canal bridge never materialized and second-rate developers moved in.

Newspaper bill boards date this photograph of a shop front at Barton's newsagents, Lancaster Road, to 1912: 'Titanic Survivors', '200 Dead in Carpathia'. Daniel John Barton ran his tobacconist business at 161 Lancaster Road from 1909 to 1919. Lancaster Road was part of the widespread business interests of a famous – or infamous – Victorian property developer, Charles Henry Blake, whose later enterprises included not only house-building but investment in railways. Perhaps he sought to balance his more dubious activities by contributing to the foundation of no less than four churches in fifteen years – St John's on Ladbroke Hill, St Mark's, St Peter's in Kensington Park Road and St Michael and All Angels in Ladbroke Grove.

Ladbroke Grove in 1866, spanned by the new bridge of the Hammersmith and City railway opened only two years earlier, linking the area with the City via Paddington. Until then development in this northern end of the Grove had been sparse (as can be seen beyond the bridge) but now advertisements for the new houses could describe their 'most convenient situation' with speedy access to all parts of London for sixpence return!

Work proceeding on the new bridge in 1938 when it became the first all-welded steel plate girder bridge to be built in England. In the 1860s hundreds of imported navvies had built the first viaduct on this spot across the swampy land of Notting Dale.

Ladbroke Grove at its junction with Holland Park Avenue *c*. 1900 (above), when a horse-drawn cab rank awaited the requirements of the affluent residents who occupied the grand houses up to the crest of the hill. St John's Church spire can be seen in the distance. Just how affluent is made plain by the interior (below) of No. 42 Ladbroke Grove in 1915. These semi-detached houses were built *c*. 1845 as part of the scheme to create a neighbourhood comparable with Cheltenham or Regents Park.

Portobello Road *c.* 1900, when the street that was to become a tourist attraction sixty years later was still a line of homely shops, with the stalls confined to a small section, and selling mostly foodstuffs. In its earlier days the market functioned only on weekdays until the stallholders won over the Vestry to allow trading six days a week. Earlier still, Portobello Lane, which passed through fields of barley, was described as 'one of the pleasantest rural walks in London, with nothing to be heard in the tranquil silence but the notes of the lark, the linnet and the nightingale'.

A.J. Symons' newsagents and confectioners at No. 281 Portobello Road. The *Daily News* bill boards announcing the historic boxing match ('Carpentier's Defeat: Dramatic Scenes') date this photograph to 1924. Street betting was illegal but Racing Advice gives the tip for the day – Miss Megan 10 to 1. The business moved away in the early thirties.

Kensington Park Road on a sunny summer day, *c.* 1905, brings out the fashionable lady with her parasol and boater-hatted escort as they approach St Peter's Church near the junction of Stanley Gardens. Both streets were fashionable addresses in the Edwardian era. The novelist Katherine Mansfield and the man she eventually married, John Middleton Murry, lived at No. 95 Elgin Crescent. Kensington Park Road was the home of poster artist John Hassall for many decades, in a house later occupied by his equally talented daughter, Joan Hassall, and his son, the poet and lyricist Christopher Hassall.

Leafy Elgin Crescent on a postcard dated 1908 as a mother, or nanny, takes a chubby toddler for an afternoon walk.

This section of Westbourne Grove, near its junction with Kensington Park Road, seen here *c.* 1905, was known as Archer Street until comparatively recent times. It was named for G.S. Archer, the Kentish absentee landlord of the old 'Barley Shots' fields on which development began in the 1860s.

All Saints Road *c.* 1900, when Thomas's Dairy sold eggs at 8*d* a dozen and country milk direct from the farm, and before the street became infamous in the Rachmanism era of the 1950s and '60s.

An early twentieth-century view of the junction of Westbourne Grove with Pembridge Villas and Chepstow Road, once known as 'Bradley's Corner' (from the fashionable furriers on the corner of Chepstow Place). The early success of the area resulted largely from the foresight of its 1844 developers who laid nearly 5,000 feet of sewers to provide modern amenities for the attractive houses. The 1861 census reveals that most of the households in nearby Pembridge Gardens had at least three servants and the occupants included merchants, stockbrokers, surveyors and a colliery owner. In Pembridge Square the number of servants often exceeded that of the family itself with not only a cook, butler and lady's maid but a footman and page. The west end of Westbourne Grove, then known as Archer Street, was a shopping centre for these fashionable folk, the traders including a milliner, dressmaker, hairdresser, stay warehouse and clockmaker.

Three

NOTTING HILL

*Notting Hill Gate near the junction of Linden Gardens and the Mall in
1908, where only the vintage vehicles date a scene which was to remain
virtually unchanged until the brutal redevelopment of the 1960s. Even now
the north side retains the old shopfront lines and Blands umbrella factory
survived until the 1980s. The High Street was on the line of the Roman
road to Silchester, later known as 'the way to Uxbridge'. Even by the mid-
eighteenth century, with gravel pits on either side and only a cluster of
houses, it hardly merited the description of a village. The 'Gate' originated
from the toll gate set up by the Turnpike Trust, situated approximately at
the present junction with Pembridge Road, an unpopular institution only
removed in 1864. It was not until the coming of the Metropolitan 'Circle
Line' railway in 1868, that its transformation into a shopping centre began.*

The north side of Notting Hill Gate *c*. 1900, showing The Plough, the Victorian successor of an ancient coaching inn, and the shop terrace which was demolished in the 1960s to provide the site for Campden Hill Towers.

This 1905 view of Notting Hill Gate looks west from the junction with Ossington Street (on the right) with the Champion public house and Wellington Terrace. The latter was a row of shops which originated when the building of the Metropolitan Railway led to redevelopment, sweeping away the tumbled down cottages of Campden Place in the 1870s.

The Coronet Theatre, Notting Hill Gate, at the height of its splendour in Edwardian days when its stage was graced by stars such as Henry Irving. Converted to a cinema in 1921, it was saved from demolition in the 1980s by public campaigns.

On 1 February 1918 Princess Louise, Duchess of Argyll, visited the Coronet Theatre to inaugurate Kensington's War Savings week. She is seen here being received by (left to right) Mr Austin Chamberlain, Lord Claud Hamilton, MP for South Kensington, and the Mayor of Kensington, Sir William Davison.

Linden Gardens in 1907 retained much of the leafy charm it had in its early Victorian days when it was known as Linden Grove. Among its famous residents were two artists, the Royal Academician Thomas Creswick and William Mulready. It was here that Mulready designed the first penny postage envelope depicting Britannia sending out messages world wide. When Thomas Creswick moved from 42 Linden Grove into Mulready's house in 1866 it was taken by the actor Alfred Wigan and was used for the wedding reception of Sir Henry Irving.

The Central Line station at Notting Hill Gate, the 'Twopenny Tube', shortly after its opening in 1900. The first tube railway of the modern type, it ran from Shepherds Bush to the Bank for the flat fare of twopence, hence its nickname.

The building of the Metropolitan Railway station at Notting Hill Gate in 1868 (above) when the line was extended from Paddington to South Kensington via Bayswater and Notting Hill, using tunnels under many of the newly-built houses. Below, as the station appeared in 1905. When its first section from Farringdon Street to Paddington opened five years earlier it was the first underground railway in the world. In the 1950s it was demolished and replaced by an underground concourse linking access to the Metropolitan, Inner Circle, District and Central lines.

The junction of Pembridge Road with Notting Hill Gate in 1905. The Edwardian fashions, a horse-drawn delivery van and handcarts turn back the clock on the building line that is practically the same today, although the traders have changed. On the opposite side of the street (below) there is a different story: a modern block has replaced Barnham and Marriages, tea and coffee importers, Adams Butchers and Goodmans Teeth, with a W.H. Smith – only the Prince Albert remains.

Norland Square, seen here at the beginning of the twentieth century, was the darling of its developer, the wealthy solicitor Charles Richardson, in the 1840s. He lived there himself, at No. 29, arranging for the maintenance of the garden, street repair and cleaning, and mains water, as he did with his other interests, St James Gardens and Royal Crescent. The aerial view (below) shows the latter, with the roller skating rink (the site of which is now a Hilton Hotel) in the foreground.

AIR VIEW OF WEST KENSINGTON

49

Horse buses in Holland Park Avenue at the turn of the century (above) share the highway with a cyclist as two little boys idle their way to school. In the same road at roughly the same date (below), looking north towards Notting Hill Gate from the entrance of Campden Hill Square, a nanny keeps up a brisk pace with her charges as elegant ladies stroll behind.

Holland Park in its Edwardian heyday – its magnificence still hardly altered since it was built in the 1860s. 'Good and substantial dwellings' was the insistence of its owner, Lord Holland, to the developer 'and all large trees to be preserved'. Some idea of their size and elegance is given by the view (below) of the garden at the rear of No. 80 in which their developer, William Radford, once lived with his family.

One of the last of the old shops in Uxbridge Street to go in recent times was Wittekind's, the bakers, in family ownership since its founders, Adam and Teresa Wittekind, came from Germany in Victorian times. They are seen here with their staff in 1906.

Not far from the Wittekind's shop was Dartmoor Street (now Hillgate Place), which shared the reputation of its neighbour, Johnson Street (now Hillgate Street), as 'a dingy ill-favoured slum', according to the vicar of St George's Church who appealed for the relief of its inhabitants. It is seen here in 1906.

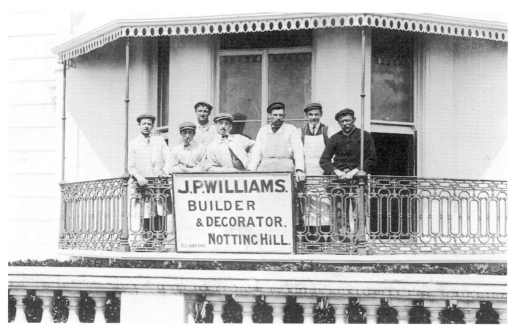

Times were changing – forty years or more separate this picture (above) of workmen employed by J.P. Williams, the builders and decorators, at work on a Notting Hill villa in 1920 and that (below) where the old shops and cottages on the north-west corner of Kensington Church Street were being demolished in 1879 to make way for the building of the new Board school, itself later demolished in the 1950s for the Notting Hill redevelopment. (J. P. Williams, builders, were established at 87 Lancaster Road *c.* 1890 and continued in business until the mid-1960s.)

Bullingham Mansions in Kensington Church Street *c.* 1903, with a carriage waiting outside. The flats were built in 1894 on the site of the house where it is popularly supposed Sir Isaac Newton lived his last years. On the east side of Church Street was glebe land of the vicar of Kensington (land assigned to the incumbent as part of his benefice) and until 1877, when it moved further to the east, a vicarage was situated at the junction with Vicarage Gate. In 1954 the Church Commissioners purchased the freehold, apart from the vicar's house and garden. Winchester Court was built in 1935 on the site, previously occupied by a large house which was converted into a convent in 1851 and later became the Orphanage of St Vincent de Paul.

This view as Church Street goes downhill towards the High Street shows the Roman Catholic Carmelite church on the right (destroyed in the Second World War and rebuilt), and in the distance the newly-built spire of St Mary Abbots, *c.* 1879. When Father Herman (Cohen), a Jewish convert to Catholicism, came to London in 1862 he rented a house in Church Street on the site of today's Newton Court. In 1865 he bought the land opposite for £3,500 on which the Church of Our Lady of Mount Carmel and St Simon Stock was built. Ten years later, the community extended its land to the west and it was here that the Carmelite Monastery (an enclosed order) was built in 1886, connected to the church by a corridor.

Four

HOLLAND PARK AND CAMPDEN HILL

Holland House c. 1900, the stately home of historic families since Jacobean times when the extravagant mansion was known as 'Cope's Castle'. It was created for Sir Walter Cope, one of the richest men in the land, property dealer, entrepreneur and money-lender; it went on to become the home of the turncoat Henry Rich, Earl of Holland. Although he lost his head in the Civil War the house remained in his family's possession until the eighteenth century, when it was the hub of social and political life in the ownership of the Fox family. It had seen drama, intrigue, romance and scandal in an elegant setting until the night of 27/28 September 1940 when it was disastrously damaged during an air raid. At one time it seemed this was the end but a vigorous campaign of public opinion saved what was left. The east wing was restored as the King George VI Memorial Youth Hostel, and the extensive grounds became one of the most attractive public parks in London.

The West Room of Holland House in 1886 when it had become the home of Lord Ilchester, a distant relative of the Fox family, and once again became the scene of balls, garden parties and lavish entertainment, in a setting of sedate opulence.

At about the same time, gardeners with a donkey-drawn mower tend the lawn outside the garden ballroom. The ballroom (now the Belvedere Restaurant) was converted from the granary in 1849; it was reached from the house by the cloistered walk and terrace above, and was adjacent to the orangery, now a venue for concerts and art shows.

It would be hard to convince today's occupants of Oakwood Court, Addison Road, that the extensive gardens and lake of Oak Lodge, seen here in 1894, stood on the site of their flats at 25 Addison Road. The site of the house had been bought from the Holland estate in the 1850s and sold again in 1862 to James McHenry who extended its grounds, making the lake out of the Old Moats fishponds of Holland House. In 1873 he offered to buy the whole of the Hollands' remaining estate from Lady Holland, who was in serious financial difficulties from both her lavish lifestyle and the maintenance of the property, but she instead passed the inheritance over to Lord Ilchester, who would in any case have received it on her death, and the beautiful remnant of another age was preserved. A plate on the wall of 13 Melbury Road inscribed 'J McH 1877' marks the boundary of McHenry's land, which in its turn was sold for the building of Oakwood Court in 1900. St Barnabas Church, consecrated in 1829, can be seen in the background.

In 1906 Holland Walk was as popular with young mothers and their babies as it is today, although fashions have changed in perambulators. A right of way since 1848, it has sometimes been disputed but has endured, despite threats of closure, or conversion to a traffic highway.

Duchess of Bedford Walk in 1930 when it was still no more than a leafy byway leading from Holland Walk between the boundary fences of secluded villas to Bedford Lodge, home of the Duke and Duchess of Bedford from 1823 to 1853. Bedford Lodge, later renamed Cam House, was demolished in 1955.

The site of Bute House, seen above in 1912, is now largely covered by the Queen Elizabeth College on Campden Hill. Built in 1812, its first resident was Richard Gillow, probably a member of the cabinet makers Waring and Gillow, but its name commemorated a later occupant (1830–42), the Marquess of Bute. The University of London took a 999-year lease of the site in 1914, after the house had been demolished, for its King's College women's department. The college, now renamed for Queen Elizabeth II, also swallowed up neighbouring Thornwood Lodge in 1956. The picture below shows the site during demolition.

Lord Leighton (1830–96), the Victorian artist *par excellence*, whose first Royal Academy painting (bought by the Queen) was hung when he was twenty-five, and who became President of the Royal Academy in 1878. His friendship with the fourth Lord Holland, which brought him often to Holland House, obviously inspired his choice of Kensington for the house which he envisaged as 'meeting the needs of a working painter with a lofty studio'. 'I am indeed truly sorry to hear of Lord Holland's death,' he wrote to his mother in 1859. 'Nothing could exceed his kindness to me.'

Five years later he obtained a 99-year lease from Lady Holland for the site in Holland Park Road to build his dream home, designed by his friend, George Aitchison. This view of the entrance hall in 1897 shows that despite his desire for a working home, he ornamented it with exotic décor, tiling and stained glass. Leighton House was much smaller as first planned in 1866 (only one bedroom was included in the plan to discourage guests who might interrupt the artist's work!), and the famous Arab Hall, intended to display his marvellous collection of tiles, was not created until 1877.

No black and white photograph can convey the extraordinary wealth of colour in the black and gold lacquered woodwork and ornate furnishings of Leighton House, seen here *c.* 1890s. It was the work of such contemporaries as Walter Crane, William De Morgan and Randolph Caldecott. After Leighton's death in 1896 several attempts were made to purchase the house for the nation, but it was not until 1926 that the freehold was acquired by Kensington Borough Council. It is now open to the public as well as being used for various exhibitions and concerts.

Campden House, seen here in an impression of its early splendour *c.* 1800, was built in 1612 for Baptist Hicks, later Viscount Campden, who as a city financier 'knew how to amass money and spend it'. The estate is bounded today by Sheffield Terrace, Hornton Street and Kensington Church Street. When Viscount Campden died in 1629 he left £200 for the poor of Kensington; as the Campden Charities, this has grown into many millions and benefited innumerable good causes.

His descendants retained the house until 1708 when it was sold and used as a girls' boarding school, seen here in an early lithograph which gives some idea of its lavish décor.

In 1691 Campden House was let for a while to Princess (later Queen) Anne and Prince George of Denmark. Returning to private occupation its residents included Mr William Wolley, who built a private theatre there in which Charles Dickens acted in *The Lighthouse* in 1854. Then disaster struck: in 1862 the house was burned down. The photograph shows fire officials surveying the gutted ruins. Although a similar, and perhaps even more ornate, house took its place, it had a short life and was demolished in 1900. The site was used to build Campden House Court flats.

Hornton Street, shortly before this terrace was demolished in 1903 and replaced by the present houses on the east side. This area is on the Phillimore estate, in the ownership of the family of that name since the early eighteenth century. The west side of Hornton Street kept the charm of its earlier life until the new town hall was built in 1972, for here was the Red House, later occupied by Herbert Hoover, who became President of the USA and who described it as 'a house with a quaint garden in the middle of a great city'. Its next-door neighbour, Niddry Lodge, was named for its second occupant in the 1840s, the Dowager Countess of Hopetown, whose husband, the 5th Earl, was also Baron Niddry.

Sir James South (1785–1867), the astronomer who bought the mansion which had once been the home of the Phillimores in 1827, constructing an observatory in the garden. Throughout his residence he refused to allow a road to be built near his house for fear that the vibration from traffic would interfere with his astronomical observances; Campden Hill Road was only opened at its southern end in 1867 after his death. He is seen here in the 1860s with his dog, Tiger.

Holland Street in 1909, when its traders included a dairy, a tailor's and a cycle shop. Known as Parsons Yard in the eighteenth century, it was a public way leading from Church Street to Holland House.

The building of Holland Street began as early as 1724 and continued throughout the next century, and in 1846 a developer built two houses on one of the remaining vacant plots, one of which, No. 15, was occupied by the poet Jean Ingelow (1820–97) (right). The site is now a block of flats named after her. The west side of this faces Kensington Church Walk, which had existed as a cartway to the parsonage since at least 1726. In 1767 the vicar agreed to allow the Vestry to make it a public pathway through the churchyard, but it was not extended to Kensington High Street until 1914.

Tower Cressy in 1930, the fanciful folly built in Aubrey Road, on Campden Hill, by the Victorian engineer Thomas Page, the year after the opening of the Great Exhibition in 1852–3. It survived until hit by a flying bomb during the Second World War, and was then demolished. Thomas Page, who built Westminster Bridge and the Albert Embankment, intended his romantic castle home to be a tribute to the Black Prince, whose emblems appeared on each storey above the arched doorway. Dr Christopher Dresser, the decorative designer, lived here with his wife and thirteen children between 1869 and 1882.

Five

KENSINGTON HIGH STREET

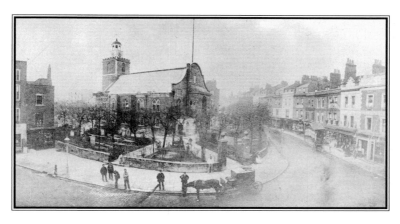

St Mary Abbots Church in 1860, a few years before the late seventeenth-
century building was demolished, an event which marked the end of the
'village' character of old Kensington. The 'High Street' was becoming too
narrow for the increasing traffic and there were constant complaints about
its poor lighting. The handsome new Vestry Hall nearby provided a striking
contrast to the shabby church, which, although rebuilt in 1696, had a
history of constant repair, possibly due to undermining by the vaults still
below it, or Kensington's unstable gravel soil. There had been a church on
the site since medieval times, and although the old tower had been retained
it had to be replaced in 1722. The growing population was also putting an
enormous physical strain on the structure, said in one report to be visibly
bulging, and in 1866 it was declared unsafe with dry rot in the beams.
Demolition began in 1869 and Sir George Gilbert Scott was appointed
architect of the church as we know it today.

This must be one of the last photographs of the old church before its demise, showing the west front and tower in 1865. Its end was controversial, criticized as extravagance by some people and as being undertaken not a day too soon by others. The *Kensington News*, for instance, declared that 'if something was not done quickly the voice of prayer would be changed to cries of terror as its frequenters were buried beneath its ruins'!

On Ascension Day 1869 the church held its last services. A few days before the demolition began the Cumberland Society rang a farewell on the bells, a ten-part peal of grandsire triples. This was followed by another marathon peal on the anniversary of the Queen's coronation; the bells were taken down the following day, 29 June 1869.

On 14 May 1872 the new church was consecrated – though without its landmark spire. This photograph was taken some weeks earlier when the site was still sealed off and the churchyard gate taken over by flyposters advertising *Sporting Opinion* and other racing journals! The spire, the highest in London and the sixth highest in England, was not completed until 1879, and the south porch and cloisters until 1893. The final stone of the spire was laid by the vicar, the Revd the Hon. Edward Carr Glyn who, with twelve parishioners, two church wardens and a correspondent of *The Times*, climbed the scaffolding by a series of ladders and held a service 264 feet above the crowd below. It was a blustery day and *The Times* reported that the scaffolding was swaying 'slightly but perceptibly in the wind'. Mr Carr Glyn nevertheless laid the capstone safely in position and blessed the 14 foot metal cross.

These new bells were added to the peal in 1879. They bear the inscription 'Those evening bells, how many a tale their music tells' and (the smaller bell) 'Invite. Warn. Rejoice. Mourn.' Standing proudly by are (left to right) Mr Reuben Green, vestry clerk, and Mr Robert Henry Pearson and Mr Jubal Webb, church wardens, whose names are also engraved on the bells.

The 278 foot spire houses the peal of ten bells, on which the church clock chimes the hours and quarters, although there is no visible clock face because it was thought it might spoil the look of the spire. The invisible clock mechanism was exhibited at the Universal Exhibition in 1862. In this picture, dated 1892, intrepid steeplejacks can be seen carrying out repairs on the spire. Of the older bells, some had already been recast in 1772 and some had to be recast in 1872. Among the inscriptions on these is the curiously pagan reference 'The ringers' art our grateful notes prolong, Apollo listens and approves the song'. The ringers' art is often heard from the belfry and celebration peals have been rung on occasions such as royal births.

St Mary Abbots School, Group I, in 1900 (above), with their teacher Miss Jewell. This photograph was supplied to Kensington and Chelsea Libraries by Walter Brown, who is seen next to her (in a sailor suit). His father was a coachman and the other children all come from local tradesmen's families. The school met at the Mission Hall in South End. The school in 1924 (left) appears much as it does today, including the painted wooden figures of a boy and girl which have decorated its entrance for nearly 300 years. The school has its roots in the days of Queen Anne, occupying a building designed by Nicholas Hawksmoor in the High Street in 1711, until the Victorian Town Hall took the site in 1871.

In 1880 Kensington Vestry Hall still
retained much of the splendour of
the time of its building some thirty
years earlier in 1851 when ratepayers
had complained of its extravagant
embellishments such as gilded
railings and chandeliers. Until then
the Vestry men had met in the parish
room. After the building of the Town
Hall in 1880 the railings and gate
piers were moved, and in 1889 it
became the central library. With the
creation of the new library in 1960,
it was taken over by the Melli Bank.

13th London Regiment (Princess Louise' Kensington Regiment) parading outside Kensington
Town Hall on 9 August 1914, five days after the declaration of the First World War, and handing
over the regimental colours to the mayor, Sir William Davison MP, for safe custody before leaving
for France. There they suffered terrible losses in the early years of the 'Old Contemptibles'.

The first scaffolding goes up in 1905 for the building of Hornton Court (above). The demolition reveals 'The Abbey', the eccentric Gothic folly built by William Abbot in Victorian times which, after extensive air raid damage in the Second World War, became the site of the new library. The architect of Hornton Court, built in 1907 (seen below), was Frank Sydney Chesterton, of Chesterton and Sons, a relation of the famous G.K. Chesterton. Frank Chesterton died in action in the First World War.

Chesterton's premises on the corner of Campden Hill Road and the High Street in 1909. The family firm had links with the Phillimore family, and this section of Lower Phillimore Place survived until 1931 when it too was redeveloped as modern flats, Phillimore Court.

Holland Park Dairy in its last days, *c.* 1914. As Holland House estate became more built up, the owners of Holland Park Farm were allowed to build a new dairy and cow sheds on the corner of Melbury Road. Although the cows left, the building, which was designed to match the nearby lodge houses, survived in use as a United Dairies shop until the 1960s redevelopment.

The 'big cheese' (in every sense) of Victorian Kensington must be Jubal Webb, the cheesemonger, whose shop was already well established next to St Mary Abbots Church in 1869. Flamboyant, publicity-seeking entrepreneur, leading vestryman and church warden, his telegraphic address was Gorgonzola, London. He is seen here with the giant cheese he exhibited at the Chicago World Fair in 1893, which weighed 207,250 pounds! In 1886 Jubal Webb moved to The Terrace (now 129–61 Kensington High Street) which ran from Wrights Lane to Adam and Eve Mews. Dating from 1690, its residents included Henry Cole, William Banting, the dietician, and artists David Wilkie and John Leech. In 1892 Webb bought the whole four and a quarter acre estate, presented a strip of the frontage to the Vestry to widen the road, and built Iverna Gardens behind.

Gardeners Buildings, seen here in its last days *c.* 1865, was one of the tumbled down yards in Market Court which originated in the 1770s behind the frontage of the High Street. They were all swept away by improvements and road widening in the 1870s. Despite its appearance, this court was not as notorious for evil living conditions as the other rookery buildings further east, notably Jennings Buildings. The 1851 census shows that over half of its residents were Irish, mostly from County Cork. Their occupations were typical and included 62 labourers, 58 women who worked in the neighbouring market gardens, 27 laundresses and 28 washerwomen (though one doubts, given the appalling sanitary conditions, how they managed to ply their trade) and 44 street traders. The area was condemned by all but neither the Vestry nor the negligent landlord took action.

From 1889 the big Kensington stores, Barker's, Derry & Tom's and Ponting's, had to compete with Pettit's and W.H. Hunt & Co. on the corner of the High Street and Allen Street, seen here in 1900. In 1919 Barker's, who wished to expand, offered £40,000 for Hunt's but were refused. The shop closed in 1923 when The Terrace was redeveloped, apart from the corner premises which can still be identified.

In 1923 the site of the Odeon Cinema was still Leonard's Place, an early nineteenth-century development. First to go were the houses removed for the premises of carriage builders which later became the motor sales and works of Strachan and Brown and then, in 1924, the Kensington Kinema was built, the largest cinema in England, seating 2,350 people. This later became the Majestic and then the Odeon.

In 1920, before the drastic reconstruction of the store which changed the whole face of the High Street, Barker's Tea Room, with potted plants and uniformed waitresses, served 'New Jersey sundaes' for a shilling to summer shoppers.

The Town Hall Tavern, seen here in 1890, was built in 1871 on land surplus to the building of the station. Known originally as the Duke of Abercorn, it survived until 1912 and the expansion of Derry & Tom's. The gateway on the right led to Francis Tucker & Co., the famous Roman Catholic family of candlemakers, whose factory was situated behind this frontage (the chimney can be seen on the right), where it had been since the 1760s. Although going into voluntary liquidation in 1908, their name was retained by Price's, who took the business over. The archway next to Tucker's became the entrance to a Lyon's tea shop.

Work began on Kensington High Street station in 1865 and the enormous 90 foot wide roof span seen here was completed two years later. The arrival of the trains set the seal on the High Street's potential as one of London's most popular shopping centres. The area to the west of the station was the home from 1821 to 1835 of William Cobbett, the radical journalist, who set off from here on his famous 'Rural Rides'.

In 1909 times were changing in the High Street, especially on the south side. Some of the businesses here, such as Keith Prowse, survived in new premises, but by the 1960s most of the terrace was taken over by Kensington Market.

The north side of Kensington High Street in the 1880s (above), where a variety of buildings and traders provided an interesting row of shops from photographic studios to provision stores. Decorations for Queen Victoria's Golden Jubilee in 1887 (right) enliven the Duke of Cumberland, Wells the jeweller's and a florist's. The whole of this side of the High Street was demolished for road widening in 1903 and advertised as a building site by the Crown Commissioners, but there were no buyers, despite early suggestions for a cinema.

Kensington House, seen here in 1880 at the end of its short life. This magnificent mansion, situated roughly on the site of Kensington Court, built to replace two earlier grand houses, was the flamboyant creation for the Victorian financier and entrepreneur Albert Grant. Begun in 1873 the grand edifice, surrounded by extensive grounds, with a lake, bowling alley and skating rink, boasted twenty bedrooms, ballroom, banqueting room, winter and summer dining rooms, billiard room, huge conservatory and grand hall, and numerous other facilities. It was completed by 1876 but Grant never occupied it, and it was eventually put up for sale, possibly as a club or a college, and finally demolished in 1882.

The Kensington toll gate, situated on Kensington Road near the junction with Palace Gate, seen here in its last days in the 1860s.

Six

CENTRAL KENSINGTON

*Young Street in the 1890s, at its junction with Kensington High Street, is
one of the oldest side streets in Kensington, having been laid out in 1685
when it was the only entrance to Kensington Square. It was named after the
square's developer, Thomas Young. Sadly, hardly anything remains of the
original seventeenth-century houses, occupied by courtiers and high-ranking
soldiers in the retinue of William of Orange, as well as by tradesmen and
shopkeepers who also served the royal household. In this it encapsulates
much of the Kensington and Chelsea story, the way in which the fancy of the
rich and fashionable gave birth to a community to support their needs.*

William Makepeace Thackeray (1811–63) took No. 16 Young Street (the house third from the left with a bow window) in 1846 and it was here that he wrote *Vanity Fair* and *Esmond*. At that time the street was still largely unchanged, but from 1860 wholesale alterations began and have never ceased, although often in the face of local opposition. The corner of Young Street and the High Street (see p. 83) was occupied in 1894 by the greengrocer, Slater, but demolition had already begun as part of the redevelopment of the main road. The corner site is now a bank.

Thackeray's first taste of domestic happiness was found at 16 Young Street, where he lived with his young daughters after many years of separation (the family was broken up because of his wife's insanity, the little girls being cared for by their grandparents in Paris). His joy in this reunion is apparent when he wrote happily about his new home, 'Kensington Gardens at the gate and omnibuses every two minutes. What can a mortal want more?' He stayed there nearly ten years, moving to Onslow Square in 1855 and finally to Palace Green, where he died in 1863. The photograph on the right was taken shortly before his death at 2 Palace Green.

These stalwarts represent about three-quarters of Kensington's fire brigade in the 1860s, photographed with their new engine after attending a fire in Lower Phillimore Mews. In 1871 the Board of Works reserved a site on the corner of Ball Street (a new, short-lived shopping street connecting Young Street and King Street – now Derry Street) parallel with the High Street, to build a new fire station with accommodation for three married men, three single men, one driver, three horses and three engines. The station closed in 1906 when a new fire station was built in Old Court Place. Within a few years, in 1912, the firemen and colleagues from many other parts of London were called to a disastrous fire at Barker's expanded premises across the road, when five staff members died. Ball Street was swallowed up in a further expansion of Barker's in 1927.

Dr John Merriman (1826–96), a member of a famous nineteenth-century medical family which occupied No. 45 Kensington Square for over half a century. The house backed on to that occupied by Thackeray, with adjoining gardens, and the story of the two homes is curiously linked. John Merriman was an historian and pioneer photographer, and his records of his neighbourhood in mid-Victorian times have provided a unique archive, all of which he bequeathed to Kensington Libraries, an invaluable visual aid to researchers. This photograph was taken c. 1870s.

Volunteers working for the war supply depot set up at Nos 11, 12 and 13 Kensington Square, here photographed rolling bandages in 1917. They also produced splints, slings and other surgical aids and dressings from material donated by the public. A report of the depot states, 'Were it not for such work the wounded would have no recovery.'

The west side of Kensington Square, *c.* 1900. The largest house here, No. 27, was occupied from the 1830s to the 1890s by the Kensington Proprietary Grammar School for Boys. When its fortunes began to fade, the back garden was taken to build the railway, and eventually the whole site was sold to the Crown and let to Derry & Tom's, who already had other houses in the square for staff accommodation. An archway was cut through No. 25 to allow vehicles to reach a warehouse.

The Convent of the Assumption in Kensington Square *c.* 1900, with girls of the junior school playing cricket – surprisingly progressive for Edwardian days. The community of nuns of the Order of the Assumption took the houses in the south-western corner of the square in 1859, adding a chapel in 1870–5. They established several schools and, in modern times, a teacher training college.

Woolsthorpe House in Wrights Lane became a 'home for crippled boys' in 1869. Built in the late eighteenth century, it was enlarged after being taken over by a charity which intended to educate, board and clothe destitute, ill-used or neglected disabled boys. The site was sold in 1935 and the proceeds used to provide a college at Stanmore. It has now become Kensington Close Hotel. In this picture the inmates in the early 1900s are enjoying a game of football despite their disabilities.

Britannia Brewery in Allen Street, shortly before its demolition in 1928. Note the imposing figure of Britannia on its roof. It was built in 1834 by Edward Herington and William Wells, with its attached pub the Britannia Tap (which survives in modern guise), but after various financial crises it finally closed in 1924.

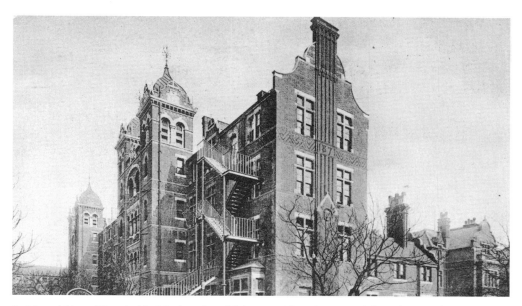

St Mary Abbots Hospital in Marloes Road (above *c*. 1900) began its life as the parish workhouse. In 1846 a small infirmary was included, and this was gradually enlarged until a new building was created in 1871, and the chapel of St Elizabeth in 1874 (below *c*. 1800). Extensions continued over the next sixty years, during which time the LCC took over the hospital and the workhouse closed. The buildings suffered severe damage during the Second World War. It was closed under the reorganization of London hospitals in the 1980s, and the site redeveloped for housing.

South End, which lies behind the south side of Kensington Square, seen here in 1900, had probably changed little since it had served as stabling for the wealthy residents of the neighbourhood a century earlier. At that time the beautiful 'Spring Gardens' and bowling green, laid out at great expense by the builder, Thomas Young, in the 1680s, had been 'digged up' to his consternation and sorrow by his successor, sold off as market gardens and later built upon. Garages replaced stables before its 'prettification' in present times.

Victoria Grove in Edwardian times, some sixty years after its construction as part of the fashionable Kensington New Town (1837–43). It was created on the estate of a wealthy importer of pipes and snuff, John Inderwick, and was earlier part of the manor of Earls Court, known as Towney Meads.

Cottesmore Gardens, a terrace of considerably varied houses, seen here *c.* 1919, was built a half-century or so earlier. The tower of the Imperial Institute can be seen in the distance.

The fashions of the early 1920s smilingly displayed by residents of No. 24 Cottesmore Gardens, from a family photo album inscribed 'E.G. Hunter of Kent House, Kensington Court'.

The cul-de-sac Kensington Gate (off Gloucester Road) in the 1920s, when Barker's delivered bread daily by horse-drawn cart. This too was on the land of John Inderwick, whose firm lives on in Carnaby Street.

The Gloucester Arms, Gloucester Road, in 1903. The pub still flourishes on the corner of Victoria Grove. It was first occupied by Thomas Hitchcock in 1839. St George's Terrace on the opposite side of the junction only changed from its Victorian guise in 1907, when the row of houses with front gardens on the west side of Gloucester Road was demolished to build the present St George's Court with shops below.

Gloucester Road station nearing its completion in 1868. The station was shared by the Metropolitan and District Railway, and in 1906 excavations were undertaken to construct the Piccadilly Line beneath it.

Bailey's Hotel, next to the station, was commenced in 1875 as the most ambitious venture to date by James Bailey, a businessman from Norfolk who lived there for a time with his family. The hotel was built to the highest standards of amenity to attract American visitors. (Note the bath chair and its attendant in the foreground.)

'Cab, Sir?' Queens Gate Terrace, where hansoms await customers in 1900. This and other developments in the vicinity were undertaken in the 1850s by the Broadwood family, the famous makers of keyboard instruments and pianos.

Queens Gate (originally known as Prince Albert's Road) as envisaged in 1853 by the area's main developer, William Jackson, whose grandiose mansions stretch westwards, away from the open country towards London. Jackson had his difficulties and nearly went bankrupt in the late 1850s.

Seven

SOUTH KENSINGTON AND THE MUSEUMS

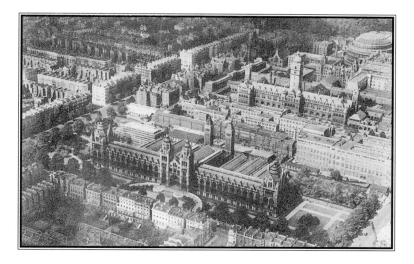

The museums area of South Kensington, a 1930s aerial view taken from the south-east with the Royal Albert Hall in the distance (right). The area is in some ways as much a memorial to the Prince Consort as the monument which bears his name, for it was the surplus funds from the 1851 Great Exhibition which helped to create this district devoted to the promotion of the arts and sciences. The Commissioners of the Exhibition were to spend the next ten years planning the complex of institutions which eventually filled the area around Cromwell and Exhibition Roads and Queens Gate. First to be established after the acquisition of the estate, which was to cover 87 acres, was the South Kensington Museum, or Iron Museum, in temporary buildings nicknamed the Brompton Boilers for their unprepossessing appearance. This became the Victoria and Albert Museum, but not for fifty years.

The Royal Albert Hall seen from the park, *c.* 1900. When Queen Victoria attended the opening in 1871, she found the occasion very moving, for the idea of such a venue for the performance of music had been dear to Prince Albert's heart and cherished by his (and later the Queen's) private secretary, General Charles Grey, who also died before he could see the dream fulfilled. Arguments over its building and the necessary finance were protracted but eventually resulted in the building of today with its magnificent mosaic frieze of Grecian figures.

This engraving in the *Stationers' Almanac* of 1870 envisages the Memorial to Prince Albert two years before its inauguration, after years of debate on its nature, detail and setting. The Prince sits in effigy (though now shrouded by scaffolding) under the ornate castellated canopy with its mosaic decorations, a copy of the catalogue of the Great Exhibition of 1851 in his hand.

Exhibition grounds in 1872. In 1869 the Commissioners announced a series of exhibitions linking art, science and commerce, held in new galleries which stretched north and south on either side of a central garden.

These ornate gardens of the Royal Horticultural Society, seen here in 1872, attracted thousands of visitors every year to the 20 acre site south-west of the Royal Albert Hall between 1861 and 1880. It is almost impossible today to imagine that huge area of arcades, topiary, mosaic pavements and statues, now built over.

This view of Brompton Park House painted by R. Collinson in 1865 shows the International Exhibition building, demolished at the end of 1864, towering behind its garden trees. The famous gardener, Henry Wise, had taken it in 1698, and successive residents lavished care and attention upon it. Although the new museum grew around it, the house itself survived to be used as a school of art, and was not demolished until 1899 when the Victoria and Albert Museum was constructed, as the photograph below, taken *c.* 1890s by Beatrix Potter's father, Rupert, shows.

Work in progress on the building of the new Victoria and Albert Museum in 1903 (above). In the forty years or so since its foundation the 'South Kensington Museum' had become a hotch-potch of buildings, among which were scattered the early collections, later acquisitions and educational departments. In the 1880s endless debates took place on its future and in 1890 architects competed to design a new building. The successful candidate was Sir Aston Webb, and in 1899 the foundation stone was laid by Queen Victoria. In June 1909 it was opened by King Edward VII. The photograph below shows it four years later, when today's plane trees were still saplings.

Onslow Square in the early 1900s. It was built between 1845 and 1865 on the estate left by Henry Smith, a wealthy seventeenth-century Alderman, as a charity 'to relieve the sufferings of Christians held in captivity by Turkish pirates', the Earl of Onslow being one of its trustees. An Act of Parliament later allowed it to be used for other charitable purposes. Among its past residents was William Makepeace Thackeray (see p. 84).

The west side of Cromwell Place in 1906 demonstrates the rivalry between the horse and the motor in public transport. This street, leading from South Kensington station to Cromwell Road, was developed by John Alexander, who had to wait until 1822 before he could build on much of the land owing to the leases on nursery gardens.

Sumner Place, seen here *c.* 1900, was also named for trustees of the Smith Charity estate (see p. 100), George and William Holme Sumner, and was known earlier as Sumner Terrace. In common with so much of this area, it was built up by Sir Charles James Freake, son of a coal merchant who became a builder/architect and used much of his large fortune to promote the arts and music and other public benefactions.

Onslow Gardens, seen here at the turn of the century, was among the later developments, but equally grand. In the 1871 census, when only twenty houses were occupied, there were 175 inhabitants of which over a hundred were servants. Famous residents included Andrew Bonar Law, Prime Minister from 1922 to 1923, and Sir Leslie Stephens, first editor of the *Dictionary of National Biography.*

The Imperial Institute seen from roof-top level in the autumn of 1903. The Institute was opened by Queen Victoria in May 1893, to 'present the Arts, Manufactures and Commerce of the Queen's Colonial and Indian Empire'. Designed by T.E. Collcutt, its 287 foot central tower was retained as a memorial when the rest of the Institute was demolished for the building of the new Imperial College in 1957–65.

Cromwell Gardens in its last years of private occupation, c. 1900. By 1914 the houses were sold off to the Office of Works, which leased them to the Institut Français. In 1937 the site was sold with the object of building a national theatre. Bernard Shaw launched the campaign in 1938 but it came to naught and the area remained vacant for many years.

Alexander Square, named for its fortunate young owner, John Alexander, who inherited an enormous Kensington estate from his godfather in 1799. When he died, his son, Henry Brown Alexander, continued its development. Although he and other landowners were happy to have the railway station, they were not so eager to have it situated on their land, and Alexander eventually had to convey a large number of houses to the railway company.

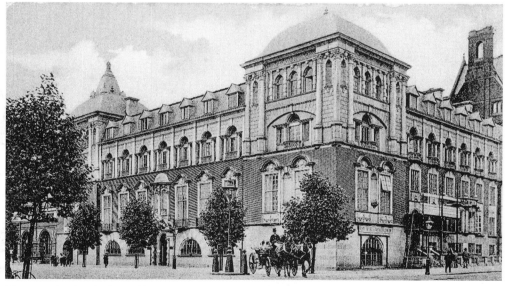

The Royal School of Needlework in Exhibition Road in 1905. The school was founded in 1872, with the purpose of reviving the art of decorative embroidery, by Princess Christian of Schleswig Holstein, third daughter of the Queen. It moved to this impressive site in 1903. In 1934 the lease was taken over by Imperial College and in 1949 the school moved to Princes Gate and later to Hampton Court. The building was demolished in 1962.

In 1864 the Metropolitan Railway was allowed to extend its 'Inner Circle' line from Paddington to South Kensington, news received with mixed feelings by the builders of the new houses when some villas had to be demolished. In 1907 the construction of the Piccadilly Line necessitated the building of the entrance on the Pelham Road side of the station as seen here. The original plan of Leslie Green, the famous architect of stations, to crown it with a handsome four-storey block of flats, never materialized.

Harrington Road, *c.* 1900. Note the young violinist crossing the street, on her way perhaps to the Royal College of Music. On her left is the still-existent Norfolk Hotel. The Stanhopes, Earls of Harrington, have owned considerable property in Kensington since the sixteenth century.

The magnificent interior of No. 39 Harrington Gardens as it appeared in 1906 (above). The house was built specially for William Schwenk Gilbert (left) in 1883 when he was celebrating the great financial success of HMS *Pinafore*. The frontage decoration of a ship did not commemorate this, but Gilbert's seafaring ancestor, Sir Humphrey Gilbert. Apart from its grand exterior and lavish internal decorations, the house had electric light, powered by a gas-engined dynamo, and a telephone with a direct line to the Savoy Theatre. The doors to the various rooms bore mottoes, such as 'Abandon hope all ye who enter here' on the dining room!

Debnam Motors *c.* 1920, soon after its opening at 8–15 Athelstone Mews. The property was leased by Henry George Debnam on 21 February 1917, and he converted the existing stables into a garage named initially Golly's Garage. Athelstone Mews, like so many others in the area, was built in the 1870s as stabling with small flats above to serve the big houses, in this case in Cromwell Road. By 1925 Henry was trading under his own name; he held the Daimler franchise in west London. Since the early days Debnam had dealings with royalty, and on his advertising he describes himself as 'an expert to the Royal Families of Great Britain and Europe'. Judging from a series of photographs given to the Kensington Local Studies Department, employees were also involved in the early days of motor racing, often with some success. The firm remained in business until 1972.

Eight

EARLS COURT

*The Edwardian shopping terrace at the northern end of Earls Court Road
c. 1904, when the homely shops of butchers, drapers and newsagents
preceded today's offices and restaurants. For centuries this had been no
more than a leafy lane leading from the high road towards Chelsea. Those
who used it might be on their way to the old manor house, or Earls Court
Farm. By the early nineteenth century, a few cottages, an inn and later
a brewery were clustered around what is known today as 'Earls Court
Village', near Kenway Road. By then Earls Court House, which had been
the home of the celebrated surgeon, John Hunter, had become a lunatic
asylum. The Gunter family of prosperous confectioners, living at Earls
Court Lodge (nicknamed Currant Jelly Hall), were beginning to move into
property development and within a century Earls Court was to become
a crowded, built-up urban area and the venue for one of London's most
fantastic exhibitions.*

Earls Court farmhouse with the Manor House behind, as they appeared in 1874. The hoarding marks the railway crossing under the road at the time of the construction of Earls Court station, which was situated on the east side of the road. The wooden construction burned down in 1875 and was replaced by a more permanent structure on the west side.

The house beyond, known as the Manor House, in 1845. Erected in the 1790s, according to the historian Thomas Faulkner, it replaced an earlier building demolished at that time. It was occupied by the Hutchins family who had been tenants of the estate for many decades. The manor courts were held there, the last recorded being in 1856.

Earls Court Farm in the 1870s. After Samuel Hutchins's death in 1844, most of the land on the western side of the lane was let to a market gardener, Samuel Alloway, who is seen here (above centre, in a bowler hat) with some of his workers, including Mr Goddard and Mr Ives. The Manor House, seen in the background, had been let to several tenants, including one who kept a menagerie there, but both buildings eventually succumbed to the development which followed the coming of the railway.

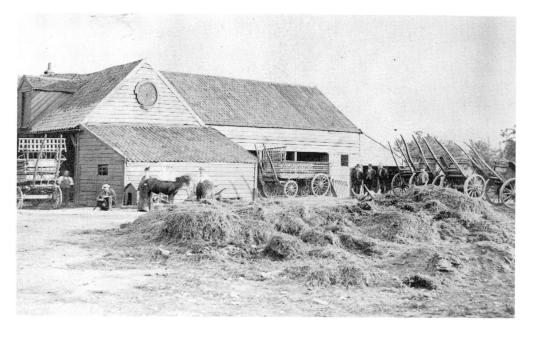

Earls Court House in 1875 about ten years before it was demolished to make way for Barkston Gardens. Situated almost opposite the site of the present station it is, of course, best known for its occupation by the surgeon and anatomist John Hunter, from 1765 to 1793. Hunter's home was the successor to an equally splendid, if not more handsome, house created in the mid-seventeenth century for the Secretary of the Treasury, Henry Guy.

John Hunter (1728–93) kept a menagerie there to further his study of body structure and for medical experiments. A subterranean passage led from the north side of the house to a cloister where the animals were housed, including a den said to have been occupied by a lion and pens for buffaloes, zebras, jackasses and rare breeds of sheep and goats. It was here that he kept the cauldron in which he boiled down the body of the Irish giant to retrieve the skeleton which is still displayed at the Royal College of Surgeons. The feet of the giant can be seen on the right of this engraving of 1814, which was based on Sir Joshua Reynold's portrait.

The southern end of Earls Court Road, near the junction of Barkston Gardens, in early Edwardian days. Parrs Bank, on the corner, was later merged with the Westminster Bank, which still exists as the 'Nat West' in the same terrace.

Late Victorian splendour in the drawing-room of a house in Earls Court Square, *c.* 1880. One of the grandest of the Earls Court developments, started in the 1870s, its residents included Sir William Palliser, landowner, who also made his name as an inventor.

Edwards Furnishing Warehouse at 146 Earls Court Road, photographed from the corner of
Trebovir Road in May 1904. The delivery van horse enjoys his nose-bag, and the window display
features 'Folding bed, spring overlay mattress and pillow for 17s 9d' and inlaid linoleum for 1s 11d
a square yard.

The Old Manor confectionery stores, 175 Earls Court Road, in 1904, 'Proprietors E. Smith & Sons'. The window tells a sweet story: raspberry and vanilla ice creams at 2*d*, 4*d* and 6*d* a glass, Cadbury's chocolate, iced lemonade at 1*d*, 2*d* and 3*d* a glass, and 'Cough No More Lozenges'.

In 1896 a Ladies Cycling Club flourished in the grounds of Hereford Lodge near the corner of Old Brompton Road and Redcliffe Gardens, as shown above. The track was described as 'a miniature Olympian', forming a circle round the grounds and running over two artistic bridges. Hereford Lodge, and its neighbour Coleherne House, on the estate of which the confectioner James Gunter was ground landlord, had already been advertised as building land in 1863 but survived for another thirty years, Coleherne being occupied by Edmund Tattersall, head of the bloodstock auctioneers. Both houses were demolished in 1899–1900 for the building of Coleherne Court, seen below c. 1907.

Clareville Cottage, Old Brompton Road, portrayed here by T. Hosmer Shepherd in 1852. The 'Cottage' was described as a new house in 1784 when it and four other villas were built on the land of the Day estate between Gloucester Road and Love Lane (Dove Mews) in 1784. It was demolished in the 1880s.

Clareville Cottage (above) was the residence of the coloratura soprano Jenny Lind on her arrival in London in 1847, when she delighted audiences who dubbed her 'the Swedish Nightingale'. Madame Jenny (Johanna) Lind Goldschmidt (1820–87; right) spent the last part of her life in England, living at 1 Moreton Gardens (189 Old Brompton Road) from 1875 to her death in 1887, when she was singing professor at the Royal College of Music.

These handsome young cowboys gave London another taste of the Wild West in 1909 at the Golden West Exhibition, which attempted to repeat the success of 1887 when the Earls Court Exhibition opened with Colonel William Cody's 'Buffalo Bill's Roughriders and Red Skins Show'. The entrepreneur John Robinson Whitley acquired the six acres of surplus railway land between Warwick Road and Richmond (now Old Brompton) Road in 1884, the rest of the triangular site being occupied by coal depots and railway works. Whitley had seen the wild west show in Washington and booked it as his opening event. At the beginning of 1887 two gangs, each of 1,000 men, worked 24 hours a day in two shifts, for four months, to construct an open arena with a covered stand as well as an exhibition building and pleasure gardens, with a switchback, huge bandstand and other attractions. During its five month season 15,000 visitors came daily to see the show, including the Queen (who was shown a shortened version and asked to meet an Indian papoose), the Prince of Wales, Gladstone and the whole of Harrow School! Whitley followed his first triumph with further exhibitions on national themes, but he never achieved equal success, and by 1891 he had retired. Within three years he had been succeeded by a new entrepreneur, the Hungarian Imre Kiralfy, who had already made a name as the presenter of circuses and spectaculars.

The Big Wheel towering above the Earls Court rooftops, c. 1903. It was Imre Kiralfy who added a new sophistication to the Exhibition pleasure gardens with the great wheel and the water chute (see below). The wheel, modelled on the great ferris wheel at Chicago, was constructed in 1894 by an independent company. It was 300 feet in diameter, weighed 1,000 tons and took 20 minutes to complete a revolution (with a pause to allow the passengers to enjoy the view). Its 40 cars, each with 40 passengers, allowed a maximum capacity of 1,600 people. It operated for many years without a serious accident, although a year after it opened in 1895 it stuck for four and a half hours: the passengers were given £5 each for their ordeal.

The water chute, c. 1903, was somewhat less spectacular, and like the switchback was said to lose some of its effect because the surrounding rocks and crags were not high enough to block out the view of surrounding chimney pots!

The Exhibition was transformed in Edwardian days to portray the Ice Caverns of Hungary in 1908 (above) and the minarets of a Balkan village in 1907 (below).

Kiralfy had switched his attention to the White City in 1906, but Earls Court continued under new management and presented a series of exhibitions similar to those he had staged with national themes. Many new buildings had been added, such as the huge Empress Theatre (the Empress Hall) – technically in Fulham, as were all the western pleasure gardens – and the Queen's Court with its lake and palace, adaptable to various themes.

Although the grounds remained open until the outbreak of the First World War, the Earls Court Exhibition slowly declined. During the war, the Empress Hall was used to house Belgian refugees, described as 'the largest clearing house in Europe for dealing with the refugee problem'. A chapel was set up for the spiritual comfort of these thousands of families displaced from the battlefields of Flanders. Here the Auxiliary Bishop of Malines, Monsignor De Waechter, is seen blessing the angelus bell presented to the camp chapel by Sir Horace Monro, on 5 February 1915. In the 1920s and '30s much of the area became derelict, apart from some small industries, although the Empress Stadium survived as an ice rink and the site of various entertainments. In 1936 a £1.5 million development roofed over the area to build the modern exhibition buildings, which in recent years have been greatly extended.

Ellen Terry (left, in 1888) moved into 33 Longridge Road in 1878, with her two children Edith and Gordon Craig and her two dogs Drummie and Fussie, soon after her marriage to Charles Wardell. It was here that Sir Henry Irving invited her to join his company at the Lyceum, thus forming one of the most famous partnerships in theatrical history. The Revd Dugald McColl, minister of the Kensington Presbyterian church (later St John's), who lived at No. 36, wrote in his memoirs of the contrast between the dullness of the street with its houses of 'sad coloured brick and window-surrounds in gritty stucco' and its inhabitants. He recalled Ellen Terry's departure for rehearsals thus: 'She appeared on the steps like an April morning . . . the air became tender and gay with wavings and blown kisses; the wheels revolved, and greyness descended once more on Longridge Road.'

Longridge Road in 1905.

Nine

BROMPTON AND KNIGHTSBRIDGE

Brompton Road in 1904, crowded with the traffic and shoppers of the time. A century earlier this was a comparatively quiet country road, only enlivened by the frequency of its inns and a few scattered cottages. In fact the name 'Brompton Road' was not applied to the old turnpike connecting Knightsbridge with Fulham until the 1860s, and Cromwell Road was non-existent. Lacking a bridge over the creek or railway at its western end, it petered out after Earls Court. Building development did not begin on any scale until the 1780s, when the young architect, Henry Holland, began to build on Lord Cadogan's estate in the north-east of Chelsea. The turnpike was still narrow and badly surfaced, but the route to London lay through Knightsbridge and Hyde Park Corner. In the 1820s further development began with the building of Brompton Square. In 1853 Charles Henry Harrod acquired a small grocery shop in one of the terraces, known as 8 Middle Queens Buildings, selling humble goods such as tea, soap and candles.

In the 1880s the magnificent Oratory of St Philip Neri began to rise among the towers and domes of the museums area, seen above in 1882. The Oratorians, founded in Rome in 1578, were introduced to England in 1847 by John Henry Newman. They came to Brompton in 1852, where they built an oratory house with a private chapel which was later extended to provide a public church. As this became too small for increasing congregations, funds were raised by public appeal to build a 'cathedral' church. The commission was given to Herbert Gribble. Sadly, Gribble died at the age of forty-seven, and although the oratory was consecrated in April 1884 it was still incomplete. The dome, seen in this 1890s picture (left), was the design of another architect, George Sherrin.

The Bell and Horns, on the corner of Old Brompton Road and Thurloe Place, in 1914, only a year before its demolition for the development of Empire House. Adjoining the nursery garden of John Harrison, the old coaching inn is recorded as early as 1722 as The Bell. The addition of 'Horns' may have originated with a merger with another inn of that name. The early building was reconstructed in 1824 and enlarged and altered in Victorian times. Work on Empire House, seen to the left and back of the Bell and Horns, was begun in 1910 for the Continental Tyre Company. It was not completed until 1916 due to the continuing presence of the public house.

Brompton Road station in 1908, two years after its opening to serve the new Great Northern, Piccadilly and Brompton Railway (the Piccadilly Line). Brompton Road was closed in the 1930s but the façade remained while the 'ghost station' below was used for defence purposes.

Brompton Square in an engraving, *c.* 1843. This was one of the earliest developments in the area, completed by 1826. The gap at the northern end was the subject of much controversy in the 1840s when the residents of Ennismore Gardens opposed the opening of a road 'to establish links with the aroma of the Serpentine'.

Joyce & Matthews, butchers, seen in 1903 proudly displaying their wares and delivery tricycle. In 1825 a row of five houses was built on the south side of the Brompton Road, now Nos 179–87. The ground floors were converted into shops and in 1888 John Joyce took over the butcher's shop, house and stabling at 183 Brompton Road. Ernest Matthews joined the firm in 1897 and they remained in business until 1927, when the shop was rebuilt as a gallery. The other four properties still survive today.

The original buildings of Harrods Stores, Brompton Road, prior to demolition in 1901. When Charles Henry Harrod opened his first shop in Middle Queens Buildings in what was to become Brompton Road, in 1853, it was hardly a salubrious situation. North Street to the rear was described as 'a mass of filth from one end to the other' and Queens Gardens (later to be swallowed up by the new store) had a rat-infested woodyard. Nevertheless the business prospered, and when he retired for his son Charles Digby Harrod to take over in 1861 it was expanding rapidly, with an extension built over the back garden and a new shop front with a plate glass window proclaiming 'Harrods Stores'. More shops were acquired and, despite a disastrous fire just before Christmas 1883, the business went from success to success. Nevertheless, Mr Harrod never pandered to his customers: he gave them free delivery but was strict about credit and in early days gave none. In 1894 the great decision was taken to rebuild. The design commission went to C.W. Stephens, a hitherto comparatively unknown architect, and the plan was to complete one block 200 × 120 feet every year until the whole store was rebuilt. The interior of the store was, of course, lavish, from its Doulton-tiled meat hall, mahogany, walnut and satinwood counters and furniture, to the ornate ceilings and cornices. The meat hall was built on the site of a small board school which Harrods had great difficulty in acquiring.

Harrods during reconstruction, *c.* 1901–5. At first the intention was to provide a two-storey shop with flats above – partly due to the current fire regulations on the height of shop premises. These flats were huge, sometimes having fifteen rooms, but they were short-lived, and by 1927 the whole building was commercial. So frequent were the alterations that in 1913 a house architect was appointed, and at one time there was a plan to reconstruct along Hans Crescent (below), but this did not materialize. Interestingly it was not until 1921 that the freehold of the site was acquired from its original owners, the Goddard family and their trustees.

The north side of Brompton Road, between Brompton Square and Montpelier Place, *c.* 1900. It has changed much less than other sections, in parts still retaining the old stepped pavements which raised pedestrians above the mud thrown up by the traffic. The big changes here were much earlier, with a row of over fifty terraced houses known as Biscoe's Buildings, then Brompton Row, built in the 1760s.

Rutland Gate in 1905, dated by the hoarding advertising Julia Neilson and Fred Terry in *The Scarlet Pimpernel* at the Vaudeville Theatre. This was a terrace, built in the 1840s opposite Knightsbridge Barracks (described then as 'a range of dull heavy brick buildings badly placed and long an eyesore to the neighbourhood').

Beauchamp Place in 1906, when its humble beginnings were still evident, in contrast to sixty years later when it was described as being 'the steady pulse beat of London fashion'. It was first developed in the early nineteenth century in the midst of financial uncertainty, owing to the many problems of its owner, the sporting gunsmith Joseph Manton. By 1871 half the houses were in multi-occupation and a complaint was made to the Vestry that two were being kept as common brothels!

Knightsbridge (looking east) in 1900 before modern development removed the terrace of houses on the left. The equestrian statue is of Field Marshal Lord Strathnairn, a hero of the Indian Mutiny. It was removed in 1933 when extensive road widening took place.

'Scotch Corner', photographed on 11 September 1902 by Ernest Milner. Officially known as Park Mansions, the imposing block of flats built between 1900 and 1902 in place of a ragged collection of old houses and shops is now best known as 'The Scotch House' from the shop which occupied its groundfloor on the apex of Brompton and Kensington Roads. In 1900 the business was run by Gardiner & Co. Park Mansions Arcade runs beneath the flats to connect the two roads, complementing Brompton Arcade opposite and Knightsbridge Station Arcade (now demolished).

Ten

CHELSEA

*The last days of the old waterfront at Chelsea, captured by the famous
photographer James Hedderley in 1870 from a vantage point in the tower of
Chelsea Old Church. Looking west, the trees of Cremorne's pleasure gardens can
be seen in the distance. Old Battersea Bridge (left), the frail wooden structure
built by Henry Holland a century earlier, was also nearing its demise. Although
the proposition to embank the northern shore of the Thames between Vauxhall
and Battersea Bridges was first made by the Commissioners of Woods and Forests
in 1839, nothing happened for many years owing to the cost of building a new
suspension bridge at Chelsea. This did materialize in 1853 but the embankment
then petered out at the end of the grounds of the Royal Hospital. The Chelsea
Embankment remained a contentious parliamentary issue for nearly twenty years
when the plan was drawn up by the great engineer Sir Joseph Bazalgatte.*

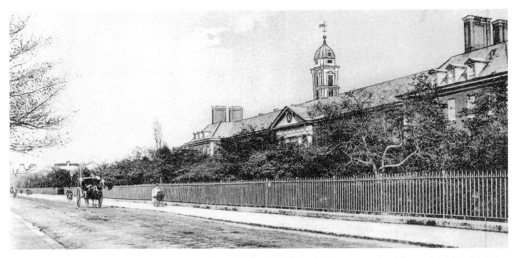

The Royal Hospital *c.* 1900, over 200 years after its foundation stone had been laid by Charles II in 1682. The King's concern for his wounded soldiers had been expressed long ago on the battlefield at Tangiers when he promised them that they would always be in his care. The site chosen was that of the old Chelsea College, a theological institution now defunct and owned by the Royal Society. The land was bought for the Crown for £1,300 and Sir Christopher Wren was commissioned to design the building, which was completed in 1692. Apart from some later additions by Robert Adam and Sir John Soane it changed very little until the world wars, when the old soldiers once again came under fire: various parts of the hospital and its grounds were hit, but despite these tragic events most of the original features remain.

Pensioners at the hospital are selected from a huge number of eligible applicants, who must all be on permanent pensions, have no dependents and have given 'good service by flood and field'. The traditional uniform, shown here in 1900, remains, scarlet coat in summer, navy blue in winter, the old fashioned army cap or the ceremonial tricorn. The military structure of administration is also virtually unchanged since its foundation. Although it was thought at first that army discipline might be unwelcome in old age, it is enjoyed by men who have spent long years in service.

Pensioners enjoying the recreation room before the First World War.

The hospital buildings, seen here *c.* 1900, are surrounded by acres of lovely grounds, which every spring house the Chelsea Flower Show of the Royal Horticultural Society, now as much a hallmark of traditional Chelsea as the pensioners themselves. The obelisk, which is now a centre point in the marquee at the Chelsea Flower Show, was erected in 1843 in memory of the officers and men of the 24th Regiment who were killed at Chillianwalla in the Sikh War in 1849.

An early photograph by James Hedderley of Chelsea Physic Garden. A young man rests beside the statue of Sir Hans Sloane, commissioned by the Apothecaries Society in 1757 and executed by Rysbrack. The four acre plot of the Physic Garden was leased to the Society of Apothecaries in 1673 by Sir Charles Cheyne as a Botanical and Physic Garden, but it was not until it came under the patronage of Sir Hans Sloane that its purpose really began to be fulfilled. Sloane studied there as a young man and made his name as a successful and fashionable physician. He had bought the Chelsea Manor estate from the Cheyne family in 1712, and in 1722 gave the freehold of the garden to the Apothecaries Society. Philip Miller was appointed director, an appointment he was to hold for nearly fifty years. Today it thrives as a world-famous centre for the cultivation and study of plants in the expanding science of their use in the treatment of disease, yet the garden still retains its ancient peaceful charm, a gem in Chelsea's crown.

Tite Street in the late nineteenth century, very early in its life. It is named for the Embankment architect Sir William Tite. Its occupants at various times make it one of the best-known thoroughfares, as they include James McNeil Whistler, Oscar Wilde, John Singer Sargent and Augustus John. Whistler's house, White House, designed by Edward Godwin with pale bricks and green slates, aroused great controversy. He only lived in it a short time owing to his bankruptcy following the famous libel action with John Ruskin.

James McNeil Whistler (1834–1903) portrayed in this etching by Paul Cesar Hellen. Whistler may be only one of the stars in Chelsea's galaxy of famous artists, but his life story competes with any of them, with his Irish-American descent and his cosmopolitan education until his settling in Chelsea. His flamboyant lifestyle, behaviour and dress, his conceit, stinging wit and sarcasm have been chronicled as variedly and as often as his artistic genius, which is undeniable.

Cremorne Gardens at the height of its popularity in the mid-1860s. Cremorne House was built in 1740 for the Duke of Huntingdon, whose widow founded the Huntingdon Connexion, a splinter group of Wesleyan Methodists. It was sold in 1785 to Viscount Cremorne who gave it its name. Its later owner, Charles de Berenger Baron de Beaufain, an entrepreneur despite his aristocratic title, opened a sporting club there for 'gentlemen to take manly exercise', and this in turn changed again in 1845, under the promotion of Thomas Bartlett Simpson, to a pleasure garden which became the delight of the masses and the bane of the more select residents of Chelsea. Among its devotees was Whistler, who visited it frequently with Walter and Henry Greaves to enjoy its vivid life and colour, which they frequently portrayed. The entertainment included bands, performances by clowns, giants and dwarfs, performing animals, every conceivable form of side-show, spectacle and sensation and, in the evenings, fireworks – which particularly attracted Whistler and the Greaves. This study by Walter Greaves, a disciple of Whistler, shows that he was an artist of repute in his own right. It includes the figures of Whistler (standing right) and Greaves and his sister sharing a bottle of beer.

CREMORNE

ANOTHER STARTLING NOVELTY

MONDAY, Aug. 7th, 1865,

WHEN THAT EXTRAORDINARY INVENTION

THE AERIAL VESSEL

OR

SAILING BALLOON!

"L'ESPERANCE"

INVENTED AND CONSTRUCTED by M. DELAMARNE.

Will ascend from these Gardens. This novel and remarkable Balloon is the first of the kind ever invented. It is nearly 200 feet in length, 50 feet in diameter, and 150 feet in circumference. Being provided with Screw Propellors and a Rudder, similar to those of a Ship, which are set in motion by machinery.

It ascends and descends at will, becoming lighter or heavier than the air, and already much progress has been made towards propelling it in any given direction.

The First Public Experiments made with this Monster Machine were from the Gardens of the Luxemburg in Paris, before the Senate of France and a vast multitude of people, and were crowned with triumphant success.

☞ Remember! on MONDAY, August 7th, at CREMORNE.

ARLISS & Co., Printers, 18, Great Queen Street.—W.C.

Ballooning was among the biggest attractions at Cremorne Gardens, as seen in this 1865 poster. A balloonist named De Groot, known as 'the Flying Man', attempted in 1874 to descend from a balloon, The Czar, from a height of 5,000 feet by the use of bats' wings thirty-seven feet wide. As the balloon drifted 300 feet above St Luke's Church, De Groot attempted an emergency landing but crashed to his death. In the afternoons Cremorne was a family outing, but after dark drink and rowdiness gave it a bad name and in 1877 its application for a renewal of its licence was refused; the estate was sold for building and the handsome trees sold off as growing timber.

The closing of Cremorne Gardens allowed the Ashburnham Park Nursery, which belonged to the Chelsea gardener and horticulturist James Wimsett, to expand. Although not as famous as his neighbours, such as Veitch, Wimsett was described as a 'distinguished cultivator of rare and valuable plants'. The nursery, seen here in 1903, was sold as a school site in 1907.

Duke Street in 1865, only a few years before it and other old streets and alleyways by the river, such as Lawrence and Lombard Streets, were swept away by the building of the Embankment. This whole area around the Old Church and the approach to Battersea Bridge was the essence of Thames-side Chelsea, with its wharves, docks and boatyards and old taverns such as the Adam and Eve. Mrs Carlyle would have shopped here, in Lombard Street perhaps, where the Elizabethan Arch House spanned the narrow road and where the 'sea tar breeze', described by Thomas Carlyle, was also spiced with the scent of the coal unloading from barges at Alldin's or Johnson's Wharf. Part of this area was used in 1910 for the reconstruction of Crosby Hall, moved from the City stone by stone. One of the objects of the embankment project was to provide a route for the newly improved sewer by reclaiming land from the river, and between Old Church Street and Oakley Street the shore line was moved outwards so that the old trees on the bank now grew in the garden space dividing the buildings from the river.

The south side of Duke Street was the first to go, in 1873, as the great embankment wall went up, putting an end to the tidal floods which could lap the front gardens and the shop doorsteps in Cheyne Walk. The north side of these by-ways also eventually succumbed to more modern buildings, and the sixteenth-century Magpie and Stump, near Oakley Street, burned down in 1886. These two photographs are part of the visual historical record made by James Hedderley of old Chelsea between 1860 and 1875. He worked as a sign writer in the riverside village and at Worlds End. His photographs were taken with a cumbersome 10 × 12 foot plate camera mounted on a tripod.

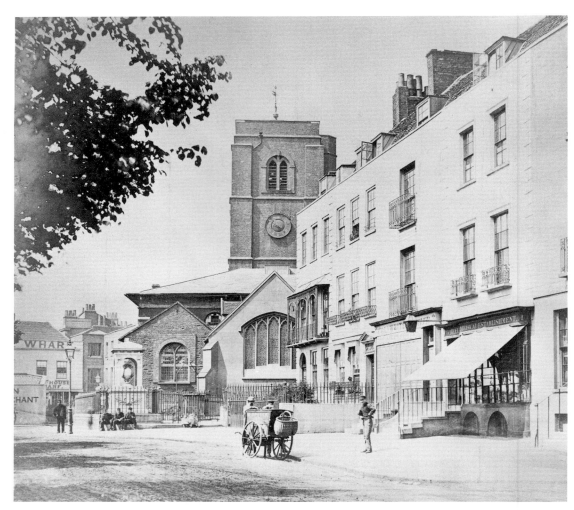

Chelsea Old Church in its 1870s setting, still the centre of the waterside village as it had been for nearly 800 years. There is a record of a church here in Norman times, but this could have been preceded by a Saxon church. In 1290 it was named as 'Chelchurche of All Saints' in papal letters from Pope Nicholas IV. As the population of Chelsea increased the little church began to be outgrown by its congregation, with noble families complaining that they could not find room in the pews, and in 1670 it was practically rebuilt with a new roof and tower and peal of bells. It was almost totally destroyed by a land mine on 16 April 1941, although the chapel where Thomas More, 'The King's good servant – but God's first –', had sung Offices as humbly as any parish clerk, happily survived. After the bombing the building was boarded up, with the exception of the More Chapel which was repaired sufficiently to enable worship to be continued. The church was rebuilt in 1958 on the old plan to the design of Walter Godfrey, including the restoration of the More Chapel and the repair and replacement of almost all the monuments.

An early twentieth-century photograph of the southern end of Old Church Street. Until the King's private road was opened up, Church Lane (as it was once known) was the only coach way to the riverside village. In later times it was the site of the seventeenth-century Black Lion with its tea gardens and bowling green. Carlyle bought his cigars from a tobacconist's shop here. Among its many famous residents over the years was Dr Francis Atterbury, politician and theologian, and Dr John Arbuthnot, physician to the Royal Hospital. Jonathan Swift lodged there in April 1711, complaining at having to pay six shillings a week for a silly room with coarse sheets!

The Rectory in its heyday at the turn of the century before it became the focus of development wrangles. The seventeenth-century house, with its two acres of garden on the eastern corner of Old Church Street, is one of the largest private gardens in London. In 1824 St Luke's in Sydney Street was consecrated as the new parish church, but the first vicar, the Hon. Revd Gerald Wellesley, brother of the Duke of Wellington, continued to live in the Rectory. It was here that Charles Kingsley, author of *The Water Babies*, was brought up when his father was rector in the 1830s.

The seventeenth-century Lindsey House *c.* 1900, now altered and rebuilt to become a terrace of seven houses, 95–100 Cheyne Walk. It was bought in 1750 by Count Zinzendorff, a religious philanthropist, who had befriended the Moravian Brethren, a displaced Protestant sect suffering persecution in Central Europe. Here they led a simple communal life, until their benefactor's death when they were forced to leave, only retaining their chapel and burial ground, which still survive. Among later famous residents were the engineers Marc Isambard and his son Isambard Kingdom Brunel, James Whistler and the boatmen artists Walter and Henry Greaves.

Walter Greaves and Thomas Carlyle, two of Chelsea's most famous residents, in life and effigy in 1890. Note that Greaves still aped the appearance of his master, even though he was rejected by Whistler in later years.

In this photograph of Cheyne Walk in the 1860s (above) the trees that now stand in the embankment gardens were on the river bank (compare the 1905 view, below). The first houses were built on the site of the gardens of Henry VIII's riverside palace, which became the home of the Cheyne family until 1712 when the estate was bought by Sir Hans Sloane, who sold some of the land as building plots. One of the largest and most magnificent was No. 16, which was rented by Dante Gabriel Rossetti in 1862 for £110 a year, where he entertained and worked with all the artists and literati of his time, and kept a menagerie of animals in his back garden.

The Thames Coffee Shop in 1865, run at this time by William Hall. It was situated at the corner of Lawrence Street at No. 51 Cheyne Walk. In the 1860s the row contained five small shops and an inn, the Cricketers, seen to the right of the dining room. All were swept away with the building of the Embankment, and in 1886 Carlyle Mansions occupied the site. The flats were described as having spacious sunny rooms overlooking the river in the front, and less spacious, sunless rooms in the back where the servants slept. Henry James took 21 Carlyle Mansions as his London home in 1913, three years before his death, and wrote to a friend 'this Chelsea perch proves just the thing for me'. The west side of Lawrence Street is believed to be the site of the Chelsea China factory, which thrived from 1745 to 1784 when the works were moved to Derby. Monmouth House, consisting of four houses, was situated at the top of Lawrence Street, and in the 1750s Tobias Smollett, the novelist, and Sir John Fielding, the Bow Street magistrate, were neighbours of the Duchess of Monmouth.

Cheyne Walk looking west from the King's Head and Eight Bells, *c.* 1871. When he came to live in Cheyne Row in 1834, Thomas Carlyle described Cheyne Walk as 'having really good old brick mansions, flagged pavement and a wide carriageway between two rows of stubbornly high old trees'. He was able to enjoy the company of his friend, Leigh Hunt, in Upper Cheyne Row and they were certainly well provided with nearby inns, from the King's Head and Eight Bells on the corner of his street ('Pale Ale 4*d* a pint, Guinness and Bitter 2*d*') to the Thames Coffee House – far from teetotal – at Lawrence Street. Although Mrs Carlyle preferred to have her ham and butter sent from their family in Scotland, she did patronize local shops, Carless the butcher, the Lombard Street fishmonger and local milkmen and bakers. When these photographs were taken by Hedderley, poor Jane Carlyle was sadly no more, having died suddenly while out driving in April 1866, and Thomas was a lonely eccentric old man, wandering about the Chelsea streets like a ghost in his long coat and wide-brimmed hat.

Dr Phene's fantastical house on the corner of Oakley Street in its brief Edwardian days. Of Chelsea's wealth of eccentrics, Dr John Samuel Phene is among the most celebrated, and the 'Chateau' he built is the most extraordinary of its buildings. The highly ornamented edifice, smothered with serpentine bodies, gargoyles, beasts, birds, gods and goddesses, dragons and serpents, picked out in scarlet and gold, gave rise to myths and rumours from its construction in 1906 to its demolition in 1917. Even before the house was built, the gardens had been filled with similar creations.

A scholar and antiquarian, Dr Phene (1823–1912) was a knowledgeable eccentric, a pioneer of the now accepted theory that trees purify the air in towns, and was able to convince Victorian developers to plant them whenever possible. He designed many conventional houses in Oakley Street (where he lived himself, never occupying his chateau) and Margaretta Terrace, said to be named for the woman he loved who is rumoured to have died shortly after their marriage.

Oakley Street in the early twentieth century, only a few years after the days when Oscar Wilde had been lionized by his mother's guests, and where he stayed in the agonizing intervals between his trials. The building of the Albert suspension bridge in 1873 made Oakley Street into a main road, although its proximity to Chelsea's Steamboat Company's Cadogan Pier and the Pier Hotel had already made it of some importance to travellers.

Argyll House in the 1900s. It still exists on the corner of Oakley Street and King's Road, and owes its name to a fairly brief residence by the Duke of Argyll, although it was built in 1723 for John Perrin, whose monogram appears on the gate. It was designed by the famous Venetian architect Giacomo Leoni, and described by him as having 'a beautiful harmony of colours in its brick work and stone decoration'.

Chelsea. Six Bells and Town Hall.

King's Road in 1900, when the eighteenth-century Six Bells public house had just been rebuilt. Once a medieval cart track used only by farmers and gardeners, King's Road attained its royal status when Charles II used it as his private road to Hampton Court. It eventually opened to the public in the 1830s.

The Chelsea Palace music hall, seen here *c*. 1900, replaced the Wilkinson Sword factory in 1902 and attracted all the leading stars of the day. After its use as a TV studio from 1956, it was eventually demolished in 1966 and replaced by shops and offices.

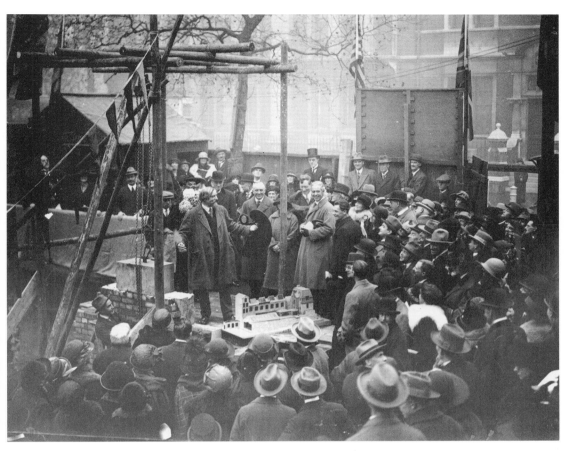

Augustus John presiding at the opening of the Chenil Galleries in 1905. Founded by Charles Chenil to help young artists show their work, it stood on the site of the famous Chelsea Arts Club, a meeting place for artists founded in 1891 by the sculptor Thomas Stirling, together with others such as Walter Sickert and Whistler. Augustus John could compete with any of his predecessors or contemporaries in the sensational Chelsea scene as he held court in King's Road, the Café Royal or anywhere else that artists congregated, in his broad-brimmed hat and flowing cravat. The Arts Club moved to Old Church Street from where it introduced the Chelsea Arts Ball, held first at the nearby Town Hall, then in 1908 at the Royal Opera House Covent Garden, and from 1910 at the Royal Albert Hall. On the opposite side of the road the Board of Guardians building can be seen, later to become Chelsea Registry Office and more recently, offices. Next to this is Dovehouse Green burial ground.

Belle Vue Lodge (above, *c.* 1870), on the corner of Beaufort Street, was occupied for a time by Luke Thomas Flood, a benefactor of Chelsea parish. Flood Street (below, *c.* 1905) was named for him, and not for its proximity to the river. Flood Street was once Robinsons Lane and it may well have been down this that Pepys rode to the Swan Inn on the river, famed for its association with the Doggetts Coat and Badge race rowed by the Thames watermen.

In 1888 Lord Cadogan laid the foundation stone of Chelsea's first public library in Manresa Road. A vigorous campaign had been conducted by the supporters of the public library movement, led by Mr B.W. Linden, resulting in the adoption by the Vestry of the Public Libraries Act, and in 1887 two rooms were fitted up as reading rooms in the old Chelsea Vestry Hall. The new library, in Italianate style, was designed by J.M. Bryden, who was also responsible for the Town Hall in 1906. After the amalgamation of the boroughs of Kensington and Chelsea the Manresa Road library was closed and the library moved to the Old Town Hall in 1978.

Sydney Street *c.* 1900, in the days of the early motor buses, bicycles and boaters. Sydney Street commemorates one of the Smith Charity trustees, Viscount Sydney. To the left was St Luke's Infirmary and workhouse and to the right, in the distance, is the ambitious buttressed tower of St Luke's Church, consecrated in 1824. Charles Dickens was married to Catherine Hogarth there in 1836.

Brompton Fire Station soon after its opening in June 1893 on the north side of Trafalgar Square (now Chelsea Square). The new building at South Parade contained one steamer, one manual, one horse cart and one fire escape, with accommodation for eleven men and one coachman. The building, with its 800 foot watchtower, cost £7,862. At the opening the Commissary General remarked that its name was a misnomer as 'it ought to have been Chelsea'. One of the station's most famous inmates in the 1930s was a dog rumoured to stamp out fires with its paws. The station closed when the new Chelsea station was opened on the King's Road in 1964.

Fulham Road at the junction with Old Church Street in 1900. The original Queen's Elm inn is meant to commemorate the spot where Lord Burghley once walked with Queen Elizabeth I and took shelter from the rain under an elm in the Fulham Road.

Fulham Road in the early 1900s. Stocken and Co. (on the right) proudly announce they are 'Carriage and Motor Builders to the King and the Prince of Wales'. The picture is taken from the corner of Drayton Gardens looking westward. The two cyclists are telegraph boys.

This very early photograph (*c.* 1864) shows the south side of Sloane Square at about the same time that the Welsh draper Peter Rees Jones came to London to seek his fortune (see p. 156). The square was only a part of the ambitious plan of Henry Holland, the eighteenth-century builder/ architect who developed Hans Town, the whole area between King's and Brompton Roads. The son of a Fulham master builder, Holland leased 85 acres of farmlands known as Blacklands from Lord Cadogan in 1771, although building did not begin for another eight or nine years. Holland retained a generous portion for his own house, The Pavilion, and its extensive gardens, most of which later became Cadogan Square, named for the family linked to Hans Sloane by the marriage of his daughter to the second Baron Oakley, Charles Cadogan. Meandering through Blacklands on its way to the Thames, the Westbourne river was crossed in the region of Sloane Square by Bloody or Blandel Bridge, and its waters still flow through a conduit over the District and Inner Circle lines at Sloane Square station. When first laid out, the centre of the square was no more than a grass patch surrounded by a chain fence, later replaced by railings, where Queen Charlotte's Volunteers drilled and boys played cricket.

The south-west corner of Sloane Square nearest to King's Road, photographed around 1890, shows some humble shops with goods hanging outside, a patent piano maker and an Aerated Bread Company shop, which were rebuilt soon afterwards. After the King's Road was opened to the public in 1830, shops began to intersperse the villas along the highway until in modern times it became one of the world's most famous thoroughfares. The road reached its zenith in the 'swinging sixties' and the arrival of Mary Quant. In a few short years all the small useful neighbourhood shops closed as the boutique owners moved in. The 'beautiful people' of the sixties were followed in the 1970s by the punks.

This photograph, taken in 1864, shows the west side of Sloane Square before another success story was written. In 1877 Peter Jones took over Nos 4 and 6 King's Road, near the corner pub, the Star and Garter, previously occupied by a linen draper. Young Mr Jones had come to London ten years earlier, and after a few years as an apprentice he saved enough to acquire two shops in Marlborough Road (Draycott Avenue) to open his own Co-operative Drapery. It was while these were being knocked into one that the building collapsed, killing an apprentice workman and burying his wife in the debris. She survived and the shocked Jones and his few assistants recovered, the shop was rebuilt and within a few more years moved to the Sloane Square premises between a boot warehouse and a grocer. The business went from strength to strength and by 1894 had spread to the twelve next door houses, and was employing a staff of 200. On his death in 1905 it was bought by another Welsh draper, John Lewis, from Oxford Street. In 1935 Peter Jones's red brick, green roofed store was pulled down and replaced by the modern six-storey building which now dominates the west end of the square.

Workmen on the roof of Sloane Square House in 1893. Over the next ten years great changes were to take place on the square, including the south-east corner with the rise of the Royal Court theatre. In 1871 the Ranelagh Chapel, built in 1817, became the Royal Court theatre, a site next to the station which had actually been used as a theatre much earlier. Its first proprietor, Bertie Crewe, was succeeded by Harvey Granville Barker and J.E. Vedrenne in 1904, in whose hands the theatre earned the reputation for progressive productions which it has never lost, despite the ups and downs of nearly a century. Under this management eleven Bernard Shaw plays were presented, six for the first time, as well as Galsworthy's *Silver Box* and Granville Barker's own play *The Voysey Inheritance*. In 1935 the Royal Court became a cinema; it suffered severe bomb damage in 1940. Rebuilt in 1954, it was soon taken over by George Devine and his English Stage Company, whose third production was John Osborne's *Look Back in Anger*, followed by a series of successes with work by young dramatists such as Harold Pinter, Arnold Wesker and Samuel Beckett.

This 1900 view of Sloane Square shows the late Victorian changes, with hotels and mansion blocks replacing domestic shops. In 1953 an ornamental fountain was set up at this end, designed by Gilbert Ledward, as a gift from the Royal Academy to Chelsea. The square continues to change as old buildings change hands or are modernized.

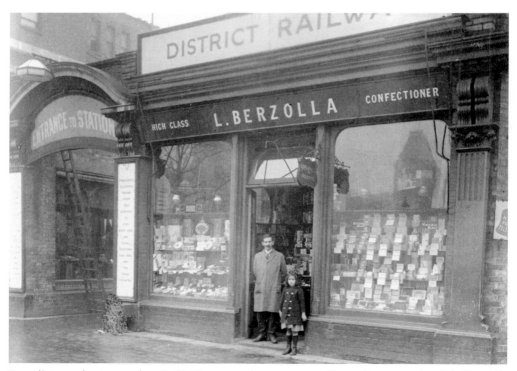

Berzolla's confectionery shop in 1927, next to the entrance to Sloane Square station. The Berzolla family, who ran the business here from 1918 to 1938, donated the photograph to Chelsea Library.

The north end of Sloane Street, *c.* 1900. In 1830 the Church of Holy Trinity was built to the design of James Savage, a Gothic revival building which lasted sixty years, being replaced in 1890 by the present church by J.D. Sedding. It has been described as a cathedral of arts and crafts, and includes decoration by William Morris and Burne-Jones. Beloved by John Betjeman, it was saved from extinction some years ago. Betjeman also immortalized the Cadogan Hotel, Sloane Street, in his poem about Wilde's arrest there in 1895.

Nathalie's at 187A Sloane Street after 1891, when she moved from No. 189. Mme Leah Nathalie, seen here at the doorway, opened her fan-making shop in the mid 1880s. She continued in business until 1912, by which time fans were no longer an essential fashion accessory.

Chelsea Creek, the boundary between Chelsea and Fulham caught by the lens of James Hedderley when it was still at the height of its industrial importance at the end of the nineteenth century. This was almost the last of the Chelsea riverside to be swept away by modern development, in the shape of Chelsea Harbour. The creek was the outlet of the stream originally known by several names, such as Billingswell Ditch and Counters Creek, which arose near Kensal Green and pursued a roughly straight course south-east along the border of Kensington and Hammersmith, crossed by bridges on Hammersmith Road, Fulham Road (Stamford) and King's Road (Stanley). In 1828 an attempt was made to convert the lower two miles into a canal which could take vessels up to 100 tons burden, with timber, coal and sand to a basin near the present site of Olympia. This was not a success, and after less than twenty years the canal was drained to create the Western Extension railway line, pilloried in the 1840s as Mr Punch's Railway, and the stream became a sewer. The inlet was described as recently as 1952 as being 'still visible as a stagnant ditch with a few disheartened marguerite daisies and thistles growing beside the green slime'. The area was chosen for an expensive development when twenty acres of coal yards were bought by P & O and Globe in the 1980s to create Chelsea Harbour, described as a 'unique world of houses, flats, offices, restaurants and shops, achieving a complete transformation'.